W9-CAT-048

REPORT 2009

A MAN'S GUIDE TO WOMEN

REPORT 2009
A MAN'S GUIDE TO WOMEN

Have the Sex of Your Dreams—and Hers!

Sex and Values at Rodale

We believe that an active and healthy sex life, based on mutual consent and respect between partners, is an important component of physical and mental well-being. We also respect that sex is a private matter and that each person has a different opinion of what sexual practices or levels of discourse are appropriate. Rodale is committed to offering responsible, practical advice about sexual matters, supported by accredited professionals and legitimate scientific research. Our goal—for sex and all other topics—is to publish information that empowers people's lives.

Printed in the United States of America
Rodale Inc. makes every effort to use acid-free ♾, recycled paper ♻.

ISBN 13: 978–1–59486–996–9
ISBN 10: 1–59486–996–0

2 4 6 8 10 9 7 5 3 1 hardcover

CONTENTS

INTRODUCTION

Want to have the sex of your dreams? We mean that figuratively—and literally. Obviously most men dream about sex—as in wish for more, better, hotter sex. But also most men *dream* about sex—as in when they're sleeping—a lot. Researchers found that men dream about sex in about one out of every 12 dreams. Because each of us dreams around six times a night, that's a sexy dream at least every other night. This book will help you get the sex of both your sleeping, and your wishing, dreams.

To create this book, we talked with dozens of experts and dozens of women—and dozens of women who believe they're experts—to gather their best tips, tricks, and techniques.

The first section of this book, Get Noticed, is all about you. Catch her eye with five simple strategies. Discover why a little vanity is good for you. Cultivate the seven financial habits of highly laid men. And increase your sex appeal in a few easy steps.

Get a glimpse inside her head in the second section of this book, Understand Women. Read her body language to tell whether you have a shot with her—in seconds. Crawl out of your dating rut by looking for *these* particular women. Discover the dozen sexy triggers that work for just about every woman. Learn why they rev her engine—and how to shift your mojo into an even higher gear.

In part three, you'll learn how to Date Great. Achieve romantic bliss while taking her away on a wild adventure. And date dangerously by following our expert-proven advice on how to make that hands-off hottie yours—whether she's the short-skirted seductress in the copy room, your friend and female confidante, or your best friend's sister.

Enhance Sex to make it the best ever in part four. This part provides everything you need to know to make, and keep, her happy. Seduce her fast and easy with our simple guide. Take the latest suburban sex toy for a test-drive. And have sex with someone new—every single night.

In our Get Better section, we talk about problems we hope you never have to deal with. You'll find a troubleshooting guide to your reproductive organs. Meet the few doctors who know how to fix prostatitis. And learn more about the most promising treatment for prostate cancer to date. Then liberate her flagging libido if the Pill is dampening her desire.

Last, keep your love alive with our Survive Relationships section. Discover which of five intriguing but possibly overrated sex scenarios are worth trying—and which you should ditch. Steal the advice of our favorite sex doc. Minimize conflict with your wife over child-rearing issues, which is a cause of serious marital strife. And learn the strategies that keep men and women together, happily ever after.

Ready for the best sex of your life? You're about to start living the dream.

PART 1

GET NOTICED

CATCH HER EYE

BEFORE YOU CAN TAKE HER HOME TONIGHT, YOU'LL HAVE TO GET HER ATTENTION. HERE'S HOW

BY SARAH MILLER

It would be nice to have been born good-looking, but even if you weren't, you can relax. Women don't care all that much if you're good-looking. But they do care if you're cool, so you can't totally relax.

Here's the paradox: In order to be cool, you sort of have to relax.

Cool is all about contradictions like this. Do this, but not always. Do that, but not for that reason.

While reading this article, you'll be forced to think about being cool, which isn't that cool. So read it in the privacy of your home. But read it. Because when you understand coolness, then it becomes possible to cultivate it.

COOL IS ABOUT BEING WHO YOU ARE

You want to convey to everyone—especially to any woman who might be sizing you up as a potential hook-up—that hey, being you is pretty good, maybe even fun. It's a simple concept that's hard to fake.

Thank God, then, that there are no rules pertaining to what women find cool. There are cool loud guys and cool quiet guys. Cool guys listen to jazz and electronica and rock and country, and so do uncool guys. (No one who listens to jam bands is cool.)

You can wear baggy sweat suits and funky hats and be sort of weird-looking but still be cool. Oh, sorry, that's only if you're Jay-Z. The point is that just about anything goes, as long as you do it with confidence and without looking over your shoulder to see who approves.

. . . BUT IT'S NOT ABOUT ANNOUNCING WHO YOU ARE

When you advertise yourself as just about anything—a star athlete, a type-A personality, a stand-up guy—you're suggesting that your demeanor won't speak for itself. Instead of telling her you got a bonus, take her out to dinner. Resist relaying the details of your grueling workout routine, and just fit into your damn pants. Never, ever use the phrase "I'm the kind of guy who. . ." If it's really true, she'll find out.

COOL GUYS REFUSE TO ENGAGE IN ACTIVITIES THAT MAKE THEM FEEL SILLY

You know that moment at a concert when the performers try to force everyone in the audience to clap or sing along? The impulse that tells you that you might die of shame if you do it is a good one. When it comes to earning a woman's respect and admiration, you are nothing without dignity. It's better to be a killjoy than a lemming.

. . . UNLESS MOTHERS OR KIDS ARE INVOLVED

If it's your nephew's bar mitzvah and your mother wants you to dance the hora, you're going to join the circle and spin. And you're going to like it. Sometimes being cool means knowing it's not just about you.

COOL GUYS RUN THEIR OWN LIVES

A cool guy has reasonable control over the way he makes his living. If he doesn't have that control, he should be taking concrete steps to change it. A cool guy values his family but doesn't live in service to them (unless they're ill). A cool guy isn't always asking everyone what his next move should be, because he should always have his next move planned.

. . . BUT THEY ACCEPT ADVICE WHEN APPROPRIATE

Yes, a renegade spirit is an important part of coolness. But don't make it your god. There are times when the beat of your own drummer should be drowned out by the counsel of good friends.

You will recognize your good friends by their excellent suggestions, such as, "That girl you're dating who has five kids by four different fathers probably doesn't have time to convert to Roman Catholicism."

You will honor those friends with your gratitude, humility, and compliance. "Whatever, dude, it's my life, and I've done a pretty good job this far without you" sounds great in the movies, but only because that guy's going to either end up being right or look really hot being wrong. You, on the other hand, are just going to look like you, only bummed, poor, divorced, or dead. "Cool" and "pigheaded" are not synonyms.

COOL GUYS ARE CHEERFUL

There's a reason the brooding antihero became popular, and that's because men look good smoking and sulking on-screen. They do not look good smoking and sulking in real life. So smile frequently. If you have to complain, make sure your complaint takes the form of an amusing and preferably self-deprecating anecdote.

. . . BUT NOT AGGRESSIVELY CHEERFUL

The only thing less cool than the perpetually miserable guy is the guy who is always telling you how great everything is. He may even believe that if he acts happy, he will become happy. And he may achieve this, in a head-bobbing-Chihuahua-dashboard-ornament sort of way. But he will never be cool, because at the end of the day being cool is about having people walk away from you thinking you know something they don't know, that you have secrets to which they may be privy should they spend a little time in your company.

COOL GUYS ARE GENEROUS

Of all the cool gestures you can make, few equal that slight lift of the chin to the waiter, coupled with the hand sliding into the breast pocket. Everyone—not just women—loves the guy who picks up the check, so do it when you can. But, more important, be the guy who lugs the sleeper sofa up five flights of stairs, feeds Snowball and Trisket while their owners are in Cabo, or lets drunk people crash on his couch. The generous guy is an object of wonder: He must have his game all figured out if he's got the time to do this.

. . . BUT THEY HAVE THE RIGHT MOTIVES

You have to mean it. Don't take a girl to the airport hoping she'll come back not only tan but suddenly in love with you. When you do nice things for people because you're looking for a return on your investment, you will find yourself disappointed. And accumulated disappointment leads to bitterness, and there is nothing—nothing—less cool than that. Take care of your own needs. Do nice things only for people who deserve it. And the next time you're at a party and the girl of your dreams walks in, let someone else go out for more ice.

>>A MAN'S GUIDE POLL

Clothes She'll Tear Off You: More than 700 women told us the dress code for sex.

1 = Not 10 = Hot

Casual blazer: 7	Slim-fit jeans: 6.5
Sport jersey: 4	Baggy jeans: 4
Denim shorts: 3.5	Black jeans: 3.5
Cargo shorts: 7	Pinstriped suit: 7.5
Baseball hat: 4	Flannel shirt: 3
A clean white T-shirt: 8	

CAPITALIZE YOUR GAINS

YOU ALREADY KNOW THAT LOSING WEIGHT AND BUILDING MUSCLE WILL MAKE YOU LOOK GOOD. NOW SCIENTISTS ARE FINDING THAT LOOKING GOOD WILL MAKE YOU HEALTHIER AND WEALTHIER THAN YOU EVER IMAGINED

BY BRYAN SMITH

Something was wrong. Rich Gamble knew it, could sense it, could feel it—the way he could tell whether a business presentation was going south, or whether his jagged-stripe tie was clowning up his striped shirt, or whether a woman's smile held promise or mere politesse. Tall, with broad shoulders and a frank, handsome face, Gamble was used to colleagues, bosses, women, and friends being drawn to him: his energy, his good nature, the linebacker's frame that he'd sweated into a lean V. But lately he'd felt a coolness, an indifference from the people around him. Nothing dramatic. Nothing rude. Just . . . different.

Cut to an office hallway, outside the elevator. Gamble, a director of finance with a large Chicago media company, was standing with his mentor and a handful of colleagues, including a couple of women he liked. Normally, this was a time for him to shine, to ply his friends with his genial good humor. But of late he had felt lumpish, slow on the draw. Thick.

Laughter now. Someone telling a joke. He felt his mentor's hand clap his shoulder. He smiled quizzically. "Oh boy!" the executive roared, slapping Gamble's belly. "When's she due?" The group exploded. Gamble winced. His cheeks burned. The laughter pounded in his ears. And in that moment, the truth dawned. That's how they see me, he thought. One of those guys—with a paunch.

He managed a grin, even laughed to show he was above such shallow worries. But the words hit him like a slap. In a wounding way, yes, but more as an epiphany. For within that little joke, he realized, lay the answer to why he'd been treated differently lately and why he felt like crap. More important, that moment of lost dignity motivated him to relocate his mojo.

Like a chameleon invisible in the grass, the secret Gamble stumbled on has always been there, hiding in plain sight, full of power and promise, yet largely ignored. It's a simple solution, available to all, blazing with the potential to extend our lives, advance our careers, improve our relationships, and lead us on that golden path to the six-pack abdomen. It has plunged countries into war, compelled men to heroic feats, and offered, to those who recognize it, transformative potential as potent as any Tony Robbins pep talk.

Such is the power of our own innate, undeniable, and often-suppressed desire to look good, achieve greatness, and make sure others know. Such is the overlooked and underappreciated exercise of our own vanity.

To put it more bluntly (and to riff off that Hollywood icon of vainglory, Gordon Gecko), vanity is good. Vanity is right. Vanity works. You may not like it (or perhaps you do), but caring about one's appearance, in the right way, is no character flaw. It is actually an essential trait in a world that lavishes its attention, money, jobs, respect, and all-around deference on good-looking people (and, perhaps more important, on those of us who are less prepossessing but who better our looks through hairstyle, grooming products, diet, and exercise).

The dirty truth is we all care about our appearance. It has always been so, from the first time a caveman dyed a pelt and wore it over his shoulder instead of that so-last-season loincloth. Those who say they don't care are lying, says Anne Hollander, PhD, a cultural-fashion anthropologist who has written several books on the social, historical, and spiritual implications of fashion. "Of course men care how they look. There's no way not to, unless you're invisible." She suggests putting such claims to the test. "Tell them, 'Here, wear this tutu and go shopping.' They'll care."

Still, raised eyebrows are understandable. Society ranks vanity right down there with lust, sloth, greed, gluttony, and envy. In Western art, the trait straddles a steed as the Whore of Babylon. Embracing it is, in a word, a sin.

But what if it were defined differently? Not as the preening office dandy fixated on his looks, the guy with hair streaks and spray tans and blush in his dopp kit, the metrosexual redux (though those *Queer Eye* guys had a decent run creating such fops), but redefined as self-possession and self-care, maximizing your assets. Women really do dig properly cut clothes and glistening abs and polished manners and really don't go for rumpled khakis with a shirt that blouses out like a spinnaker on an undersized dinghy. What if vanity meant simply knowing that attentive hygiene, a healthy body, confidence, and clean, white teeth could actually pave the path to a happier, healthier, more fulfilling life?

The wisest among us, even history's sages, believe that it just may be possible. "Most people dislike vanity," Ben Franklin wrote, "[but] I give it fair quarter, wherever I meet with it, being persuaded that it is often productive of good to the possessor . . . therefore, in many cases, it would not be altogether absurd if a man were to thank God for his vanity."

As it happens, "productive of good" could summarize the findings of nearly every major study on vanity. The benefits of caring about one's appearance are real, they're spectacular, and they're quantifiable.

The kicker is that although we all have vanity, and to some extent indulge it, we have been conditioned to reject it, scorn it, make fun of it, avoid it, and underrate it. To act otherwise would open the door to admitting the unthinkable: that the most self-centered of sins could actually be our salvation.

For Gamble, the potshot at his belly "was a wakeup call," he says. "A way of someone saying, 'Dude, get your shit together.'" That evening he ignored the siren song of the McDonald's drive-thru and instead filled a grocery cart with fresh fruit, salad, and lean cuts of meat. He cracked the Yellow Pages in search of home gym equipment. And he tracked down his old personal trainer.

A growing body of research suggests Gamble could scarcely have chosen a better or easier way of enhancing his career. Study after study has found that leaner, fitter, better-dressed, better-groomed, and therefore better-looking people are paid more, promoted faster, and rewarded with more positive evaluations.

Unfair? Perhaps. "In an ideal world, no, looks wouldn't matter," says Daniel S. Hamermesh, an economics PhD from Yale University and the author of *The Beauty Papers*, a series of six studies on vanity and its effects in the business world. But "people aren't stupid about this. If I'm an employer and I think that my customers care about your good looks, I'm going to be better off and make more money hiring you," whether or not you're actually the most qualified. "And you're going to reap the benefits from my use of your looks."

When Hamermesh conducted a study titled "Beauty and the Labor Market," he discovered that people with above-average looks received a "pay premium" of as much as 5 percent, whereas people with below-average looks suffered a salary penalty of up to 9 percent. In another study, this one on the earning power of a group of graduating law students, Hamermesh determined that 5 years into their careers, attractive men were earning about 10 percent more than their less-attractive classmates.

This superficiality even extends to the classroom. In 2004, researchers at Medaille College in Buffalo asked students to rate 400 professors on their helpfulness, clarity, and looks. When they evaluated the results, they found that the hottest teachers also rated highest in the other categories.

As for whether investing in vanity truly pays dividends for employers, scientists have studied that, too. Last year, researchers at the Stockholm School of Economics gave participants pictures of a good-looking salesclerk and a dud and asked which one gave them better service in a mock sale. In both attitude toward the clerk and the encounter itself, the looker earned far higher marks. Then there's the study in which researchers sampled data from Dutch advertising firms and discovered that companies with attractive executives had higher revenues—higher, in fact, than the extra wages those good-looking executives commanded.

Should any of these researchers ever want a compelling case study of vanity's power, they need look no further than Rich Gamble. As Gamble slimmed down, he looked better in his suits, which led him to start dressing better. He paid more attention to his grooming. The sharp creases returned to his dress shirts. The better he looked, the better he wanted to look. "It's a snowball effect," he says. "I was paying much more attention to the image I was projecting, realizing I needed to look the part and have more energy."

Gamble's career, like newly rippling muscles, pulsed with fresh vigor. Promotions, pay raises, and a corner office followed. How much credit is due to his rededication to his appearance and health, he isn't sure. But there's no doubt, he says, that his attitude, energy, and focus on the job expanded as his waistline shrank.

If vanity is an essential tool in the workplace, it can be a lifesaver in the area of health. A fit body isn't only pleasing to the eye; it leads to decreased blood pressure, a reduced risk of some cancers, less chance of a stroke, improved immune function, and increased energy. Visceral fat—the dreaded potbelly—has been called the most powerful predictor of liver disease, diabetes, and a range of other ills.

But a paunch may pose its biggest threat to a man's heart. Spare-tire syndrome accounts for nearly 33 percent of a person's infarction risk—just behind smoking, according to a 2004 study from McMaster University, in Hamilton, Ontario. In that context, a flat stomach not only looks buff on the beach, but it can also actually increase the number of years you'll be around.

Muscles, likewise, can serve the dual masters of vanity and health. It's hard to beat a woman's gasp at squeezing diamond-hard biceps. Or a curving quadriceps muscle flared over a flexed knee. But consider the health benefits of such satisfactions.

Muscle strength and mass are crucial to a person's ability to recover from such traumas as surgery and severe disease and to prevent killers that include colon cancer and diabetes. How? Extra muscle provides a larger storage area for glucose, and exercise burns that glucose as fuel, reducing the risk of insulin resistance and diabetes. Strenuous exercise, such as weight training, hastens the emptying out of the sewage plant that is your large intestine, removing the toxic sludge that can leach into healthy tissues and cause cancer.

"If you dismiss the importance of exercise and protein intake because you're not interested in sports"—or because you feel that doing so is vain—"you're underappreciating other roles that muscles play," says Robert Wolfe, PhD, the lead author of a 2006 study examining the role of muscle in health and disease.

The health benefits of vanity, however, flex beyond muscles, researchers say. Healthy skin both looks better and is a powerful indicator of inner health. Conversely, skin conditions such as moles, wrinkles, and age spots can sometimes indicate serious internal maladies.

In fact, according to a study by the University of Pennsylvania's department of dermatology, people with a prematurely aged appearance not only have lower self-esteem and less confidence, but are also less healthy than those who have aged well. The report recommended that doctors encourage their patients to slap on the skin cream, "not simply as an expression of vanity, but to add to self-esteem and improve social relations."

But skin? Men can be expected to care about muscles, but are they really exfoliating en masse? Yes, according to the numbers. Global spending on grooming products for men is nearly $22 billion, a 50 percent increase since 2001, reports Euromonitor, a London-based marketing and research company. In the United States, more than 1 million men had cosmetic procedures last year, the most popular being Botox injections. Sounds like we care.

Rick Patrone, a 38-year-old senior account manager in Chicago, certainly does. His Hugo Boss suits, crisp haircuts, and leather Italian shoes make that obvious. But he's also sensitive to the negative connotations associated with vanity. The men on his hockey team sometimes bust his balls. "That's fine," he says. "I just laugh that kind of thing off."

What's important to him, he says, are the benefits he derives in his career, his relationships, and his health. "The benefits aren't just what you look like," Patrone says, but "what you feel like, and what you can do with that feeling. You walk into a room and you know you look good and that people are looking at you and they're thinking positive thoughts, and you know you can hammer that meeting, or whatever it is."

This spring, after a winter spent gorging on pizza and pasta, Patrone challenged his buddies to a competition: Who could lose the highest percentage of body fat in 12 weeks? The entry fee was $500 apiece, winner take all. The idea, Patrone says, was that with their shrinking guts, they'd improve their health, physically and mentally. Call it vanity, call it whatever you like. "One guy is in it for the money," he says, "the other for bragging rights. I'm in it because I want to look better. It doesn't really matter why. What matters is how we'll all feel in the end."

Okay, so vanity is good for your career and your health. But your relationship? Surely vanity fails here. Self-absorption, narcissism, selfishness, and pride, after all, hardly seem to be the box of chocolates from which healthy relationships are plucked.

True, those extreme forms of vanity could land you more mirror time with yourself than quality time with her. But the kind of self-confidence that comes from caring about your appearance is indispensable if you want to maintain a healthy relationship, or form one in the first place.

For example, if you're single, there's no better wingman than vanity. A 1992 Yale University study found that attractive people are perceived to be "more sociable, dominant, sexually warm, mentally healthy, intelligent, and socially skilled than unattractive people." And that is before you even open your mouth to verify everything her eyes assume.

From the bar to the bedroom, vanity also figures into sexual satisfaction. In this area, "the importance of looks cannot be overestimated," writes Nancy Etcoff, PhD, a Harvard psychologist, in her book *Survival of the Prettiest*. "Good-looking men . . . are more sexually experienced and engage in a variety of sexual activities." Etcoff also cites the work of two researchers, Randy Thornhill and Steven Gangestad, who suggest good-looking men "are more likely to bring their women to orgasm and to simultaneous orgasm."

Nor does attention to appearance become less important after she's been successfully wooed, wowed, and wedded. Let yourself go within the safe status quo of marriage and your declining self-esteem could cause trouble, says Sandra Murray, PhD, a professor of psychology at the State University of New York at Buffalo. In the journal *Personal Relationships*, she warns that overly sensitive and insecure partners may "read nonexistent meaning into their partners' ambiguous cues, thus leading their relationships to the outcome they wish to avoid." Misreading cues may seem to be a greater danger in nascent relationships, but research shows that even after 10 years of marriage, people with low self-esteem believe their partners love them far less than they actually do.

Patrone and Gamble both affirm that vanity has been vital to the health of their own relationships. "To me, people continue their commitment to each other by staying fit and healthy," says Patrone. "I see a lot of people letting themselves go after they tie the knot. Why? It should be the opposite. It's important to remain attractive to your spouse, whether it's 5 months or 5 years."

Patrone says he and his wife look at their thrice-weekly trips to the gym together as a kind of continued courtship. "We flirt with each other as if we've never met," he says.

Gamble believes he never would have met his fiancée had he not had the extra energy he gets from working out. And if he had met her, he might not

GREAT MOMENTS IN THE MIRROR

SEVEN MEN WHOSE VANITY CHANGED HISTORY

1841: William Henry Harrison

Even though it's a cold, windy March day, President-elect Harrison refuses to wear an overcoat to his inauguration. After delivering a 2-hour address, he catches fatal pneumonia.

1926: Harry Houdini

Escape artist Houdini is so proud of his abs that he's said to have dared anyone to punch him in the stomach. A student obliges, aggravating undetected appendicitis. Houdini dies 3 days later.

1943: George Patton

When he takes command of the demoralized II Corps in North Africa, Lt. General Patton orders soldiers to shave daily and wear neckties. Two months later, the Axis desert forces surrender.

have approached her with the same confidence he felt from being in shape and well dressed.

"I remember I was driving on the expressway, and it was a cold, rainy night, and I wasn't sure whether I wanted to go to this work function. Finally I decided to go, and that's where we met," he says. She was a former competitive athlete. Gamble, who has studied martial arts for most of his life, was lifting weights and kickboxing. He says his comfort with his looks made him at ease in a way that let his humor and sociability shine.

With them, vanity isn't one-way, explains Gamble. "It's what we give each other: healthy attitudes about everything from food to exercise to clothes. You name it. We support each other."

"Well I hear you went up to Saratoga, and your horse naturally won.
Then you flew your Lear jet up to Nova Scotia
To see the total eclipse of the sun."

1956: Elvis Presley

For his second movie, *Loving You*, Elvis dyes his hair, sandy blond since birth, to black and never goes back. Would we have called Elvis "The King" if he'd looked like Kevin Costner?

1960: John F. Kennedy

In the first televised presidential debate, Kennedy agrees to wear stage makeup, but Nixon refuses. Although radio listeners say Nixon won, TV viewers favor Kennedy—and he goes on to win the election.

1984: Steve Jobs

Macintosh makes PCs cool, while its founder—wearing button-downs and mock turtlenecks—popularizes casual work clothing. Relaxed dress makes employees more creative and productive.

1996: Michael Johnson

Sprinter Johnson dons blindingly bright gold running shoes. The Nike shoes, half the weight of his old pair and made with 24-carat gold flecks, propel Johnson to two Olympic gold medals.

Despite the scientific studies and anecdotal evidence, male vanity can't be exonerated without confronting the Carly Simon conundrum. Written in 1972, composed of 24 searing lines, Simon's "You're So Vain" was more than a song. It was an anthem, a paean, a musical bitch-slap that seemed to indict the trait and anyone with the balls to back it.

Simon herself, however, has been a surprise witness for the defense. The song may indeed chide her lover for leaving, but she was in no way dissing his panache, his flair, his swagger. "Hardly objectionable!" she said, referring to the lover's traits in a 1994 interview with Bob Costas. "I think

ARE YOU VAIN ENOUGH?

Find out whether you need a shot of superficiality.

1. Do you smoke?

Yes/No

Cigarettes are wrinkle sticks. "They lead to the loss of collagen and elastic fibers," says Mitchel Goldman, MD, a professor of dermatology at the University of California at San Diego. Smoking can also color your skin a yellowish tint, give you wretched breath, and hurt your hairline.

2. Do your hands look like hell?

Yes/No

"I have nothing against a mechanic's hands as long as he takes care of them after he's done with the carburetor," says Lisa Petty, RHN, a health consultant in Ontario, Canada. Use Kiehl's Ultimate Strength hand salve ($13) twice a day.

3. Do you use nail clippers?

Yes/No

Unkempt fingernails are an eyesore, and the edges can cut when you're trying to caress. "Guys have problems with nails because they bang them up all the time," says Dr. Goldman. Try the Denco Stainless Steel Clipper ($7); it has a nail catcher to keep clippings off the floor.

4. Do you sleep 8 straight?

Yes/No

it's [about] a very attractive man." (Presumably Warren Beatty, widely believed to be the song's model.) "It's a very complicated man who is obviously concerned with his image but obviously worthy of my love or my interest. I don't love just anyone. You know, he's gotta have a certain amount of . . . " Integrity? Chasteness? "Character," she said. But a little vanity never hurt, either.

Which means it was okay that one day, a year or so after "the joke," Rich Gamble walked into the office as if he were walking onto a yacht. And a female colleague stopped him in the hallway.

The vain man knows when to call it a night. Sleep lowers stress hormones and improves the immune system—all helpful for looking good, says Phyllis Zee, MD, a professor of neurobiology at the Northwestern University School of Medicine.

5. Do you have a "healthy" tan?

Yes/No

No such thing—even from a tanning booth. "They give early wrinkles and can cause skin cancer," says June Robinson, MD, a professor of dermatology at Northwestern University.

Score Your Level

1. Yes 0, No 1
2. Yes 0, No 1
3. Yes 1, No 0
4. Yes 1, No 0
5. Yes 0, No 1

Totals

0–1 point(s): Doh! Homer would be proud.

2–3 points: Close, but no Carly.

4–5 points: You probably think this quiz is about you.

"I don't know what it is," she said, "but you look incredible. You're confident, you're projecting energy. What's different about you?" Gamble considered telling her—how much weight he'd lost, how his gut, rather than resembling a woman in her second trimester, now bulged with muscle. But he didn't. Instead, he relied on the fruits of his vanity. "I know," she said finally. "You have your swagger back." Gamble smiled and shrugged. Who was he to disagree?

WOO HER WITH WEALTH

FLASHING MONEY WON'T IMPRESS HER. CULTIVATE THE SEVEN FINANCIAL HABITS OF HIGHLY LAID MEN, AND SHE'LL PAY YOU BACK WITH HER INTEREST

BY ANYA KAMENETZ

You just treated her to a five-star first date: cozy table at an exclusive new restaurant, seven courses of amazing food, and the best bottle of wine on the menu. The bill arrives and, without glancing at it, you slip the waitress your AmEx. Smooth! Next, you sign the credit-card receipt, add a 15 percent tip, and . . . go home alone.

What went wrong? According to a *Men's Health* magazine survey of 160 women, you made three major mistakes. First, only 3 percent of them would have been impressed by your ability to land a table at Chez Overprix, and even fewer lathered up over pricey wine. (You should have cooked dinner at your place, said 68 percent of the women, and introduced her to your favorite pinot.) Second, your indifference to the final tally suggests you're irresponsible or, worse, a show-off. (You should have double-checked the total quickly, said our survey respondents.) Finally, your tip was insulting, according to 36 percent of them. (Give at least 20 percent on a first date, in case she notices.)

So three strikes and you're out. Perhaps you're thinking, Screw her. I won't use money to impress women. But you're missing the point. Your money didn't do you in; how you wielded it did. But if you take our rules to the bank, you just might be able to take her back to your place, too.

UNDERSTAND YOUR EARNING POTENTIAL

Women aren't interested in men who earn less than they do. Sorry, K-Fed. In fact, 41 percent admitted they actively seek men who earn more. Precisely zero told us they prefer to earn more than their men do. "There's still a stigma attached to men who don't contribute at least equally," says Mari Adam, a certified financial planner in Miami.

This doesn't mean, however, that you can date only within your tax bracket. "Know exactly where you want your career to take you and how much you can potentially earn along the way," says Adam. "Having confidence and a plan will appeal to any woman."

Why is your earning potential so important? A majority of single women—53 percent—told us they're looking for a man who can single-handedly support the family for a few years while she stays home with the kids. And another 25 percent would feel more secure knowing the family doesn't need her salary to make ends meet.

SET SPECIFIC LONG-TERM GOALS

You're lying in bed, engaging in pillow talk, when the conversation turns to the future. Seventy-eight percent of women are hoping you'll say, "I'm saving up to buy a house in the country someday." Only 16 percent want to hear "I'm planning to retire a millionaire by age 40."

"It's sexy when a man has a specific vision for his money," says Adam, "and the patience to wait for it."

As for that very manly goal to "live fast, die young and broke, and leave a good-looking corpse," women aren't buying it. In fact, 98.72 percent don't want to date you.

COME CLEAN ABOUT DEBT

The average guy has 8,562 skeletons in his financial closet, in the form of credit-card debt. Revealing your little secret to a potential mate isn't a deal breaker, but timing is key. Nine out of 10 women would rather you put off that talk until you're dating exclusively. "Once the relationship becomes serious, tell her, 'This is my situation, and this is how I'll pay it off,' " says Mary Durie, a certified financial planner in Dallas.

The women in our survey agreed. One said, "As long as he takes his debt seriously and is trying to pay it down, I'll stick with him. That means he shouldn't be suggesting really fancy dinners. Spending time with me is better than spending money on me."

LOSE THE STATUS SYMBOLS

Seventy percent of women say the hottest men are those who "spend wisely," compared with 19 percent who say they are attracted to big savers; only 8 percent say they like big spenders. The biggest money-related turnoff: a man who's a walking logo.

"Seeing a man flash his money suggests he's more interested in the present than the future," says Durie. That's a problem for women. Half of those we surveyed said a man with money is attractive because the "feeling of financial security is sexy," not because "money brings a sense of adventure to a relationship" or they'll "be able to enjoy the finer things in life."

So how can you let a woman know you're doing just fine financially without coming across like a show-off? "It's wise for a man to be frugal and live within a budget," one woman told us. "But I'll know he has money if he can just let loose for a day."

BE CLEAR ABOUT THE PRESENT DANGER

When we asked women to name their most romantic gifts ever, only 25 percent mentioned jewelry. At the beginning of a relationship, presents should be simple and inexpensive, said 89 percent of those surveyed. In fact, during the first month, no gift should exceed $100, said 97 percent.

As for what to buy, our women were unanimous: Aim for that elusive combination of thoughtful and unexpected. Said one, "Once, a guy gave me a very cool vase and promised to keep it filled with flowers. And he did."

Said another: "At the end of our first date, my boyfriend filled my gas tank so I couldn't use 'no gas' as an excuse not to see him. It was cute, surprising, and memorable."

SHOW YOUR MANY GENEROUS SIDES

The ideal man donates more than his money. He gives his time as well, whether it be to a local soup kitchen or Habitat for Humanity. Almost

40 percent of the women said this is an important trait in a man. By contrast, only 11 percent said writing checks to a charity is appealing.

And while you're helping those less fortunate: Tipping your waiter or waitress 25 percent is a major turn-on, said 57 percent of respondents. Who knew?

KEEP YOUR HOT STOCK TIPS TO YOURSELF

Financial knowledge is sexy in a man, according to 60 percent of the women. But only 42 percent want your advice on money matters. That's because they don't need it. "Women are often better investors," says Durie. "They rarely make rash decisions."

"If anything," says Durie, "men should be asking their girlfriends for tips."

>>A MAN'S GUIDE POLL

Money Talks

Money doesn't make you attractive. How you spend it does. Do this, say 160 women . . .

When She Expects You to Pay

Take turns from the get-go: 41%

Dates 1, 2, and maybe 3: 30%

Dates 1 to infinity: 8%

The Smartest Splurges

A surprise vacation for two: 34%

Concerts and entertainment: 20%

Your appearance: 9%

Dates That Put Her in the Mood

Great dinner and conversation: 39%

Front-row seats at a concert or show: 21%

Limo service all night long: 13%

Her Biggest Money-Related Turnoffs

Wearing too-obvious logos: 31%

Referencing your bottom line: 19%

Clipping discount coupons: 11%

Financial Qualities She Finds Sexy

Being knowledgeable: 59%

Being generous: 23%

Just plain having a lot of money: 6%

(Percentages reflect the most-common answers.)

INCREASE YOUR SEX APPEAL

HERE'S THE BEST (AND SIMPLEST) ADVICE FOR LOSING FAT, BUILDING MUSCLE, AND LOOKING SHARP

FROM THE EDITORS OF *MEN'S HEALTH*

Employ these strategies, and you'll instantly upgrade every aspect of your life.

GET GROOMING

You brush your teeth twice a day, shave every morning, and get your hair cut every 6 weeks. But the places you neglect to groom leave a lasting impression on women in your life. A bad one. So tend your lawn, men.

THE INSTANT TURNOFF: Dry elbows and feet

REPEL FACTOR: "I don't want a guy's rough, sandpapery skin touching all the places I spend hours on making soft and lovely," says Kate, 27.

THE FIX: Slap a moisturizer on the rough spots after you shower. But opt for a hand cream rather than a body lotion. "It has a richer formula that penetrates deeper into the skin," says Brian Boyé, *Men's Health* magazine fashion director. Try Kiehl's Ultimate Strength hand salve ($13).

THE INSTANT TURNOFF: Chapped lips

REPEL FACTOR: "There's nothing worse than a guy going in for a kiss with dry skin hanging off his lips," says Kerri, 24.

THE FIX: Make a habit of applying lip balm twice a day, even when your lips aren't chapped. The best times: "In the morning after you eat and at night before bed," says Pirooz Sarshar, cofounder of the Grooming Lounge. We like Brave Soldier Lip Defender SPF 15 ($8, groominglounge.com).

THE INSTANT TURNOFF: Neck hair

REPEL FACTOR: "If it looks like a reverse beard, I head in the other direction," says Kristen, 23.

THE FIX: Hair on the neck grows just as fast as facial scruff, so don't rely only on your barber to trim it. When your hair is dry, lift it off your neck and shave any hair that's creeping below the hairline, says Vaughn Accord, a men's grooming specialist at Bumble and Bumble in New York City. Work it into your morning routine twice a week; a regular razor works best.

THE INSTANT TURNOFF: Ear hair

REPEL FACTOR: "Once I catch sight of it, I can't look away," says Jaclyn, 23. "And I don't mean in a good way."

THE FIX: A certain amount of hair is nature's way of keeping bad things out of your ear canal, but most women have limits to what's acceptable. "It's tough to see in a bathroom mirror, but you should take inventory every time you shave to keep it under control," says Accord. Invest in a Panasonic Nose and Ear Hair Groomer ($20, panasonic.com); it'll clean you up in seconds.

SAVE YOUR SKIN

Korean researchers found that fish oil may help prevent wrinkles. When the scientists treated skin with eicosapentaenoic acid (an omega-3 fat in fish oil), then exposed the epidermis to light, the number of collagen-destroying proteins dropped by 75 percent.

GOTTA WEAR SHADES

Along with protecting your eyes from damaging ultraviolet rays, sunglasses can help you avoid jet lag, according to Scottish researchers. In a study of 1,000 international travelers, those who wore sunglasses for the first few hours of the morning after arrival recovered from jet lag up to 3 days sooner than fliers who skipped the specs. Choose shades that wrap around your eyes and offer 100 percent UV protection, say doctors at Henry Ford Hospital, in Detroit.

BEAT BALDNESS

Flax may halt a receding hairline. In a study, Taiwanese scientists gave a daily 50-milligram dose of lignans—disease-fighting compounds found in flaxseed—to 10 men who were losing their hair. After 6 months, 9 of the 10 men showed slower hair loss.

Lignans are found in the flaxseed's shell, so buy ground whole seeds in your supermarket's health-food section. Taking 1½ tablespoons provides the lignans you need.

GRAB HER ATTENTION

Your scent will stick in her memory as much as anything you say or wear, according to a Cornell University study. So choose a cologne she'll remember. Not sure what the ladies like? These three scents have stood the test of time: Acqua di Gio by Giorgio Armani, Eternity by Calvin Klein, and Dolce & Gabbana by Dolce & Gabbana. Have a female friend help you pick the one that fits you.

EXTEND YOUR "SMILEAGE"

The sharper you look, the more trustworthy you look, according to a Rice University study. Furthermore, the researchers discovered that smiling people are thought to be more trustworthy than those with straight faces. Self-improvement doesn't get much simpler.

SHINE ON FOR YEARS

A brighter smile could mean stronger teeth. American Dental Association researchers found that teeth-whitening products containing "amorphous calcium phosphate" can cut down on enamel damage and tooth sensitivity by 40 percent, compared with other whiteners. Ask your dentist about Nite White and Day White whitening systems ($40).

FIND YOUR ABS

Nutrition science isn't rocket science, so why confuse the two? Instead, use this simple eating guide from Alan Aragon, MS, a nutritionist in Thousand Oaks, California. It doesn't require calorie counting or complicated calculations. All you have to do is eyeball your portion sizes and eat. Then watch your flab melt away.

STEP 1: Divide your daily menu into the following six food groups, which include every category except "junk."

STEP 2: Eat two servings a day from each food group, split any way you want into four meals. Also, regularly drink 50 ounces of water, or 80 ounces on days you hit the gym.

FOOD GROUP	FOODS	1 SERVING
Protein	Meat (beef, pork, poultry, fish), eggs, or protein powder	1 piece of meat the area and thickness of your palm; 1 egg; 2 scoops of protein powder
Fruit	Do you really need a list?	1 fist-size piece of fruit, or a heaping cup of it
Fat	Oils, butters, nuts, seeds, and avocados	2 tablespoons of oil, butter (regular, peanut, almond), or avocado; a handful of nuts and seeds
Dairy	Milk, yogurt, and cheese	1 cup of milk or yogurt; 1 slice of cheese
Vegetables	Any fiber-rich vegetable that's green or that you'd eat raw	It doesn't matter. Feel free to indulge.
Starch	Any plant food not catego-rized as a "fruit" or "veg-etable"	1 cup of cereal or cooked pasta, rice, or other grain; 2 slices of bread; 1 medium potato

STEP 3: Two meals a week, eat whatever you want.

STUBBORN FAT? Reduce your starches to one serving or less on days you don't work out; ramp back up to two servings on days when you exercise intensely.

THINK BACK BEFORE YOU SNACK

British scientists found that people who reviewed their last meal before snacking ate 30 percent fewer calories than those who didn't stop to think. The theory: Remembering what you've already eaten makes you less likely to overindulge.

KEEP A RUNNING TOTAL

Throughout the day, scratch a tally mark each time you eat a serving from one of the six food groups on the opposite page. University of Pittsburgh researchers discovered that dieters who keep only a basic food journal are as successful as those who record every bite.

TURN OFF THE TV

University of Massachusetts scientists found that men who watch TV during a meal consume, on average, 288 more calories than those who don't eat with the tube on.

STAND IN THE PLACE WHERE YOU WORK

Quit sitting down on the job. Australian scientists found that workers who log more than 6 hours of chair time a day are up to 68 percent more likely to be overweight than those who sit less.

One solution: Ask HR for a stand-up desk. You burn one more calorie each minute when standing than when sitting. (Do the math.) Request denied? Create your own stand-up workstation: Place your monitor on a box, with the top of the screen at arm's length and at eye level, and elevate your keyboard so your elbows are bent 90 degrees. A bonus: Your posture will improve from standing instead of slumping.

KNOW THE FAT-LOSS FORMULA

When it comes to exercise, hit the gym, road, or court. Your abs aren't picky. French scientists determined that men who spent the most time moving, regardless of the type of activity, had the leanest midsections. The magic numbers? Three or 4 days a week, for a weekly total of 4 hours.

A SWEET SOLUTION

You don't have to give up sweets to give up your gut. In a study of 14,000 people, Cornell scientists found that those who ate the most candy also downed the most fruit. The connection, of course, is that both taste sweet. But the same amount of fruit, by weight, contains far less sugar and packs a healthy dose of belly-filling fiber. Case in point: A regular package of Skittles has 47 grams of sugar, while ½ cup of blueberries serves up just 8 grams. Craving sweets? Try these fresh-fruit substitutes instead.

YOUR CRAVING	EAT THIS
A tangy candy, such as Starburst, Skittles, or Mike and Ikes	Orange, pineapple, or mango
A tart candy, such as SweeTarts or Smarties	Blackberries, blueberries, or raspberries
A soft candy, such as marshmallows	Banana, cantaloupe, or honeydew
Pure sugar (think cotton candy)	Figs (one of the most sugary fruits)

MAXIMIZE YOUR WORKOUT

Don't waste another minute in the weight room. Instead, build muscle fast with this "three-and-out" routine from Bill Hartman, CSCS, a strength coach in Indianapolis. It works your entire body with just three exercises to help you achieve the best possible results in the least amount of time.

This workout uses only what Hartman calls "big" exercises—those that work multiple muscle groups. There are exercises for your lower body and pushing and pulling movements for your upper body. Choose one workout (A, B, C, or D) from this menu of total-body routines. Then perform the exercises as a circuit, doing one set of each exercise in succession, resting as prescribed. Complete a total of four or five circuits, 3 days a week, resting at least a day between sessions. After 4 weeks, select a new workout.

	BIG LOWER BODY	BIG PULL	BIG PUSH
A	Squat	Chinup *	Shoulder press
B	Front squat	Bent-over row	Push press
C	Deadlift	Pullup*	Bench press
D	Split squat	Seated row	Incline bench press

*If you can't do chinups (underhand grip) or pullups (overhand grip), substitute lat pulldowns.

EXERCISE 1 (BIG LOWER BODY): Do 6 to 8 repetitions; rest for 75 seconds.

EXERCISE 2 (BIG PULL): Do 6 to 8 repetitions; rest for 75 seconds.

EXERCISE 3 (BIG PUSH): Do 6 to 8 repetitions; rest for 60 seconds, go back to exercise 1, and repeat until you've done four or five circuits.

LIFT FOR YOUR LIFE

Here are three more reasons to hit the weights.

BOOST YOUR METABOLISM. A University of Wisconsin study found that when men performed three "big" exercises, their metabolisms were elevated for 39 hours afterward. In fact, scientists in the Netherlands calculated that men who lifted weights twice a week for 18 weeks burned an average of 9 percent more calories a day beyond what they expended during exercise—enough to lose 25 pounds in a year.

FIGHT OFF HEART DISEASE. Researchers at the University of Michigan reported that men who completed three total-body weight workouts a week for 2 months lowered their diastolic blood pressure (the bottom number) by an average of 8 points. That reduces your risk of stroke by 40 percent and of a heart attack by 15 percent.

LIFT FOR HAPPINESS. In a study at the University of Alabama at Birmingham, scientists discovered that men who performed three weight workouts a week for 6 months not only built muscle and lost fat, but also improved their scores on measures of tension, anger, and overall mood.

DRINK TO YOUR BICEPS

Now you can build muscle at the office. French researchers found that men who drank small amounts of a shake containing 30 grams of protein every 20 minutes for 7 hours boosted muscle growth more than those who downed the entire drink in one sitting.

Want to try it? Mix 30 grams of whey protein powder with 16 ounces of water and sip on it during your workday. Besides giving your muscles a steady flow of raw materials for growth, whey protein has been shown to improve immune function.

We like Optimum Nutrition 100 percent whey protein, available at www.optimumnutrition.com.

INJURY-PROOF YOUR BODY

Research in the *American Journal of Public Health* shows that scrawny men are more likely to die from an impact—think a car crash or a fall—than their brawny brothers are. The reason: Hard muscle may help shield a man's internal organs from damage.

ALL ROADS LEAD TO ABS

Turns out, any exercise can help you carve a six-pack. "All you have to do is make the right adjustment," says Alwyn Cosgrove, CSCS, owner of Results Fitness, in Santa Clarita, California. The trick? Tweaking the exercise to throw your balance off-kilter. "This tactic forces your core muscles to contract maximally in order to keep your body from rotating or falling over," says Cosgrove. Here's how to convert five classic movements into instant ab builders.

SPLIT SQUATS AND LUNGES: Instead of holding two dumbbells at arm's length next to your sides, use just one dumbbell and hold it at shoulder level. On each set, alternate the arm holding the dumbbell.

PRESSES AND ROWS: Work just one arm at a time, leaving one hand free. When you finish all your repetitions, switch hands and repeat to work the other side.

CHINUPS: Use a mixed grip, with one hand grasping the bar underhand, the other overhand. Flip your grip each set.

EAT YOUR BROCCOLI

Australian scientists found that men felt like their workouts were easier when they were regularly eating lots of antioxidant-rich fruits and vegetables. When they downed only three daily servings of produce, their workouts seemed harder.

SKIP THE SMALL TALK

Twenty seconds before you pick up the dumbbells, start focusing on the task at hand. UK researchers recently discovered that men who psyched themselves up prior to a lift were able to hoist 12 percent more weight than when they were distracted.

CHIN UP

If you can't yet do one chinup, you're missing out on the most effective way to build upper-body muscle. And why in the name of great Arnold himself would you want to do that? Use this workout from Cosgrove 3 days a week, resting for a day between sessions. It emphasizes the negative, or lowering, portion of the chinup—a proven technique for quickly raising your strength levels.

Eliminate excuses. Buy a doorway chinup bar at jumpusa.com or pullupbar.com.

THE MOVE: Set a bench or sturdy box under a chinup bar. Then step on the bench and grasp the bar with an underhand grip. Jump up so your chest is next to your hands, then cross your feet behind you. Try to take 10 seconds to lower your body until your arms are straight. If that's too hard, lower yourself as slowly as you can. That's one set.

THE ROUTINE: Do three sets, resting for 90 seconds after each. Once you can take a full 10 seconds to lower your body from start to finish in all three sets, add a fourth set. In your next workout, though, reduce your rest between sets to 75 seconds. Do your fourth set only if you're still able to complete all three 10-second sets.

THE PROGRESSION: Each time you make it to set number 4, reduce your rest period in your next workout by another 15 seconds. Typically, once you can complete three 10-second sets with 45 seconds of rest, you'll be able to perform at least one chinup. Go to MensHealth.com, keyword chinup, to find out how to do more.

TALK YOURSELF UP

NEGATIVE SELF-TALK CAN RUIN YOUR DAY. WELL, WE THINK IT CAN, BUT MAYBE WE'RE WRONG

BY CARL SHERMAN

True story: Guy walks into a bar, chats up the hottest babe in the joint. He's feeling hip and funny. She's gazing dreamily into his eyes, obviously impressed. When she goes off to the restroom, a buddy walks up to the guy. "Know who that is?" the buddy asks. "She used to date Al Pacino."

Gulp.

Somehow, when Miss Lovely reappears, our man isn't so fast with the repartee. His confidence is gone; the conversation sputters. She's no longer looking into his eyes. In fact, she seems to be looking for an escape route. He's become another wannabe player shot down by negative self-talk.

We all talk to ourselves. It's the way the mind works. And it's terrific when it makes like your own personal Laker Girl. Who doesn't like hearing, "Smart move . . . she liked that." Or, when you start a new job, "I have great ideas." Positive self-talk bolsters confidence and boosts energy.

But sometimes our inner cheerleader changes sides. Instead of encouragement, you get zingers like, "Pacino! Man, I'm so average. What'll she think when she sees my ancient car? And my pathetic apartment—not that we'll get that far."

What's a guy to do? There's no off button for your inner motormouth, and demoralizing thoughts can pop up anytime. But there are ways to keep your head out of trash-talking mode.

Bad thoughts are inevitably triggered by events, however minor. The boss looks your way—is he frowning?—and you think, "I'm gonna lose my job." Or your dinner date's giggle reminds you of that leggy brunette who laughed so cruelly when you brought a bottle of cheap white zinfandel to her classy dinner party. "Doofus!" Instantly, you're reliving a moment you'd rather forget.

But that's just the beginning. Electrochemical activity in the brain's frontal cortex, where thoughts are born, jumpstarts the limbic system, a primitive brain region known as the seat of emotion. Specifically, thoughts that suggest something is wrong rev up the amygdala, an almond-shaped parcel of gray matter that functions like a panic button.

From there, circuits light up in the hypothalamus, which links the mind with the body. You start to sweat. Your pulse quickens. Now you're really nervous.

Upstairs, the frontal lobes are generating even more discouraging words. Soon a killer monologue is going on inside your skull, and it's not the kind that knocks 'em dead at the Laugh Factory. It's the voice of doom—hypercritical and looking for anything to feel terrible about.

The mischief that bad thoughts can do is something athletes know better than anyone. "Negative self-talk hurts your self-confidence, and when confidence goes down, so does performance," says Shane Murphy, PhD, the former head of the U.S. Olympic Committee's sports psychology program.

Self-doubt produces muscle tension, which screws up timing and coordination. And by torpedoing your mood, self-doubt makes it difficult to focus. "You can't concentrate on pitching the ball when you're thinking, Last time, this batter hit it out of the park," Murphy says.

The same thing can happen in daily life. Thoughts like "I have nothing interesting to say" become self-fulfilling prophecies. Self-doubt shows in your facial expressions, tone of voice, and even in your posture. You become so focused on how you're coming across that you can't keep up with the conversation. Bye-bye, playful banter; hello, strained silence.

At work negative self-talk has a similar effect. "If you focus on how difficult a task is—how you won't do a good job—you'll find it tougher to start," says psychologist James Pretzer, PhD, director of the Cleveland Center for Cognitive Therapy. "You're likely to procrastinate, which will turn the task into a real ordeal."

If you're giving a speech or typing a report, an inner critic that keeps jabbering "This sounds so lame" is all but guaranteed to tie your tongue and freeze your fingers at the keyboard.

Worst of all are the missteps that keep replaying like some sadistic tape loop. Maybe it's the way you blew that great thing you had with Liz. Or that time you sneezed in your boss's coffee.

This is a milder version of the intrusive thoughts that bedevil combat veterans and other trauma victims. According to John Ratey, MD, a psychiatrist at Harvard University and the author of *A User's Guide to the Brain*, those thoughts "come when the mind has no focus or directed attention."

True, an office cubicle isn't exactly a battlefield. Nor is a bar or your bedroom. But threats to your self-esteem in these everyday settings can rev up the amygdala just as effectively as a mortar attack will.

So what are you going to do? Here's your battle plan.

KNOW THE ENEMY. Zeroing in on your negative mind chatter isn't easy, but with a little practice, you'll be able to pick out the sentence fragments that constitute a sort of lingua franca between "you" and your limbic system—brief phrases such as "Blew it, as usual," or names that are freighted with personal meaning: "Dad all over again." Sometimes it's just images, such as the face of an old girlfriend. You'll see it coming.

DON'T IGNORE THEM, AND RESPECT THEIR POWER. Don't try to eliminate negative thoughts. "The more you fight them, the more they come back," says clinical psychologist Gregory Markway, PhD, author of *Painfully Shy*. "Instead of trying to suppress negative thoughts, let them stay as background noise."

ARGUE WITH YOURSELF. Identify the putdowns you typically say to yourself, and then jot down a rebuttal for each. Your goal isn't to pump yourself up with false optimism; it's simply to recast unrealistically negative thoughts in a more positive light. The rebuttal to "I sound like an idiot" isn't "I'm as smooth a talker as Humphrey Bogart in *The Big Sleep*," but rather "If I say something dumb, she'll like me anyway."

PUT ON AN ACT. Imagine yourself in a stressful situation, first with the negative voice-over and then with the good stuff. Run mental rehearsals until it feels natural. Or simply act like everything's copacetic and positive thoughts will follow. Just putting a smile on your face reinforces the notion that all is well (while telling the other person "I'm glad you're here").

SLAP ANOTHER LABEL ON IT. Another good way to reverse a downward spiral in your thinking is to give it a positive spin. If you relabel "Uh, oh. I feel nervous" as "I'm psyched!" your brain automatically shifts from take-cover mode into let's-roll mode. That helps rechannel a surfeit of adrenaline into positive action.

SING SOME SENSE INTO YOURSELF. Discouraging words that keep coming back call for a special strategy. "It's easier going toward these thoughts than going away," says R. Reid Wilson, PhD, a psychologist at the University of North Carolina and the director of anxieties.com, a self-help site.

Wilson says you can blunt the sting of endless self-reproach by putting it to music (in your mind, please). "I lost the only woman I'll ever love, because I was a jerk" sounds pretty silly once you sing it like Merle Haggard.

Too nutty for you? Studies suggest you can ease negative self-talk simply by rapidly sweeping your eyes from side to side about 25 times. "It stimulates both sides of the brain and briefly disrupts your thinking patterns," says Matthew McKay, PhD, clinical director of Haight Ashbury Psychological Services, in San Francisco, and the author of *Thoughts and Feelings: Taking Control of Your Moods and Your Life*. "It makes it hard to hold onto a disturbing thought."

SEDUCE HER WITH SMARTS

KELLI GARNER, THE REAL GIRL IN THE MOVIE *LARS AND THE REAL GIRL*, PROPOSES TWO STEPS FOR SUCCESSFUL SEDUCTION

BY MIKE ZIMMERMAN

"No way. How do you do that?" pleads Kelli Garner.

"Well," I say, "you suck air in like you're inhaling, but instead of going into your lungs, it goes into your stomach. Then you blast it out."

I've never taught anyone how to belch at will, let alone a gorgeous 23-year-old California blonde in a dark-blue tank top and Mets cap. "I can't do it," Garner says after a few attempts. "I need carbonation."

Kelli Garner is an interesting specimen. Yes, she has all the physical

THE ONION APPROACH

Here's how to peel back a woman's layers.

Explore her music. Notice we didn't say embrace. You don't have to love chick music. Garner cops to digging Led Zeppelin and early Prince, but also says that men who want to connect with a woman should have a familiarity with gynocentric artists such as Feist, Fiona Apple, Cat Power, and especially Jenny Lewis. "She's awesome—really sexy," Garner says.

Enjoy what gives your face character. Don't worry about your hairline or big ears, Garner says. Women gravitate toward features that give a man character. "I'm really attracted to interesting noses," she says. "Some people just have great noses. I don't feel like I'm one of those people." She pushes hers up to make pig nostrils. "Nothing wrong with it, but there's nothing to it, either."

Let yourself go (just a little bit). "One thing I can't stand is when men care too much about how they look," Garner says. "Leave that to the women. Look good, but don't obsess about it. That's not attractive at all."

requirements: the drive-up-a-lamppost body, blue eyes that invite you in, and long, blonde hair. Yet there's more underneath. She, unlike others her age who seem to feed off closing nightclubs and driving up lampposts with their own cars, has no interest in being cool. "In fact," she says, "I'm a geek."

She sure makes a good case: She's a science-fiction addict who just finished Neal Stephenson's novel *Snow Crash*. She loved *Transformers*. She plays World of Warcraft online, and doesn't dabble, either—she's a level 38 night elf for the Alliance. She plays guitar and writes her own songs.

Also, she prefers dark beer—we're sharing a few Fat Tires at a Sunset Boulevard bar—and doesn't go out much. If she hits the town, she does so with close friends or her boyfriend of 2 years. As far as being that hot young Hollywood thang posing for 200 cameras on a Saturday night—well, "I'm just not that girl," she says.

All of which, despite her best efforts, makes her extremely cool. So does her résumé. The edgy, dark, teen stuff? Check—Larry Clark's *Bully*. Scorsese?

Beware the other man in her life. Garner says that every girl has one guy she'll always compare you to: her dad. In Garner's case, she really does think his style is worth emulating. "He's simple but charming, never boring," she says. "He's also multifaceted and layered. He's a butcher. He restores cars. He also likes to play poker. His hobbies as a man are really attractive."

Dredge out some depth. No matter how good-looking a man is, Garner says, there eventually has to be something beneath the facade—and allowing a woman glimpses of that depth adds to the attraction. She uses two of her former costars, Ryan Gosling and Leonardo DiCaprio, as examples. "Ryan's mysterious and open at the same time," she says. "You can have a conversation with him, but there's a lot going on in his head. And Leo is smart and sweet, but also quiet. That surprised me, and it's really sexy."

For a backstage look at Kelli's photo shoot and a slideshow of outtakes, go to MensHealth.com, keyword Kelli.

Yup—*The Aviator*. Oscar buzz? Not yet, but maybe soon. Garner's latest, *Lars and the Real Girl*, had some potential thanks to a clever story line and above-average acting.

Margo, Garner's character in the film, is desperate to draw the attention of Lars (Ryan Gosling), who's painfully shy. Of course, the traits of Lars that catch Margo's fancy are the same ones that snare Garner's attention.

"The first thing that catches my eye is demeanor," she says. "I seem to be attracted to the quiet, brooding type. But not too brooding. Too brooding can be narcissistic. Or psychotic. I like quiet. I like a little withdrawn. I like men who are more in their heads."

In fact, extroverted guys get into trouble with Garner. "Lascivious stuff infuriates me," she says. "Once I was with my boyfriend in Vegas. We were at Caesar's in the high-roller section. And I had my expensive clothes on. We were having a really great time, losing way too much. This guy came over and says to him, 'Damn, how much did you pay for her?' I was like, 'Excuse me?' And he goes, 'I'm not talking to you, hooker'—except he didn't say hooker. I was like, 'Let's go.'" Security had to pull her off the guy.

"I don't understand that mentality," she continues. "I want a guy who can clean my gutters and kill my spiders—who's simple, yet layered."

"Simple, yet layered" is a theme with Garner. That combination—"simple" meaning unpretentious, "layered" meaning true depth of character—sums her up, too. Could that be the crucial clue to what women really want?

STREAMLINE YOUR LIFE

SURE, TOSS IT. BUT NOT EVERYTHING. SOME JUNK HAS THE POWER TO MAKE YOU A BETTER MAN

BY MARK MILLHONE

I am a pack rat. Actually, that's being modest. I'm one of the finest examples of *Rattus maximus* you'll ever meet, with caches of personal excrement up and down the East Coast. When confronted by the threat of seasonal global purging (a.k.a. spring-cleaning), I take refuge in "higher priority" behaviors such as work, income-tax preparation, and March Madness. The female of the species characteristically retaliates with ultimatums aimed at the male's genitalia. Example: "Don't touch me until you throw out that ugly chair/*Penthouse* collection/Budweiser beer lamp." Such was my uncompromising position one day last spring. The list of items my wife, Rose, felt simply needed to go included the following:

ONE (1) SHEET OF CORRUGATED FIBERGLASS: It was left over from a home project. Perfectly good, no sense in throwing it out. Might be useful, you never know. Rose knew. Out it went.

ONE (1) SUPER-8 FILM PROJECTOR AND SCREEN (BROKEN): This equipment had been passed down by Rose's great-uncle Abe. He told me he didn't need the projector because all the home movies he shot after World War II had been transferred to VHS. When I asked if we could watch them, he told me that the box with the tapes had been lost, but that this was okay because he had the memories.

At age 85, Uncle Abe still has the proverbial steel-trap mind. I have a mind like one of those windup egg-beating thingies you see at garage sales—kind of fun to play with and good for stirring life up now and again. But I retain next to nothing. Without a specific prompt, like a photograph or souvenir, I can forget days, weeks, entire years. I think this is why I'm such a pack rat—if I throw away something, I'm chucking a piece of my life.

THREE (3) SETS OF DISHES (A CLEAR-GLASS DINNER SETTING FOR FOUR, A "HAND-PAINTED" FLORAL COFFEE SERVICE, AND A CONTEMPORARY-STYLE SALAD SET): These were given to us 3 years ago at a housewarming-cum-birthday party for our son Sam. In drawing up the invite list, my wife and I decided it would be poor form not to include Sam's preschool caregivers. How could we overlook them when we were inviting all his classmates and their parents? When we did not receive RSVPs from Mesdames Yolanda, Colleen, and Shauna, we inquired in person. They looked at one another. Miss Shauna, the appointed spokeswoman, finally replied, "How much do you pay?"

It took us several minutes to convince them that we were asking them to come as guests, not as the help. Reflecting on the moment now, I can think of nothing sadder than the wide smiles that graced their faces, that a simple act of common decency could be so unexpected, so dear.

They arrived early, dressed in their Sunday best, while the rest of our friends trickled in fashionably late in their fashionably shabby clothes. The three women each brought one of the aforementioned dish sets as a present, all wrapped in the same paper, as if they had pooled their resources, gone to the same sale at Macy's, and shared paper to pinch pennies. We received many more-impressive gifts that day, but none more generous. I wanted them to feel welcome in our home, to feel comfortable, but they ended up spending the entire party in a corner of our son's room, seated carefully on his bed so as not to wrinkle their good clothes, or his sheets.

As moving as the gesture was, we had no use for the dishes. The unopened sets lived at the bottom of our hall closet, a sort of compost heap of memories. Over time, any keepsake that goes in there gets broken down, first into mere stuff and then, inexorably, into plain junk. The lucky ones are regifted or donated. I gave the dishes to the Salvation Army. They deserved better than Rose and me.

ONE (1) OFF-WHITE COUNTRY-CUTE BEDROOM SET: The set consisted of the following: a distressed antique dresser that Rose found at a chic store in Manhattan back when distressed furniture was still chic; a vintage sideboard purchased at an antique store in upstate New York that is no longer in business, transported by a Volkswagen van that we no longer own, to a house in which we no longer live; two faux-antique bedside tables from Crate & Barrel; and one faux-antique king-size bed frame from Ikea.

Of all things, it was the Ikea bed I couldn't bear to part with. Ikea breaks my heart every time. It's those cute little Swedish names for everything. You go in looking for something cheap to hold your crap and end up bringing home Vestby or Pax. It's like adopting a puppy. Rose and I got Tromsnes—just about the cutest little metal bed frame you ever did see—6 years ago during that nowhere week between Christmas and New Year's.

We were in Virginia visiting my folks and stepped into the local Ikea during a 3-day lull in conversation. (I've given up trying to explain to Rose that my family isn't rude, just Midwestern. Every meal in my parents' house starts with my father calling for "a moment of silence," and one time Rose just blurted out, "How about a moment of conversation?") After picking out a Tromsnes of our very own, we waited like expectant parents for her to show up at the customer-service desk, then carefully shepherded her past the long lines of those dangerous Ikea carts that never, ever, roll straight, and then, with tender loving care, tied her to the roof of our car.

The bed became a vital part of our household. It's where we retired to read our books, watch our TV, have our fights, make our love, and, occasionally, sleep. Our eldest son was conceived on that bed. I was sure of this. But Rose wasn't sure, not 100 percent, and this inch of doubt gave her the necessary emotional wiggle room to kick Tromsnes to the curb. There was this Jonathan Adler bedroom set Rose just had to have. I don't care much for sleep in general, and, no offense to Mr. Adler, I care even less about sleeping stylishly. But I do enjoy sleeping with my wife, which is why, over the years, I have largely delegated the responsibility of winning arguments to her. So, dear Tromsnes, fare thee well. Play nice with the other stuff in the landfill.

It strikes me now that the more stuff we have, the harder it is to possess belongings of real value. I find myself longing for what it must have been like back when my parents grew up, when people still "paid good money" for things, still "shopped for necessities" instead of just running to the store "to pick up some stuff." Back then, "getting a good value" meant buying something valuable instead of something inexpensive.

By the time I came along, my parents were enjoying a certain level of suburban affluence, but my mother always retained something of the little girl who grew up poor in Indianola, Iowa. She could say things like "brand-new" and "store-bought" without irony. She took tremendous pride in her jewelry collection. Each bauble, mainly inexpensive silver rings picked up at the mall or by my father on some business trip, resided in its own zipper-lock bag, along with a brief note cataloging its provenance in my mother's distinctive and, to the end of her days, perfect script.

"Sterling silver and turquoise necklace purchased summer 1983 on trip to Solvang."

"Silver ring set with azurite stone . . . gift from John, Christmas 1999."

Mom brought the same curatorial eye to care packages. No grease-stained boxes of busted peanut-butter cookies for us. I will always remember the magnificent teacup she sent me in college. It was the color of buttermilk, with a blue stripe lining its rim. What made the cup unique was a sort of kangaroo pouch on its side for holding your spent tea bag. In the same package was a sparkling tin filled with assorted tea bags in a zipper-lock bag for freshness. Also a barn-red electric teapot that was just the right size for my dorm room.

Because I never throw anything away, I know I still have that teacup somewhere. The reason we pack rats save everything is because there's no way to predict what will become invaluable; the only way to identify a precious keepsake is by looking in the rearview mirror.

ONE (1) LARGE IRON KEY WITH A LEATHER-SHOELACE FOB: Just as I was finishing up my wife-mandated spring-cleaning, I came across this key in the hall closet. It was heavy and impressive in the way of all very old things. I remembered vaguely that my mother had given me this key and told me its story. But now, because of my egg-beater brain, the story was gone, and, because of a heart attack, Mom was, too.

There was no way I'd ever know what lock the key turned, what door it opened. Maybe it was the key to a city. Maybe just to some old barn. All I knew was that it represented a memory, a little piece of my mother's life that, because I was too busy to listen to an old woman's story, was now lost forever.

I hung the key back on its hook and shut the closet door. Without the memory attached, the key was worthless. But as much as I wanted to toss it, I just couldn't. Throwing away junk is easy. Letting go of regrets is much more difficult.

ASK THE GIRL NEXT DOOR

THE HONEST TRUTH ABOUT WOMEN FROM OUR LOVELY NEIGHBOR

How do I meet more women?

Obviously there aren't many attractive, available women at the usual places guys hang out—sports bars, the gym, a buddy's living room. So go where the babes are. They're meeting each other for coffee at cafés, browsing the green market, working out at the gyms with the cleanest locker rooms, and eating and drinking at trendy restaurants and bars. Find yourself a wingman (or, even better, a wingcouple, because being the third wheel is a neon sign to women that you're unattached) and start hitting new venues. You see, the bane of the single man isn't a receding hairline or a potbelly. It's a stale routine.

The wink as a flirting device—effective?

If a man winks at me just right (while he's talking to someone else, and so fast the other person can't see), it's totally hot.

Will shaving my Sasquatch-like chest help me attract girls at the beach?

Sure, if what you're looking for are one-night stands with shallow bimbos (and, hey, I'm not judging). But any woman with a brain will recognize the razor burn and stubble as signs of insecurity. To find your Naomi Watts, you need to brandish your hairy torso with King Kong–like confidence.

What's the best pickup strategy at the gym?

First, pick a realistic target. The Kate Moss look-alike with the perma-frown who never glances at anything but her own reflection doesn't want to talk to you, and never mind that her translucent white sports bra is telling you otherwise. Girls who want to meet guys will look around, walk around, and even smile. When you see such a creature, make eye contact and grin. Then wait. Next time she's nearby, break the ice with a cookie-cutter comment: "Crowded in here today" or "Wow, it's dead." Then wait until you see her another day. You'll show that you're not desperate. If the idle chatter goes well, bring up a movie and ask if she's seen it. No? Would she like to? Men aren't willing to go slow and feel a woman out. And that's why most are shot down.

How can I charm a woman at a classy dinner party?

It's all about being polite. Offer to fill her glass when it's almost empty, say "please" and "thank you" to your fellow guests, take time to play with the dog or baby, and offer to help the host do the dishes. You could be slicker than Colin Farrell, but she still won't think you're a slimeball.

I've only met her once, but I was floored. Should I send flowers?

How old is she? If she's in her early to mid-20s, you're better off sending an e-mail—like "Hey, we met the other night. Just wanted to say hello." Recent college grads aren't used to receiving flowers. And while you might think she'd be charmed for that exact reason, the truth is she'll just think it's weird. If she's over 28, yes, send flowers (anything but roses). She'll have been dating long enough to appreciate a rare romantic gesture. Keep the card short and sweet.

I'm a broke writer wooing a woman who makes bank at a law firm. Where do I take her for New Year's?

Insider knowledge will always wow a girl more than money. So where's the coolest, least-known wine bar in town? How can you get access to the rooftop of a tall building and view the romantic city lights at midnight? Which underground venue is featuring live bands until 2 a.m.? Where is there a cabin where you can build a roaring fire, listen to Leonard Cohen on vinyl, and ring in the New Year in the middle of a forest? Find it and the girl is yours.

I have a crush on my roommate. How should I let her know?

You can't. Right now she believes that every time she passes you in the hall wearing nothing but a towel, you're looking at her with the blasé affection of a brother. If you announce that you "have feelings," she'll know that you were mentally undressing her all along. She'll feel betrayed and violated. If you really think you're head over heels for this woman, you should move out before coming clean. It will show that you care enough not to make her feel uncomfortable when she's at home. Sound like way too much trouble? Then I'm guessing you're not so smitten after all.

I think I made a bad first impression. How do I get a second shot?

Stop worrying. First impressions are powerful, but they're not everything. I can't tell you how many of my friends are dating or married to men they first wrote off as jerks. The best move: Acknowledge that you may have stumbled. Admitting that proves you're more perceptive and polite than she thought. Ask if you can start over. We find that charming; it makes us feel like we're in a Hugh Grant movie.

She asked for my number and then never called. Should I track her down?

If "tracking her down" means asking one friend for her e-mail address, then sure, yeah, why not. She may have simply lost her liquid confidence when she woke up Sunday morning. But if you have to resort to Google or calling friends of friends, that's approaching stalker territory.

I've been dating a great woman, but it seems as if I like her more than she likes me. How should I proceed?

You could play it cool and see if she comes running. Or you could redouble your efforts to try to win her over. But a far more confident, dignified way to handle the situation would be to put her on the spot. Show her that you're perceptive, straightforward, and far too smart to be screwed over. Start by telling her that you sense she's having second thoughts about you. Then go ahead and say you're wondering what's up with the two of you. Soften your comments by adding that you'd like nothing more than to keep seeing her because you think she's amazing. Now the onus is on her to decide whether she's willing to give up such an insightful, honest guy. If she is, you've avoided wasting time on a girl who isn't worth it. But I'm guessing she'll be impressed enough to stick around.

BOOST YOUR ANIMAL MAGNETISM

Courtship in the wild is more Sadie Hawkins than seize-and-conquer, says Dan Wharton, PhD, director of the Central Park Zoo, in New York City. "It's a scientific tenet that mate selection is almost always female driven," he says. We've plucked the wildest wilderness moves for this mating-game cheat sheet. Go get 'em, tiger.

LION

THE MATING DANCE: The lioness might signal interest with a paw to the jaw of her prospective king. If the lion approaches before he gets the green light, she bolts.

THE LESSON: Learn her cues. "If a male lion tries to take any shortcuts, it's a turnoff," says Wharton. Sound familiar? A single glance across a crowded bar could simply be a woman's way of beating boredom. Use this test: Ask a buddy to keep an eye on her while you go to the jukebox. If she looks up when you pass or leans in to a friend to whisper, she's probably interested. The next signal she sends is her paw to your jaw.

BABOON

THE MATING DANCE: Baboons become nervous and shy when they encounter a potential mate, says Barbara Smuts, PhD, author of *Sex and Friendship in Baboons*.

THE LESSON: Strike the right pose. Signal that you're sufficiently moved by her presence, but exude confidence as well, says David Givens, PhD, director of the Center for Nonverbal Studies. Stand up straight, chest out; keep eye contact, and slip your hands into your pockets a few times as you're talking. This gesture shouts strength and a bit of vulnerability, Givens says.

CUTTLEFISH

THE MATING DANCE: When on the prowl, he swims solo toward a potential mate and flashes his skin patterns to assert his masculinity.

THE LESSON: Break away from the pack. "Too much testosterone can be a major turnoff for women," says Janice R. Levine, PhD, author of *Why Do Fools Fall in Love?* To stand out, start by sartorially outflanking your posse. If they dress down, throw on a blazer. If they tend toward stripes, button up a crisp, solid oxford. And once you're at the watering hole, hit neutral nooks alone: the pool table, the patio, the other side of the bar.

SNOW LEOPARD

THE MATING DANCE: A few swats, a tackle, some bloody clawing: Play fighting helps the snow leopard create sexual tension and demonstrate strength.

THE LESSON: "Being a pushover won't further her attraction," says Levine. Create friction with some playful verbal sparring: If you find her list of favorite books ridiculous, rebut with your own. If she rags on your music selection, snap back about her stack of *Star* magazines. "The sexual tension will feed her desire for you," says Levine. "Without it, things will fizzle."

GORILLA

THE MATING DANCE: The patient male makes it clear he's ready to rumble but leaves it up to her to make the mating move.

THE LESSON: Leave her wanting more. Start with the postdate callback. It's not when you say it, but how and what you say that counts. Send her a short text: "Great time last night. Call me if you want to do it again." You'll send the right message but add a dose of uncertainty. "Anxiety increases the dopamine in her brain, which heightens the feeling of romantic love," says anthropologist Helen Fisher, PhD, a relationship expert and the author of *Why We Love*.

GO WILD

New research confirms it: Active women are more fun (in many ways). Here's how to land one.

Olivia Munn has cold feet. A minute ago, she was tearing through the brisk Pacific surf on an 8-foot longboard, canines bared, hair horizontal in the spray. But now the actress and host of the G4 cable network's *Attack of the Show!* has dropped her board and is screaming loud enough to scatter seagulls.

"Aaah! Damn it! My feet are freezing!" she yells, wading out of the water. We're pierside in Santa Monica, California, to solicit Munn's advice on wooing adrenaline-seeking Athena types like her. Back on the beach, we'll have a chance to hear her out.

See, Munn is a case study of sorts. Women like her—the tomboy-gone-hot type you're more likely to find in the barrel of a killer wave than grinding to Sir Mix-a-Lot during happy hour—aren't just more fun to hang with. They're also better partners, lovers, and friends.

"High sensation–seeking characteristics translate into curiosity, explorative urges, and openness to new experiences," says Marvin Zuckerman, PhD, author of *Sensation Seeking and Risky Behavior*.

What's more, "Women who participate in physical activity are more easily aroused, have a stronger libido, and have an improved ability to reach climax," says Cedric Bryant, PhD, chief science officer for the American Council on Exercise. (He had us at libido.)

If what these docs say is true, guys ought to quit playing courtship games with happy-hour girls and start looking for love at the front of a cycling peloton or the top of a 5.14c-rated climbing pitch. Munn is exhibit A: Her bikini comes with a warning label, but her confidence comes from having the tractor-beam personality to back it up. She'll disarm you with wit, woo you with a charley horse, then win you over with a wink. She's almost daring you to keep up with her. Here are six ways to woo an adventurous woman.

GO HARD, FALL GRACEFULLY

Adventurous men and women naturally have higher levels of libido-boosting testosterone, says Zuckerman. And you don't have to be great—or even good—to see the benefits. But be humble, warns Munn. "Too many guys substitute being an asshole for being confident, or funny, or anything else," she says. "I love it when a guy admits he has no idea what he's doing." The "asshole" trait she's referring to is a guy's natural defense when cornered by his own weaknesses. Munn wants you to disable that mechanism. So try new things—hitting the break at high tide, dancing the rumba, speaking Italian—and if you flop, fail with a smile. A woman will sense—and evade—any false swagger.

STOP TRYING FOR CLEVER

The hard part about approaching a woman like Munn? Keeping her interest. "Sensation seekers are less tolerant of people who are considered boring," says Zuckerman. But save the blistering wit for later in the conversation. "Just say 'Hi,' at first," Munn says. "I'll know if it's the right match from the beginning just by the feeling. And if something weird comes out of your mouth—a pickup line or a false compliment—you're dead in the water." Munn might have a soft spot for dark humor and scathing sarcasm, but she says your initial goal should be simply to prove you're "a normal, well-adjusted guy." Once you've learned more about her through conversation, turn on the charm.

DON'T MAKE EVERYTHING THE APOCALYPSE

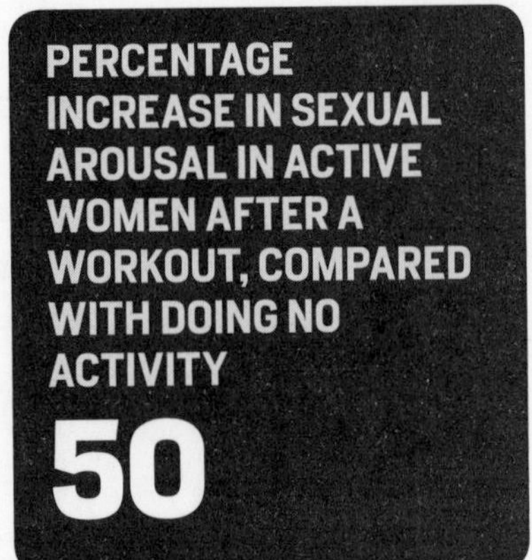

Our surfing stint fizzled, thanks to the frigid Pacific waters. But as Munn points out, you don't always have a storybook scenario at your disposal. "Sometimes the best memories are made when everything goes wrong," Munn says. "Spontaneity shouldn't seem forced. It isn't saying, 'Okay, we're going to leave at 2:00 because it gets traffic-y, and when we get there, I want flowers on the bed, and champagne.' If you're cool, the ending can fall through whenever and you'll be fine with it." Sensation seekers usually understand that you can't control every detail, says Zuckerman, but showing you can find your way helps them trust your compass.

HELP SPIKE HER ADRENALINE

Risky behavior—of all kinds, not just the Red Bull variety—boosts arousal, says Alan Booth, PhD, a professor of sociology and human development at Penn State University. Munn says she's just as likely to score a rush from beat-boxing in public or belting out a karaoke version of Mariah Carey's "All I Want for Christmas"—in July—as she is from whitewater rafting or skydiving, two of her other favorite pastimes. And if you can't keep her on her toes, you'll pay the consequences, she says. "When life is boring, sex is boring. It's routine: You're on top, I'm on top. You're from behind, I'm on top. Then we finish. You have to find new ways to make the same thing interesting. And sometimes that means being wild."

LOVE HER MOST EMBARRASSING TRAITS

About that Mariah Carey song: Taking risks means failing sometimes, often visibly. Munn says the best move a man can make is supporting a woman's risky ideas. "I'm not singing 'All I Want for Christmas' as a joke," she says.

"I know it's the worst song ever. I know it's way out of my range. But I love it. You have to embrace everyone's stupidest traits. There's nothing worse than a guy who second-guesses you when you're likely to second-guess yourself. It's the easiest way to ruin a woman's confidence. I've always been the one who goes for it. And if you're going to make me think twice, I'm going to think twice about you."

HOOK HER ON YOUR OWN INTERESTS

There's a difference between being the center of a man's universe and being the only solar body in orbit. "There's nothing worse than when a man says, 'You are my entire life,'" Munn says. "I'm like, 'Uh . . . do you like puzzles?' That's too much pressure. You have to be passionate about something else. I dated a man who loved guitar, and now I can pick out the different parts of a song. Passion is contagious. That's great, because I always want more out of myself. So if you open me up to new things, it makes me want you more."

RIPPED FROM THE RESEARCH

Active women are more likely to have ripped bodies and boatloads of energy—so you might not even need another reason to seek out these tigresses. But here's how they stack up to less-adventurous women.

Active women have a . . .

17% increase in desire for more adventure

5% increase in extroversion

10% decrease in neuroticism

25% increase in postexercise testosterone levels

7% decrease in inhibition

24% increase in testosterone levels when anticipating competition

HOLD YOUR HORSES

Here are 16 tempting urges that must always be controlled if you want to get noticed—in a positive way.

1. PERFORMING THE CHEST BUMP. Sporting celebration should be proportional to the peril faced in the pursuit of victory. If your game involves an underhand toss, midgame brews, or Velcro-backed flags, dial it down, champ.

2. BUYING ALL THE EQUIPMENT AFTER TWO LESSONS. Holster that credit card until you're certain the novelty of fly-fishing, snowboarding, or competitive bird-watching won't wear off.

3. BEING OVERPOLITE. Social pleasantries should be dispensed with grace. Saying "bless you" after each of nine successive sneezes makes you an automaton, not a gentleman.

4. WRITING A LOVE POEM IN THE FIRST 3 WEEKS OF DATING . . . AND NOT KEEPING IT TO YOURSELF. Her hair might indeed remind you of the first new morning rays of sun. But those rays may fade, and there's no reason to leave a paper trail.

5. FINDING EXACT CHANGE. Picking through your pocket lint for 11 cents isn't helping the barista churn through the morning rush any faster. Do everyone a favor and stockpile your coinage at home. Trade it for cash once a year, then treat your girl to a dinner you otherwise couldn't afford.

6. MARKING AN E-MAIL "HIGH PRIORITY." Just because Bill Gates dreamed up a button doesn't mean you should press it. Pick up the phone.

7. YELLING OUT A SONG REQUEST. Sorry, but the lead singer is only paying attention to the braless blonde in the front row. Channel all that energy into clapping, Casey Kasem.

8. OVERVALUING YOUR WISDOM. Just because you understand the intricacies of the global currency market doesn't mean you should share them. Unless there's a point to your pontification—you're a doctor, someone has symptoms—give it a rest. Saying, "Enough about me . . ." is often the best conversation starter.

9. FLIPPING THE BIRD. There's no better way to make sure you meet the recipient of your gesture at the next stoplight.

10. TALKING BETWEEN BATHROOM STALLS. No matter is so pressing that it needs to be discussed with your pants down.

11. SCREAMING AT THE CUSTOMER-SERVICE REP. Actually, check that: Go ahead and scream. Just make sure there's a method to your madness. You're mad at the company, and you're this close to taking your business elsewhere.

12. OVERPRONOUNCING FOREIGN WORDS. Granted, you spent a magical week in Baja, but that doesn't give you license to pronounce "Guadalajara" like you're clearing hair from your throat. There's a middle ground between butchering a word and being the pompous protector of its linguistic sanctity. Find it. (We're talking to you, Giada De Laurentiis.)

13. SENDING AN ANGRY E-MAIL. Along with drunk-dialing your ex and drinking appletinis, this one fits in the category of things you will always, without fail, regret. Here's a rule of thumb: The more bridges you'll burn, the longer you should let that e-mail smolder in your drafts folder.

14. TAPPING THE BRAKES. Avoid reckless drivers, don't antagonize them. Let him pass, then watch him get pulled over.

15. OVERSANITIZING. Washing your hands carefully after going to the bathroom: normal. Reaching for the bottle of Purell each time you exit a taxi: compulsive.

16. OBSESSING OVER YOUR FANTASY TEAM. If you're really that into a sport, play coach in a way that actually matters: Teach a kid to love the nuances of the game as much as you do.

SHOW YOUR STRENGTH

Here are 18 suck-it-up moments that pack a serious payoff.

1. RETURNING A WALLET. With all the dough. Witnessing the owner's delight is worth more than money.

2. ABSTAINING. If the Starbucks line snakes out the door, thou shalt not whip, frap, steam, cream, or half-caf. When time is of the essence, take it like a man: straight up.

3. WAVING. Your entire hand, not just the middle finger. Thousands die each year in aggressive driving-related accidents. Showing up 5 minutes late to work is better than showing up 60 years early to your funeral.

4. STOPPING AT SECOND BASE ON A FIRST DATE. Especially when she's waving you in from third. Settling for a stand-up double almost guarantees fireworks next time, when you put it over the fence.

5. DONATING PLATELETS. One apheresis session yields the same amount of clotting factor as six standard transfusions—and provides crucial help for burn victims, cancer patients, and organ-transplant recipients. Whose life have you saved today?

6. FIGHTING A BOGUS TICKET. The day we're too tired to fight even the smallest of insults is the day the bureaucrats break out the tattoo needles and bar codes.

7. VOTING. If you don't weigh in, you don't measure up.

8. HOLDING YOUR TONGUE. Every man possesses a simple superpower: silence. Too few flex it on a regular basis.

9. DANCING. Especially if you can't. No woman can resist a man who puts her pleasure ahead of his ego.

10. LAUGHING. At that humorless "joke" your dad trots out every Thanksgiving.

11. NOT LAUGHING. When your boss ponders what his secretary might do in a closed room with a clown. And in a wading pool. And with the Dallas Cowboys' defensive line. Standing up for your beliefs doesn't always require a lecture. See number 8, Holding Your Tongue.

12. CASHING IN YOUR CHIPS. In a perfect world, the dealer would continue to bust and the Niners would be a lock at +3. But Lady Luck is a fickle lover. Take the money and run.

13. DONATING TO CHARITY. Anonymously.

14. ORDERING SALAD IN A STEAK HOUSE. So what if your buddies are biting down on 24-ounce porterhouses and taunting you midchew? Your payoff comes at the beach; theirs vanishes with a belch.

15. WEARING BLINDERS. When the attractive blonde with the heaving chest and tiny tank top bends over. So what if she wouldn't notice, or wouldn't mind: You gain more power by exercising restraint when sin comes in the form of 42DD cleavage. To wit . . .

16. FORGOING. As in "Thanks, but I think I'll pass on that lap dance."

17. PUTTING IT IN WRITING. It's too easy to dismiss a casually uttered "thanks" or "sorry." If you really mean it, commit it to paper.

18. CONCEALING YOUR CONNECTIONS. At least at first. Sure, mention your father's frat days with the mayor and you might score the job. But saving it until you're already on board earns you respect.

THE NAME GAME

Sorry, Ned: A Miami University study found that people have an expectation of how others will look based on their names. Here's a sampling of the stereotypes.

Andy: long head, cleft chin
Tom: narrow-set eyes, pointy nose
Joe: cleft chin, pear-shaped head, full lips
Bill: small head, wide-set lips, squinty eyes
John: wide-set eyes, low-set eyebrows
Rick: pointed chin, tightly pulled-back ears

SMILE POWER

Don't underestimate the power of pearly whites. A strategic smile can make you instantly more attractive, according to a study in the *Journal of Nonverbal Behavior*. When the researchers asked 50 women to analyze videos of men

MINUTES PER WEEK THAT AMERICANS SPEND HAVING SEX—ABOUT 14 MINUTES BELOW THE GLOBAL AVERAGE

57

smiling, the guys who let a smile spread slowly across their face were rated as more attractive and trustworthy than those who flashed a grin.

"Women see this subtle delay as being more genuine," says study author Eva Krumhuber, PhD. To reinforce that perception, tilt your head slightly sideways when you smile, a move that tells her you're caring, not conceited.

FACE TIME

What's in a face? A lot, according to a study in the journal *Personal Relationships*. Researchers had 854 Americans view computerized images of male faces that were modified to look either more or less masculine by adjusting features such as jaw size and lip thickness. Manlier faces were judged aggressive and likelier to cheat, while more feminine ones were labeled hardworking, compassionate, and faithful.

Turns out these assessments aren't far off: "Facial masculinity relates to high testosterone levels, which have been linked to infidelity and violence," says study author Daniel Kruger, PhD. Next up: an international study to see whether the findings are universal.

DEAR OLD DAD

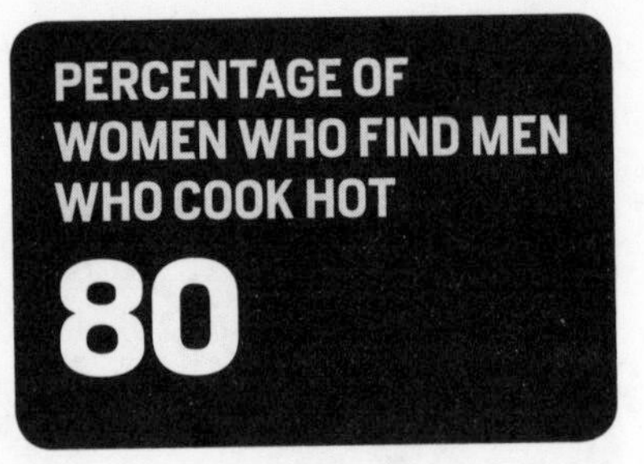

Move over, Oedipus: Daddy's girls tend to choose partners who look like their fathers, reports research in the journal *Evolution and Human Behavior*. Investigators asked 49 women how much time they spent with their fathers growing up and how close they felt to them, then measured the facial features of each of the women's dads. When they showed the women photos of 15 male faces, those who had loving relationships with their fathers rated faces that most resembled their dads' as the most attractive.

"It could be simple associative learning," says study coauthor Lynda Boothroyd, PhD: "This person is nice to me, therefore I like people who look like him."

MUSCLE MADNESS

Women love a hard male body, but they don't always buy into the beefcake. In a study published in *Personality and Social Psychology Bulletin*, researchers asked 141 women to view six silhouettes of men ranging from brawny to slender and rate them in different categories. Subjects identified the beefiest boys as more domineering and less likely to commit and labeled the "toned" guys—two notches away from the muscle men—as the most desirable.

The more muscular the men appeared, the more volatile and less likely to be faithful and sensitive they were rated, explains study coauthor David Frederick, a PhD candidate in UCLA's department of psychology. Women perceive men with big muscles as threatening and also know that it takes time to build all that beef—time you might not spend with them.

"They're looking for signs of not only health and fitness but also a potential commitment," Frederick says.

HOT OR NOT?

A roomful of George Clooney look-alikes shouldn't keep you from approaching the hot girl. Men and women overrate the attractiveness of members of their own sex, suggests a study in the journal *Evolution and Human Behavior*. Researchers showed 282 people photographs of the opposite sex and asked them to rate their sexual desirability from 1 to 10. Then men rated men, and women rated women, based on how hot they thought each would be to the opposite sex. Men and women rated others of their own gender one-third and one-quarter higher, respectively, than the opposite sex did. Why? We're programmed to see the same sex as a threat so that we work harder to attract mates, says study author Sarah Hill, PhD.

HELPER BEES

It's not what's in your wallet that makes you a better catch, it's how much you give away. Women find charitable acts sexy, reveals a study from England's Newcastle University. Researchers asked 146 women to rate a group of men on their attractiveness before and after experiments that uncovered each man's altruistic nature. The result: Men who were the most giving experienced a 10 percent increase in their appearance rating.

"From large-scale philanthropic gestures to wearing a LiveStrong wristband, incurring a cost to help someone signals that you'd be a good romantic partner," say the study authors, who add that simply having a reputation for helping others ups your desirableness.

NUMBER OF SINGLE MEN AGE 18 AND OLDER FOR EVERY 100 SINGLE WOMEN IN THE UNITED STATES

86

WINGWOMEN WORK

British psychologists have proven that you'll look better to women if you have a female looking at you. In a study, women rated photos of male faces—when the guy was alone, and then with a woman looking at him. Seeing other women smile at men increased women's preferences for those men.

On the flip side, male opinions of other men dropped if women were smiling at the men. So make 'em smile: "There's an advantage to being nice to people when you're at a bar or club," says study author Ben Jones, PhD, of the University of Aberdeen.

>>A MAN'S GUIDE POLL

You've Got Skills: We asked 1,000 women how various guy skills affect your hotness factor.

1 = Geeky 10 = Sexy

Playing an instrument = 7	Carpentry = 7.5
Cooking = 8	Throwing pottery = 3
Fishing = 4	Rock climbing = 7.5
Photography = 6	Foreign language = 7.5

PART 2
UNDERSTAND WOMEN

LISTEN UP!

WOMEN EVERYWHERE ARE TRYING TO TELL YOU SOMETHING IMPORTANT: THAT THEY WANT YOU. BUT AS THIS MAN LEARNED, YOU PROBABLY AREN'T PAYING ATTENTION

BY GRANT STODDARD

During my freshman year of college, I attended a traffic-light party at the student-union bar. Attendees were to wear red, yellow, or green to indicate their degree of sexual availability. In my naïveté, I cobbled together a green outfit entirely in hues of forest, lime, and olive. I earnestly believed that traffic-light parties might be a step toward a society where our wants and needs—my wants and needs—were out in plain view, and then we—I!—could transcend the folly of posturing, artifice, and coded messages and begin the business of living and loving!

As it turned out, I was the only partyer wearing an all-green outfit. I took my social beating and left the bar, alone. On the way home, I made peace with the fact that (a) my perpetually burning green light might never provoke a rush of traffic, and (b) posturing, artifice, and coded messages are systemic in human beings.

Since then, however, I've always held out hope that there might be a way to reckon the workings of the female mind and, like some libidinous supervillain, that I could harness that power. It would be like donning x-ray specs for a look at her horny soul.

So imagine my surprise when I learned that there does, in fact, exist a way to discern women's wants and needs, likes and dislikes, with nary a word being uttered. What's more, it's not an unwieldy thought-helmet; it's grounded in scientific fact. I'm learning how to hone this ability, and within the next several pages, you can, too.

The "secret" is nonverbal communication. You probably think of it as simple body language, but lately researchers have identified a slew of indicators that can signal what a person may be thinking.

Nonverbal communication predates spoken language in humans by hundreds of thousands of years, is used by just about every species on the planet, and is almost certainly a more reliable gauge of someone's thinking than the torrent of garbage that spills from our mouths. In his 1872 work *The Expression of the Emotions in Man and Animals*, Charles Darwin theorized that not all facial expressions and their corresponding emotions are culturally determined but are, in fact, universal to human culture and biological in origin.

What does that mean to you? That you can figure out whether you have a shot with a girl, whether you're in Akron or Addis Ababa.

Dana Carney, PhD, is a postdoctoral fellow in the department of psychology at Harvard. Blonde haired, blue eyed, and stunning, she doesn't look like your typical scientist, but she is a renowned expert in the fields of social perception, social neuroscience, and nonverbal communication. Put bluntly, Carney can read what's going on in a social situation like Keanu can see the Matrix. During a few hours in New York City, Carney will be informing my behavior so I can up my game through the cunning use of semiotics, the study of social signs and other visual cues.

In the broadest terms, her lesson is that a man should communicate the following:

I'm here, I'm male, and I won't hurt you. Unfortunately for us, it's a little more complicated than storming into a bar blasting an air horn and wearing nothing but a Lilith Fair shirt.

"According to evolutionary scientists like David Buss, women want men who express alpha status," says Carney, simultaneously enlightening me and dashing my hopes forever. "Research indicates that perceived dominance is expressed through using a loud voice, speaking a lot, making eye contact, touching, taking up lots of space, and successfully interrupting others."

For a soft-spoken, 140-pound, 5' 8" man-boy like myself, this isn't the news I'd been dying to hear. I take up very little space, and continually interrupting others has, in the past, yielded only a fat lip.

"Should a non-alpha-type male just lower his expectations?" I ask.

"No, not at all," she says in a comforting tone. "Women are also attuned to a man's intelligence, which indicates potential resource stability. This can be expressed through being engaged when another person is talking, nodding one's head, and making 'back-channel' comments like 'Ah, I see,' 'Yeah,' and 'Oh.' Engagement is also expressed by making lots of eye contact and asking questions."

"Ah, I see," I say, nodding and making lots of eye contact. "So what is a man attuned to in a woman's behavior?"

"Well, there are 'immediacy behaviors' that are predictive of affiliation, intimacy, and interest," she says. "They include (1) gazing in your general direction, (2) making mutual eye contact, (3) smiling, and (4) establishing closer physical proximity. You also want to pay close attention to her baseline demeanor—that is to say, notice whether you see a change in her behavior when she becomes aware of you. Deviation from her baseline plus one or more of items 1 through 4, and you're in good shape."

When body signals betray a pitcher or a poker player, they're called "tells." Among psychological scientists, it's known as "nonverbal leakage." Psychologist Paul Ekman spent decades studying these pinhole ruptures in our psyches, exposing the "micro-expressions" that give us away to those we are trying to deceive. One practical application of Ekman's life's work has been his assistance in putting together the Transportation Security Administration's revised behavioral-screening procedures post-9/11. It turns out that Shakira wasn't speaking metaphorically when she said her hips don't lie. They can't.

So, given how fully and rapidly a person can be assessed using semiotic data, I ask Carney what she's learned about me in the 30 minutes since I sat down with her.

"From your behavior today, I know you're funny and very emotionally demonstrative, and you put on a little show for people when you first meet them," she says.

I always felt that being "emotionally demonstrative" was my Achilles' heel. After two or three beers, my poker face inevitably becomes my poke her! face. But now all that might change: I have a scientist perverting her training to get me all up in some unwitting girl's business.

So we hit the town in earnest.

SCENARIO #1: THE BOOKSTORE

For the first field test, we head to the nearest Barnes & Noble. Some of my female friends suggested that a bookstore was a place where men and women are constantly throwing out the vibe. My esteemed PhD wingwoman concurs.

"I've always thought bookstore cafés are interesting," says Carney. "There seems to be a lot more going on in this situation than people reading books and drinking coffee. I mean, look at all the preening and primping going on here among the females; they seem very aware and self-conscious. This can give us a lot of information about whether or not they're open to being approached."

Together we single out a woman in her mid-20s who is both attractive and more concerned with fixing her hair and furtively looking around than with the tome she's idly flicking through. The plan is for me to initiate contact as Carney analyzes the interaction from a respectful distance. As I ready myself to join the woman at the table, our mark rises and strolls over to the New Nonfiction table.

"Damn, I've spooked her!" I hiss.

"Don't worry," Carney assures me. "Follow her over there and start chatting."

In the interest of science, I saunter over. She is reading a biography of Chairman Mao during the People's Revolution.

"That looks like a fun read," I say with an awkward grin.

She presses her lips together in a contemptuous smile. Silence.

"But when it comes to tyrannical despots, you really can't beat Stalin, for my money."

She laughs at my joke quite loudly, cutting the tension, though I notice that her shoulder is positioned so that she's showing her back to me a little. The torso unwittingly orients toward people we like, admire, or agree with, and angles away from those we dislike or disagree with. Richard Nixon was often pictured rotating his torso 90 degrees from his advisors (0 degrees meaning completely facing and 180 meaning turning one's back completely). With her body at about 110 degrees, she resumes reading the jacket cover.

"I'm more of a creative-nonfiction fan myself," I offer, to keep some momentum going. I reach out for the nearest book of that sort. "I can totally recommend this one." She nods her head but keeps her eyes fixed on Mao. Silence.

"Okay, see ya!" I say, admitting to myself that it was a bust, and begin to slink off, my tail between my legs somewhat.

"Have you read *Running with Scissors*?" she asks, resuscitating the exchange after I'd presumed it dead.

"Um . . . no," I lie.

"It's good," she says, then turns back to her book.

"Okay, I'll check it out," I say, and again begin to retreat.

I make it a few steps before she calls out, "It's by Augusten Burroughs. It's over there." As she says the words "over there," she motions over her shoulder with her thumb in a hit-the-road-Jack–type way that makes me think she's had enough of me.

"Ugh, that didn't go so great," I say as Carney and I hit the street again.

"I wouldn't say that," she says in a knowing tone. "There was some hair fixing, and I noticed that she really laughed at what you said. But she was talking to you over her shoulder, and eye contact was fleeting, so there were conflicting signals. She didn't seem to make an effort to close the distance between you, but she did seem somewhat interested. Both times you began to walk away, she started up the conversation again. After you walked away the second time, she turned to see if you were looking, then immediately started reading the back of the book you pointed out to her."

"Damn! Should I go back in there and try to get her number?" I ask Carney.

"No, we learned what we could. Let's try somewhere else. There are plenty of experimental subjects around." Read: "cute girls."

Even a psychology PhD from Harvard will confess that meeting women is, at its root, a numbers game.

SCENARIO #2: THE DIVE BAR

Entering a dive bar in the East Village, we immediately head for a table in a shadowy back corner. It's only around 7 p.m., but this is the sort of joint where no one hesitates to get their slur on. There are about 20 people in the place. Sitting at the bar is a cluster of women, all with badass sleeves of tattoos, cockatoo hairdos, and stripy clothes in all the colors of the Day-Glo rainbow. I am about to go up and squeeze in among them to order drinks when Carney stops me.

"It's important to establish a baseline first," she says. "You have to get a feel for a woman's normal social behavior, and from that baseline, you can discern where that behavior deviates when you establish eye contact or move into close proximity."

To paraphrase my girl whisperer: If you go charging in, you might find out the hard way that a woman's apparent flirtations with you are actually her normal mode of interacting with people.

From our vantage point, we concur that the seven women and one man are friends, since they are all interacting and involved in one conversation. All the women are fairly attractive. We spend the next few minutes taking a baseline reading for each of them. There's the quiet one, the cute one, the alpha one, the sullen-looking one, the lustful-looking one; it's like we're deconstructing the Pussycat Dolls, great fun in itself.

Satisfied that we have the lay of the land, I walk the length of the bar, then double back and insert myself into the thick of them and order drinks. I get the briefest of little smiles from "cute," but otherwise I can't discern much change in behavior. From her vantage point, however, Carney is able to observe some interesting things.

"Out of all the girls, the quiet one with the brown hair showed the most extreme behavioral deviation from neutral," she begins. "First, as you approached, she sort of stiffened up and sat at attention. There was some lip pouting, which can be associated with desire. Though she didn't gaze at you, she was very aware of you in her peripheral vision and immediately touched her face and then her hair with her hand, which can also be associated with desire."

"As you walked by," she continues, "she looked over her shoulder at you, and when you leaned in among them all, she suddenly got bigger: Her voice got louder, and her facial expressions and gesticulations became more exaggerated. Then she glanced at you as you walked back over here."

"Wow, you saw all that?" I ask.

"Sure. So we can say that she was probably acutely aware of your presence and possibly somewhat desirous. As she seemed to be concerned with where you were going, she did some preening and then made pains to stand out from the pack, maybe aware that she typically has less presence than some other members of the group. So if you're thinking of making contact, I would initially single her out as being quite receptive."

With a behavioral scientist like Dana Carney as my permanent pickup consigliere, I could truly be the scourge of the female population. It'd almost be unfair.

"Should I go over and start chatting her up?" I ask, emboldened by Carney's observations. "What if she just becomes fidgety?"

I look over at our mark.

"Well, go to the bar again and we'll see if she exhibits any more telling behavior, and then . . . Look!" Carney is suddenly excited. "She's making an unnatural series of orientation and posture changes so she can remain visible to you in the crowd of girls. I'd guess that she knows you have a lock on her."

The girl in question isn't necessarily the first woman in the group I'd gravitate to, but the idea that she's interested in me suddenly makes her much more attractive.

"So, now that we can assume she's somewhat interested, go up to the bar and see if she makes any slipups in her speech: mispronouncing words, forgetting what she's saying, trailing off midsentence. It could be indicative of cognitive load—her mind is so preoccupied with your presence that it exerts a strain on what she was initially doing."

I stand up and catch our target's eye. We both look away and then catch each other in another fleeting glance. As I approach, she dives into her purse and pulls out a compact, then checks her lipstick and tousles her bangs. Preening, I think to myself.

"So, go on!" says the friend perched on the bar stool next to her as I get closer.

"Um . . . yeah, so . . . uh . . . I was like, 'I'm not coming' . . . and then . . . um . . . "

Either my would-be girlfriend has a mental impairment or, as Carney suggested, her speech is faltering under the cognitive load of my approach. Retreating to my table one last time, I ask Carney if there are any nonverbal-communication techniques I can utilize when approaching a woman within a group.

"Research shows that in a group of women, each individual is less of an independent entity than individuals in a group of men would be," says Carney. "For instance, in my experience, if a woman in a group just left the bar out of the blue, it would be a big fuss, as if a child had been lost. 'Where did she go?' 'Is she okay?' 'Did you call her?' 'When did you see her last?' Right? There would be calling and finding and then a big fuss with her about why she left—it would be a fairly big deal.

"Contrast that with a guy unexpectedly leaving his group at a bar. You'd say, 'Oh, he probably met some girl,' and that would be that. So, because of the inherent structure of female groups, I think it's safe to say that you do want to talk to her friends, engage them, be interested in them, and convince them to trust you. I imagine the approval of her friends can make or break your chances sometimes."

I'm here, I'm male, and I'm not going to hurt you!

With an atypical swagger brought about by feeling like the Jedi master of seduction, I accost my raven-haired subject as she's paying her tab and hit her with a corny line that I'd used before with marginal success.

"Hey, I was sitting over there figuring out what I was going to say to you and I had a bunch of great stuff, but now you're leaving!"

"You snooze, you lose!" she says as I take in the nonverbal indicators as per Carney's tuition:

Cocked eyebrow—disdain/superciliousness. Bad.

Wry smile—interest/like. Good.

Angular distance—45 degrees/guarded. Bad.

Pout—desire/interest. Good.

It's a bit of a mixed bag.

"It's all too late now, but I really think you ought to hear some of the lines I had worked up. Then you can use them on cute guys if you like."

Laughing—like/amusement. Good.

"Oh yeah?" she says.

Touches hair—preening/interest. Good.

"Yeah, give me your number and we'll get together and you can write them all down."

More laughing—like/amusement. Good.

Closing the distance—like/affiliation. Good.

Angular distance decreasing—15 degrees. Bingo.

Becky writes her number on a napkin and puts it in my hand. Then she zips up her coat and leaves the laboratory. Lab rat gets girl.

SCENARIO #3: THE BLIND DATE

Flush with that success, I feel ready to go solo and then recount my evening to Carney for the postdate analysis. This is a blind date, set up by a mutual friend. I'd met Adrianna before in passing and, with some cajoling, had imposed on our mutual friend Lisa to relinquish her contact details. We arranged over e-mail to meet and get together two nights later at a bar. I remembered that Adrianna is attractive, but I didn't recall her being quite as beautiful as she appears, striding in out of the cold.

"Hey!" she says with exuberance—big smile, wide eyes.

I hesitate over whether to shake her hand or give her a hug, given that we'd spoken only for a few minutes all told, but she initiates a warm clinch that lasts at least several seconds.

"It's great to see you," I say, smiling but replaying my mantra Stuart Smalley–style in my head: I'm here, I'm male, and I'm not going to hurt you.

"It's so great to see you," she says.

We're facing each other squarely, our hands on each other's elbows.

"Can I get you something to drink?"

"What are you drinking?" she asks.

"Brooklyn Lager."

"Nice, I'll have one, too."

A manifestation of mimicking, perchance?

We sit at a high table for two. Initially the stools are positioned on opposite sides of the square table, but I notice that a few minutes into a very lively and natural-feeling chat, she's seamlessly shuffled her stool so that it's perpendicular with mine and now our knees touch slightly.

Closing distance/touching . . . It's looking good!

Am I putting a disproportionate amount of stock into Carney's tutelage? Did Adrianna know that she was effectively saying, "Take me, I'm yours"?

One thing I notice is that we're giving each other plenty of eye contact, back-channel comments, and relevant questions. We're telling each other that we are mutually engaged, interested, and not even mildly cretinous. After we finish our beers, Adrianna says she is in the mood for a really spicy Bloody

Mary, and, in the spirit of mimicry, I order one, too. When I get back from the bar, she places her hand on mine.

When I later recount the hand touch to Carney, she says, "Touching in this intimate setting is very telling. There are two of you alone in close proximity. She didn't need to work to get your attention, nor was she trying to persuade you, or enlist you in some activity. So it seems the touch had no other purpose than to signal approach. Although I don't necessarily agree with this, in the 21st century, the onus is still on the male to make the advances."

After 90 minutes with both of us faithfully mimicking each other—right down to the swaying and slurring of words—we come to the conclusion that we are hungry and head off to one of my favorite eateries. We are put at a corner table and again sit perpendicular to each other. Knees touching, leaning in so that our faces are just less than a foot apart.

"My intuition and anecdotally based sense, colored by my scientific expertise, suggest that face closeness in the absence of necessity is certainly a sign of approach, feelings of liking, feelings of intimacy," Carney later observes. "There is little doubt in my mind that close faces are more indicative than close knees. Further, you can think practically about kissing behavior and how having your faces close is a prerequisite for that."

All the signs look good as I walk Adrianna to the subway stop, and I feel that the arctic wind whistling around us may have made our goodbye shorter than I would have liked. After dinner, the prospects of a hook-up—something that had seemed a foregone conclusion until then—seem to recede slightly. We hug briefly, and she mentions getting together in a group-of-friends scenario, which after all my analysis seems like a bit of a letdown.

I ask Carney if I might have interpreted Adrianna's nonverbal behavior early in our date too optimistically.

"No. Nonverbal behavior, which is often emotionally based and automatic and uncontrollable, can be much more telling than controlled responses, like what you say. Maybe she felt insecure about all her approach behavior, since you didn't kiss her or otherwise clearly indicate your interest."

This is how a scientist calls you a pussy.

THE NONVERBAL HALL OF FAME

Here's how selected women say everything about their sexual intentions without saying anything at all.

"I like to do an eye/lip gaze combo. It works pretty well, too: When you want a guy to kiss you, look him in the eye, then down to the lips, then up to the eyes again, down to the lips, back in the eyes again, and by the third time you look at his lips, he'll kiss you. But it has to be done subtly so you don't look like a weirdo."—Emily, 32

"When I'm around a cute guy, I act shy and flirt with my eyes. I look him in the eye and, when he notices me, I flash him a smile and nod my head to acknowledge his glance. If he's interested, he'll come over and initiate conversation."—Molly, 22

"I stand close to him, and, if we're in a crowd, I make sure to lean in toward his ear, which is more about him feeling me inches away from him than just hearing what I have to say. And I'll look at him intently. I have no proof, but I believe people can tell when you're really engaged and focusing on them."—Amy, 31

"I grab his drink out of his hand without asking and take a sip."—Kiki, 26

"I turn my body toward him and lean in to show interest in what he's saying. And there's more touching, usually just teasing jabs in the arm."—Sarah, 33

"Perhaps her mention of a group date was her effort to mitigate the clear clues she sent before. Maybe she was trying to 'correct'—that is, use choice words to artificially pull back her previous automatic nonverbal expressions of liking."

This makes me feel even worse.

Unlike the 2 million other species on this planet, humans alone have the ability to "take back" or otherwise qualify instinctual nonverbal behavior through spoken language. A female baboon can't present her big red ass all day, then suggest to her suitor that they just be friends. It's because she can trust the male baboon to do what's right for her and her species.

I encouraged Adrianna into major presenting behavior, then failed to answer. A nonverbal illiterate!

Since meeting with Dana Carney, I've noticed that women seem more nuanced in this form of communication and therefore have greater control over the messages they're sending. So when they utter the universal female complaint—"Guys are so stupid"—maybe they're right. And it might just be because of what we don't say, and how we don't say it.

THE NONVERBAL OFFICE

Dana Carney, PhD, a Harvard University specialist in nonverbal communication, translates innocuous office gestures into emotional telltales.

THE COWORKER AND SITUATION	THE SIGNALS	THE EMOTION IT BETRAYS	THE MOVE
The boss, during or immediately following an interaction	Lower-eyelid twitching Nose crinkling Single-sided smile	Anger Disgust Contempt	Have a friend casually mention your name to the boss to see whether any "tells" occur; if so, you have some work to do.
The gang at the watercooler, when you approach	Engaged gazing Touching Orienting body toward you	Admiration Affection Interest	All good; if they're shorting you on these engagement techniques, it means you may have some fences to mend.
Your copy-machine crush, when you corner her near the Ricoh	Tightly folded arms Looking over your shoulder as she talks Head or body orientation away from you	Defensiveness Disinterest	Find a different copier to use.
The covert office couple, in the lunchroom, interacting with one another	Touching their own faces Mimicking each other's posture and hand/arm positions Licking or puckering lips	Self-consciousness, desire Mental synchronicity, emotional bonding	Start saving for a wedding gift.

MEET SOMEONE NEW

HERE ARE SIX WOMEN YOU NEED TO MEET TO CRAWL OUT OF YOUR DATING RUT

BY SARAH MILLER

Sure, you've gone out with 20, 30 women. But we're willing to wager that you're actually dating the same woman over and over again.

"We often return to similar patterns, to familiar personalities and modes of interacting," says anthropologist Helen Fisher, PhD, a relationship expert and the author of *Why We Love*. Not only does dating the same type of woman become a little boring, but it also doesn't allow you to evolve. But with our roster of classic womanly personalities as a guide, we'll sort out what you like, why you may be stuck in that pattern, and what you could be missing out on—both romantically and sexually—by not mixing up your playlist.

THE URBAN SOPHISTICATE

HER STRENGTHS: This woman is funny, hot, and spontaneous. When you walk into a room with her, everyone stares at you in envy. Neil Strauss, author of the best-selling dating memoir *The Game*, puts it simply, "This is the kind of girl everyone wants, and it makes you feel awesome when you're the one who has her."

HER WEAKNESSES: "You need enormous confidence to date a woman like this," Strauss says. "She gets off on attention, but you can't get jealous." If you're independent, you'll dig her ambition, but make sure she wants you—and not just the ego boost you provide.

HER BEDROOM PERSONA: She's uninhibited and nicely groomed. Tell her you like her on top, preferably wearing something expensive that makes her breasts look hot.

THE ARTY HIPSTER

HER STRENGTHS: She knows where all the dive bars are and all the art shows with free wine. She's exciting and stylish, but not as untouchable as the urban sophisticate. "She actually likes nerds and intellectuals," says Ian Coburn, author of *God Is a Woman: Dating Disasters*. And she actually cares about culture. "She can be great for a guy who wants to learn more about art and music," says Ian Kerner, PhD, a relationship therapist and the author of *She Comes First*.

HER WEAKNESSES: Do you keep going after her because you hope her cool will rub off on you? If your interests don't match, don't expect to just coast along on her taste. "Girls like this have opinions," Kerner says. "And they want you to know the difference between Jonathan Adler and Jonathan Richman."

HER BEDROOM PERSONA: The good news: She's dirty. The bad news: Her bed's not that clean. Tell her if she changes the sheets before you come over, you'll take her to see Blonde Redhead—in Japan.

THE VEGAN YOGA GAL

HER STRENGTHS: She's got great skin and a long neck, and she gives you long back rubs with wacky oils. All that deep breathing means she rarely flies off the handle, and you value this perhaps even more than you value her amazing, high, tight rear, which is saying a lot. Strauss says, "This is a woman who really wants to make a deep connection with life, and a man who wants the same could be really into her." Fisher says that independent, analytical, or creative guys could find her alternative view fascinating.

HER WEAKNESSES: Remember, Strauss notes, "These women are almost exclusively interested in men who are into the same stuff they are." Love her, love her lifestyle.

HER BEDROOM PERSONA: She's just as *Kama Sutra*–esque as you were hoping—but no quickies. She likes it slow and soulful.

THE ALPHA FEMALE

HER STRENGTHS: She graduated from college in 3 years and went right to law school without taking a vacation. She's hard to keep up with. Ironically, it's not the alpha dog who should try dating her. "A scientist, artist, or teacher will do well with this woman," says April Masini, author of *Date Out of Your League*. "If you're not interested in power plays, she won't fight you."

HER WEAKNESSES: She has a lot in common with alpha males, but these relationships are too intense. "They can't make time for each other," Fisher says. Coburn cautions that pushover types are often attracted to such women, and some alpha females—the sadistic ones—are attracted right back. "Obviously, if this is your dynamic, it isn't good."

HER BEDROOM PERSONA: She's efficient and skilled, but she can be more than sufficiently animal if you help her let her guard down.

THE INTIMACY JUNKIE

HER STRENGTHS: She goes to yoga, too, but it's the easy kind that's more about "connection to the self" than sculpting a smoking bod. So what if she's a little in your face. The sex is amazing. Strauss likes women like this. "She is the best kisser in the world. Very intense, very into connecting." Fisher says independent men will love such a deeply verbal gal, and Kerner thinks all men should date someone like this. "Most men need help learning to communicate, and she will help them."

HER WEAKNESSES: The intimacy junkie makes you feel great at first. She's so into you and your feelings. Analytical men will find themselves easily ensnared in her macramé web. "He will be super into her at first, but there's going to be a lot of talk about the 'meaning' of the relationship, which might cause it to implode," Fisher says.

HER BEDROOM PERSONA: She'll do anything, including some things that scare you. The word *harness* comes to mind. Tell her you'll do it if she gets waxed.

THE HAPPY HOMEMAKER

HER STRENGTHS: She's no gold digger—all she wants is a Volvo wagon and a nice, cozy three-bedroom. She wants to have your kids, take care of them, and take care of you. "Some guys draw a great deal of ego satisfaction from providing for a family, and there is nothing wrong with that," says Masini. A man who grew up in a very traditional household will love her, and, conversely, a guy who grew up with domestic chaos craves this woman for the stable home she provides.

HER WEAKNESSES: Remember that when she says she's not going to work, she means it. Career-minded men could be happy with an arrangement that allows them to focus on their work while she manages his domestic life. But if the financial stress builds, you may not be able to convince her to get a job.

HER BEDROOM PERSONA: She'll be accommodating and eager at first, less so with each offspring. Find a good babysitter so the two of you can steal away.

>>A MAN'S GUIDE POLL

Romantic Typecasting: We asked 764 women to tell us which combos would make them most want to hitch a ride.

1 = No thanks 10 = Let's roll

Tattoos and a Harley: 2.5	Oakleys and a Tahoe: 7
Jeans and a pickup: 7	Pressed shirt and a BMW: 7.5
Cashmere sweater and a Jag: 5	Team jersey and a Mustang: 3
Blazer and a Lexus: 6	Bomber jacket and a 'Vette: 2.5
Gold chains and a Ferrari: 2	Track suit and a Cadillac: 2
iPod and a Prius: 3.5	Fleece vest and a Jeep: 6.5

LIGHT HER FIRE

STUDY AFTER STUDY SUGGESTS THAT BEING HAPPY BETWEEN THE SHEETS LEADS TO A LONGER LIFE, A HEALTHIER HEART, AND FEWER INSTANCES OF DEPRESSION. AND IT ALL STARTS WITH ONE SPINE-TINGLING TRIGGER KNOWN AS THE TURN-ON

BY KRISTINA GRISH

Sex is more than just a way to bond with your girl and send your senses into overdrive (as if that weren't enough). To light your fire—and keep it burning at record high temperatures—we conducted, along with *Women's Health* magazine, their biggest online survey to date. More than 1,000 women confessed their biggest turn-ons, and we discovered a dozen sexy triggers that work for just about everyone. Here's why they rev her engine—and how to shift your mojo into an even higher gear.

No matter what you may have heard, the secret to being sexy is being in tune with the sensations that make her want to drop her dress and get it on. "Knowing what turns you on—and why—is key to a great sex life because it gives you control over your own pleasure," says Scott Haltzman, MD, clinical assistant professor of psychiatry at Brown University. Instead of waiting for randiness to come along, learn how to make it happen when and where you want it to. It's as close as you're ever going to get to having an "on" button.

PERCENTAGE OF WOMEN WHO SAY IT'S POSSIBLE FOR A GUY TO TURN THEM ON EVEN IF THEY'RE NOT IN THE MOOD

86

To give you a handle on what makes her horny, we pinpointed the top 12 sexual triggers for women via *WH*'s biggest online survey yet. Then we asked psychologists and sex therapists why these fleeting moments—the sweaty rush of a hard workout, flirtatious eye contact with a hot stranger—make a woman's thighs go up in flames. And because enough is never enough when it comes to sex, you'll also find innovative tips on how to take each turn-on to the next level, plus (thanks to a MensHealth.com survey) which fire starters work for guys, too. Is it getting hot in here?

PERCENTAGE OF GUYS WHO LOVE IT WHEN A WOMAN RUNS HER FINGERS THROUGH THEIR HAIR

71

SURVEY SAYS: HER #1 TURN-ON

TO AROUSE HER SENSES: "WHEN A MAN TOUCHES MY HAIR"

WHY IT WORKS: The scalp contains millions of nerve endings (a fact not lost on the folks at Herbal Essences—Yes!). And a man's fingers running through her locks is a primal form of nurturing that makes her feel loved, says Laura Berman, PhD, author of *The Passion Prescription*. You know, like when monkeys pick nits from their partners. Don't scrunch your nose: It's evolutionary psychology at work.

NOW TRY: Amplify the feeling by brushing her hair—or even better, wash it with warm water, which increases bloodflow and therefore pleasure to your scalp. When a woman puts herself in a man's care, it arouses both of them, Berman says. While women are attracted to good caregivers, "men love when we surrender to their touch," says Patti Britton, PhD, clinical sexologist and author of *The Art of Sex Coaching*.

WHAT ELSE WOMEN LIKE: "WHEN HE KISSES MY SHOULDER"

WHY IT WORKS: Because he approaches you unexpectedly. "Surprise kisses send a message of attraction and affection," says Joy Davidson, PhD, a New York City sex therapist and the host of the online video series *The Joy Spot*. "They're sweet and attentive and suggest that he can't keep his hands off you." Few things make our knees buckle more dramatically than being the object of someone's lust.

But affectionate surprises aren't just about take-me-now urges, says Molly

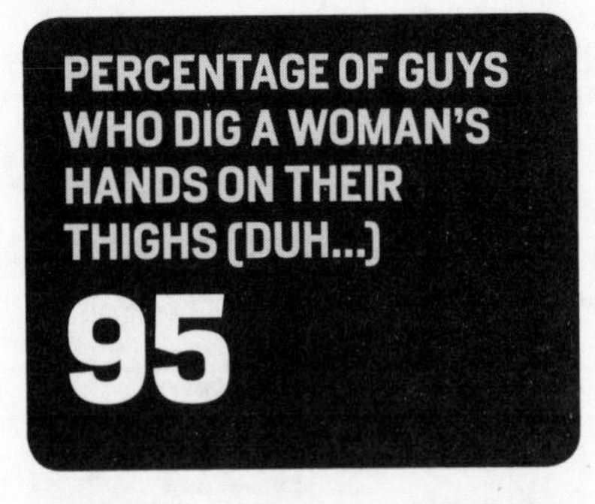

Barrow, PhD, a psychotherapist in Naples, Florida, and author of *Matchlines*. "We're taught from childhood that when a guy pays attention to the 'big three' (breasts, butt, and V-spot), it means he wants sex." So when he attends to other parts of your body, he's saying your pleasure is more important than his. "He's not going for the imme-diate score," Barrow says, which makes us less defensive—and more receptive—than when he comes on strong.

NOW TRY: Barrow suggests that you and your partner each write down things you wish the other would do to often-ignored parts of your body (smooch your collarbone, flick your earlobe with her tongue, stick her toe in your navel—just kidding!). Then drop them into a jar, pull out one or two before your next romp, and set a rule to avoid the big three for as long as possible during foreplay to heighten anticipation. "Men can go from zero to full-throttle in 6 seconds or less, while women take about 20 minutes to feel ready for intercourse," Barrow says. Prolong your start-up time and make those 20 minutes work to your advantage.

WHAT ELSE WOMEN LIKE: "WHEN HE PUTS HIS HAND ON MY THIGH"

WHY IT WORKS: "Certain parts of your body, like your inner thigh, are impossible to touch by accident," Dr. Haltzman says. "When you're close enough emotionally to someone to allow him into that space, it's very arousing and reflects the trust you have in each other."

NOW TRY: Gravitate toward other spots on her body that are off-limits in public, Dr. Haltzman says. Reach for the back pocket of her jeans or slide your fingers between the bottom of her foot and the inner sole of her high heel. (Makes those Marc Jacobs slingbacks totally worth the price tag.) Then start to explore other personal spaces on your own, he says.

SURVEY SAYS: HER #1 TURN-ON WHEN IT COMES TO THE GYM: "THE RUSH AFTER A LONG RUN"

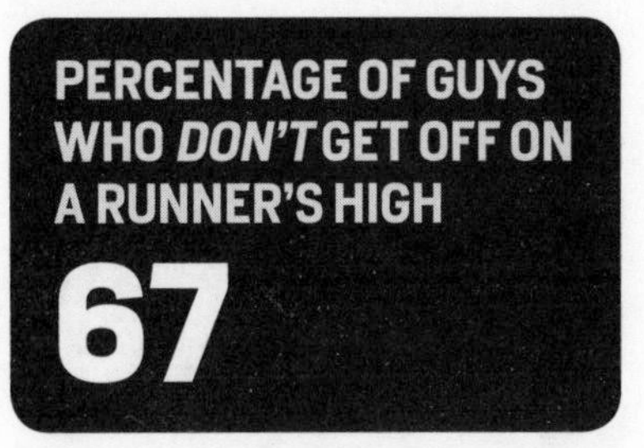

WHY IT WORKS: Exercise triggers the release of dopamine and norepinephrine—the same neurochemicals that surge when you first fall head over heels. It also releases endorphins, increases bloodflow, and allows more oxygen to reach your brain, which makes you more alert and heightens your senses. "This parallels what happens during sex," Britton says.

NOW TRY: When she gets home from work—and before she hits the couch for her *Lost* fix—encourage her to take a walk outside with you. "Even walking home from the office or up the stairs with groceries gets your blood pumping," Britton adds. If your heart is pounding, you're more likely to feel in the mood.

WHAT ELSE WOMEN LIKE: "WATCHING MY MUSCLES WHILE LIFTING WEIGHTS"

WHY IT WORKS: "Not only does building muscle support testosterone, a hormone that plays a vital role in sexual desire and sensation," Berman says, "but when a woman sees her muscles get stronger before her eyes, her body image skyrockets." When you feel good about your body, she says, you'll have a stronger libido and better sexual response.

NOW TRY: Channel the power and control she feels in the gym into her sex life by being more physical in bed. Experiment with positions that require her to support her own weight, getting on her hands and knees while you enter her from behind, for example, or by resting on her feet and squatting over you. If she likes watching her muscles in the gym, she'll love seeing them flex in a strategically placed bedroom mirror. And you will, too.

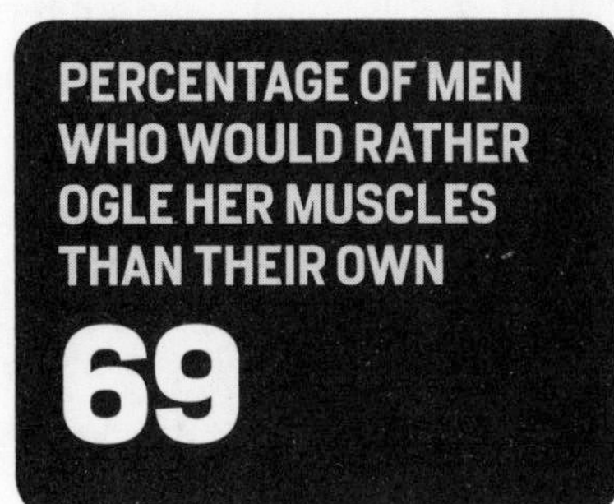

PERCENTAGE OF MEN WHO LIKE MAKING EYE CONTACT WITH ATTRACTIVE STRANGERS

77

SURVEY SAYS: HER #1 TURN-ON WHEN IT COMES TO THE SOCIAL SCENE: "MAKING EYE CONTACT WITH A CUTE STRANGER"

WHY IT WORKS: "When eyes meet for the first time, it's profoundly dramatic," Davidson says. "You get a thrill because it carries a sense of sexual possibility." So it's no surprise that "harmless flirtation even though you're taken" came in a close second in our survey. "There's a tinge of naughtiness here," Davidson says. It's also a reminder that even if you "belong" to someone else, you still have independent feelings and desires—and the ability to make heads turn. "Flirting is a provocative thumbs-up to your ego," she says.

NOW TRY: "Whether it was playful banter, arm touching, or subtle innuendo, create a snapshot in your mind of your interaction with the outsider," Davidson says. "Then repeat it with your partner."

SURVEY SAYS: HER #1 TURN-ON WHEN IT COMES TO EYE CANDY: "SEEING MY MAN LOOK SEXY IN HIS JEANS"

WHY IT WORKS: Jeans are the male equivalent of the push-up bra. We love our guys in Levi's because the look is synonymous with "sex symbol"—James Dean, Clint Eastwood, Taye Diggs, Brad Pitt, Matt McConaughey . . . Um, where were we? Oh yeah—but biology has a say in this, too. A nice-fitting pair of jeans shows off defined abs, tight glutes, or sexy hipbones, all of which "promise a healthy, virile partner," Barrow says. "That ideal is hardwired in a woman's brains when she's looking for a mate." Why? Because women seek out the best possible genetic material to pass on to their offspring. When that material is covered in denim, all the better.

NOW TRY: Ask a trusted female friend which pair of your jeans are the most flattering—or take her shopping with you. When you wear them, you'll feel sexy because you know your woman thinks you look sexy. You both win.

WHAT ELSE WOMEN LIKE: "A MAN WHO SMELLS LIKE SOAP"

WHY IT WORKS: Wanting to jump a man who smells like he just got out of the shower is like craving a croissant when passing a bakery. The scent triggers an appetite you didn't know you had until it wafted your way. Why? Because, according to Barrow, our olfactory system is one of our most powerful sensory pathways, and smells travel directly to the most primal part of our brain. Unlike a heavy cologne, which would block your natural scent, the smell of a mild soap mixes with your pheromones, natural chemicals released by the body that play a role in sexual arousal and attraction, Berman says.

NOW TRY: Warm up. Go for a walk or run together to raise your body temperature and intensify your natural scent, Davidson says.

SURVEY SAYS: HER #1 TURN-ON WHEN IT COMES TO FEELING PRETTY: "LOUNGING IN A BUBBLE BATH"

WHY IT WORKS: "A bubble bath is like a sensory-deprivation tank: It shuts out noise, work, and responsibilities," Dr. Haltzman says. "One of the fundamentals of female sexual arousal is being able to push daily concerns out of your mind." And, he adds, because women are usually busy managing their mental to-do lists, they often miss the signs of their own physical arousal (increased

GET DOWN TO THIS: FIRE STARTERS

"Start Me Up," Rolling Stones
"Steady as She Goes," The Raconteurs
"Addicted to Love," Robert Palmer
"Thing Called Love," Bonnie Raitt
"I Touch Myself," Divinyls
"Do You Want To," Franz Ferdinand
"One Way or Another," Blondie
"Mony Mony," Billy Idol
"Urgent," Foreigner
"Give It to Me Baby," Rick James
"The Way You Move," Outkast
"All Right Now," Free

PERCENTAGE OF GUYS WHO THINK THAT HOT BATHS ARE OVERRATED

61

vaginal lubrication and extra sensitivity in their erogenous zones). But warm water increases bloodflow to the nerve endings just under the skin's surface, making skin more receptive to touch. "Hot water is an automatic lubricant," he says. It helps a woman tune in to being wet and warm in other sexy ways.

NOW TRY: Make hot baths a regular part of your nighttime routine. The more relaxed and aware she is of her body's sensations, the more enthusiastic she'll be about getting it on. And never underestimate the added power of a pulsing handheld showerhead.

WHAT ELSE WOMEN LIKE: "WEARING SEXY LINGERIE UNDER UNSEXY JEANS AND A T-SHIRT"

WHY IT WORKS: There's nothing like the feel of lace and silk on bare skin. But a lot more is going on here than a synapse party. "There's a contrast between our private and public selves," says Terri Orbuch, PhD, a marriage therapist in Detroit and the project director of the Early Years of Marriage study at the University of Michigan's Survey Research Center in Ann Arbor. "It's incredibly sexy for a woman to think to herself, 'Since he's special, I'll show him my secret private side,'" Orbuch says. And by holding on to a secret, even for just a little while, she builds sensual anticipation, knowing that once she reveals it, you'll turn to jelly.

NOW TRY: "Establish a signal that only the two of you understand," Berman says. "And put it to work when you're out together." So if, say, flashing the Vulcan salute means "ravish me as soon as we get home," make like Spock just as the waiter brings dinner—you'll definitely be skipping dessert.

SURVEY SAYS: HER #1 TURN-ON WHEN IT COMES TO HARD WORK: "GETTING A BIG FAT PAYCHECK IN THE MAIL"

WHY IT WORKS: Money represents power, achievement, and control, Orbuch says. Power and confidence boost self-esteem, which makes a woman feel more desirable. "A fat paycheck is also intoxicating because of what you can do with it," she adds.

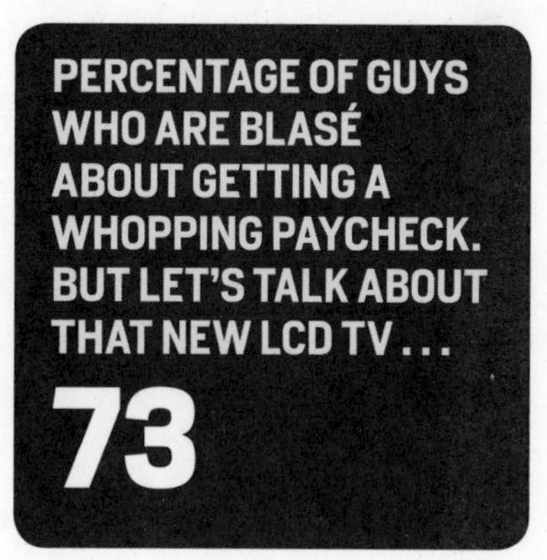

NOW TRY: Reward yourself a little bit each day. Whether it's a $5 Starbucks or a quick flirtation with the receptionist, a regular, self-affirming treat kickstarts your energy and sex drive. "Thinking of a brilliant new idea" and "shining in a big corporate meeting" ranked second and third in our survey, but they underscore the same kind of thrill: achievement, control, success.

SURVEY SAYS: WHEN IT COMES TO WHAT TURNS HER ON THE MOST: "BEING IN LOVE"

"There are more layers to excitement than having your dopamine levels rise and your heart race so fast that you can't catch your breath," Dr. Haltzman explains. "Feeling a high level of trust and comfort also makes sex more rewarding. What's really exciting for a woman is a sense of completeness. When all the dots are connected, emotional fulfillment takes precedence over biology." Gotta love that.

GET DOWN TO THIS: A LITTLE BIT NAUGHTY

"Hey Baby," No Doubt

"London Bridge," Fergie

"Hot in Herre," Nelly

"In Da Club," 50 Cent

"Black Sweat," Prince

"SexyBack," Justin Timberlake

"Naughty Girl," Beyoncé

"Oh My God," Pink

"Closer," Nine Inch Nails

"Vertigo," U2

"Welcome to the Jungle," Guns N' Roses

"Everybody Wants Some," Van Halen

GO WITH THE FLOW

THERE ARE UPSIDES TO HER MONTHLY CYCLE. SERIOUSLY, WE CAN PROVE IT

BY MORGAN LORD

You already know the crappy side effects of her period: Those sudden urges to devour Ring Dings and strangle incompetent cashiers come and go like clockwork. But with a little planning, you can harness hormonal ups and downs to your advantage. Witchcraft? No, science! During certain stages of her cycle, researchers have found that women have an especially easy time communicating, canoodling, even burning calories. Based on the average 28-day cycle (everyone's a little different), here's how to surf the crimson tide instead of cursing it.

DAYS 1 TO 10: IT ALL STARTS HERE

In your mind, the start of her period probably signals the end of the month, but from now on, label it the start of her cycle. In the first few days of bleeding, estrogen and progesterone levels hit rock bottom. Now's the perfect time for her to:

GRAB THE WHEEL. Scientists don't know exactly why, but lower estrogen levels give women an edge in what researchers call "male cognitive skills," such as spatial thinking. We thought said researchers were just sexist jerks until we saw the slew of studies proving that guys really are superior at rotating three-dimensional objects in their heads and keeping track of north and south. But during this 10-day window, women are better than usual at both—which means she'll have no trouble cramming a ton of camping gear into a tiny trunk or figuring out how to get back on the highway after that wrong turn in Poughkeepsie.

CEASE FIRE. If she's ready to stop spending $1,500 a year on her pack-a-day habit, now's the best time to stub out her last cigarette, says Louann Brizendine, MD, author of *The Female Brain* and a neuropsychiatrist at the University of California at San Francisco. Nicotine cravings are typically strongest in the first 2 weeks after quitting, but going smoke free early on in her cycle will make them easier to manage, because withdrawal symptoms are weaker when progesterone levels are low, according to a review of studies from the Medical University of South Carolina.

DAYS 11 TO 14: THE DROP ZONE

At midcycle, estrogen levels soar, causing a surge in LH, a hormone that signals her ovaries to roll out her little chromosome bomb of an egg. The exact day it's released is different for everyone, but ovulation typically falls around day 14, says Mary Abusief, MD, a clinical fellow in reproductive endocrinology and infertility at Brigham and Women's Hospital in Boston. Given that she's brimming with estrogen, now's a good time for her to:

DON A PAPER MINIDRESS. Smear, speculum, swab—feeling squeamish yet? "Women often complain about the discomfort of Pap tests, in which a tiny brush pulls a few cells out of the cervix," says Toni Weschler, MPH, a women's health educator and the author of *Taking Charge of Your Fertility*. Yeeeesh. But in the days before ovulation, her cervix softens and opens up to let cervical fluid out—and sperm in, if that's what you're after. If she schedules a ride in the stirrups now, she'll avoid a lot of pinching.

COMMAND THE CONFERENCE ROOM. She can probably argue circles around you any night of the week, but on these days she could moderate an O'Donnell/Trump smackdown. A flood of estrogen boosts her brain's ability to nail word-related tasks, says Pauline Maki, PhD, associate professor of psychiatry and psychology at the University of Illinois at Chicago. Several studies, including one that Maki led for the National Institute on Aging, have found that women are more verbally agile and can access their vocabularies faster at midcycle than at other times of the month. Translation: time to give a presentation, go for a job interview, or finally settle that long-standing Beatles vs. Stones debate.

GO FOR THE O. Right now she may be hornier than Hugh Hefner at a twin convention, so take advantage. A 2004 University of Chicago study proposed renaming this part of the cycle the "sexual phase," because participants had stronger sexual desire, increased fantasies, and more randy activity while ovulating. And a 2005 study from Milan noted that during this phase, women had higher blood levels of oxytocin, a brain chemical that increases during orgasm.

DAYS 15 TO 28: THE FADE-OUT

After ovulation, there are about 2 weeks until Big Red strikes again. In this phase, the ovaries secrete less estrogen and more progesterone, a hormone that helps maintain the lining of the uterus on the off chance her waiting egg is fertilized. If the miracle of life goes untapped, another menstrual cycle ensues, which means you should brace yourself for PMS. Now's a good time to:

KEEP HER AWAY FROM PRETTY-BOYS. Ladies prefer softer jawlines and pouty lips, particularly at this time of the month, according to the brains at the University of Aberdeen in Scotland. "After ovulation, increased levels of progesterone prep the body for pregnancy, regardless of whether the egg is fertilized," says lead researcher Ben Jones, MD. Being preggo requires sympathy and support, and feminine faces are perceived as more caring, he says. That means Tobey Maguire's in, Matthew McConaughey's out.

BURN BELLY BULGE. She'll do more to fight flab if she hops on a treadmill preperiod, claims a 2003 study published in the *European Journal of Applied Physiology*. A woman's body burns more fat at the end of her cycle because the progesterone promotes the use of fat as an energy source, says lead researcher Leanne Redman, PhD, of the Pennington Biomedical Research Center in Baton Rouge. She even recommends planning workouts around her menstrual cycle: yoga, Pilates, or strength training when she has her period and high-intensity cardio postovulation.

THE PILL FENDS OFF MORE THAN JUST RUG RATS

Birth control pills override her natural cycle so she doesn't ovulate. And because estrogen and progesterone are kept on an even keel, the perks described in this article won't always apply. Still, those tiny pills offer their own Shaq-size benefits.

She's less likely to . . . face the big C. If she takes the Pill for 6 months, she'll slash her odds of getting colorectal cancer by 39 percent, according to a 2007 study published in the *American Journal of Epidemiology*. Keep it up for 3 years and ovarian cancer risk drops by 30 to 50 percent, says a 2002 study reported in the *Journal of the National Cancer Institute*.

She's less likely to . . . spaz when the deli is out of Diet Coke. Steadier hormone levels keep mood changes minimal, according to a 2006 study in the *American Journal of Obstetrics and Gynecology*, which means no crying during *Extreme Makeover: Home Edition* commercials.

She's less likely to . . . need an orthopedic surgeon. Female athletes who take the Pill may have stabler knee joints, according to a 2004 study published in the *Clinical Journal of Sport Medicine*. That could mean fewer serious running injuries.

She's less likely to . . . use concealer like it's going out of style. Certain brands of low-dose birth control (such as Ortho Tri-Cyclen or Yaz) are FDA-approved to keep acne (not just pink plus signs) at bay.

REV UP HER LAGGING LIBIDO

THE NEW SCIENCE OF SENSATIONAL SEX: RESEARCHERS ARE UNVEILING THE BREAKTHROUGHS THAT TRULY WORK FOR GROWN-UP WOMEN

BY NANCY KALISH

A fulfilling sex life is one of the most important ways to stay connected to your partner and boost self-esteem. But great sex doesn't just happen on its own—and less so as women age. Their need for intimacy changes, and their bodies may not respond the same way they did when they were younger. Here are five common reasons that women over 40 find their libidos lagging and the scientific interventions that can get them happily humming along again.

REASON: SHE HAS LOW TESTOSTERONE

We tend to think of testosterone as a "male" hormone. But small amounts—delicately balanced with estrogen—fuel a woman's sex drive. Unfortunately, at menopause testosterone starts to decline, which can cause desire to plummet. Hormone therapy throws off the balance even more. With a blood test, her gynecologist can determine if low testosterone is to blame. Luckily, studies show that stabilizing testosterone levels can rev up arousal in postmenopausal women—and improve all areas of sexual response, from lubrication to stronger, more powerful orgasms. Here's how science can help.

TESTOSTERONE GEL: Although the FDA has not yet approved a testosterone gel specifically for women, many doctors simply prescribe the male version off-label or have a compound created by a pharmacist. (A female gel is in the works. See "Two Libido-Enhancing Drugs" on page 98.) And no, it won't make her grow hair on her chin or give her huge muscles. "The doses prescribed for women aren't large enough to stimulate male characteristics," says Anita Clayton, MD, clinical professor of obstetrics and gynecology at the University of Virginia and author of *Satisfaction: Women, Sex, and the Quest for Intimacy.*

LIBIDO-BOOSTING HERBS: Certified sex researcher Beverly Whipple, PhD, professor emerita at Rutgers University and coauthor of *The Science of Orgasm*, recommends ArginMax for Women, which is a nutritional supplement containing ginseng, ginkgo, multivitamins, and minerals. Science backs her up. ArginMax increased sexual desire, including clitoral sensation and orgasm frequency, in several studies. In one, women taking the supplement daily for 4 weeks reported a 74 percent improvement in satisfaction with their sex lives. In another study, men taking the male version of ArginMax experienced similar results.

BIRTH CONTROL WITH BENEFITS: "Ironically, oral contraceptives increase levels of a protein that binds with testosterone and makes it less available to get womens' brains thinking about sex," says Clayton. But hormonal contraceptives that are inserted into the vagina and release a minimal amount of localized hormone (such as the NuvaRing), or are administered through the skin (such as a patch), and nonhormonal methods (such as condoms or spermicides) can free up that testosterone—and her sexual desire.

REASON: SHE'S DISTRACTED DURING SEX

It's not just those endless to-do lists that make her mind wander. She's wired that way. According to brain scan research, women's brains are naturally more active than men's, even during sex. The reason: lower levels of the neurotransmitter dopamine. "Dopamine creates the desire to go after a reward—in this case, an orgasm," explains Clayton. Dopamine also increases the flow of sensory impulses to the genitals, essential for arousal. But low levels of dopamine caused by chronic stress or medical conditions can distract her during sex. Here's how science can help.

A SUPPLEMENT THAT CONTAINS THE HORMONE DHEA: This hormone (dehydroepiandrosterone) may increase dopamine production and normally spikes right before orgasm to enhance desire and focus. Taking 300 mg of DHEA an hour before sex significantly increased both mental and physical arousal in postmenopausal women, according to a study published in the *Journal of Women's Health & Gender-Based Medicine*. Clayton recommends only 25 to 50 milligrams and warns that DHEA can affect some people's cholesterol levels. So tell her to be sure to check with her doctor before taking it.

A SIMPLE TEST FOR ADD: Up to 2 million adult women in the United States suffer from attention deficit disorder, which may be associated with low dopamine levels, says Daniel G. Amen, MD, a psychiatrist and brain imaging specialist, author of *Sex on the Brain*. This can literally make it difficult to pay attention during lovemaking. However, "when a woman is finally treated for ADD, usually with a combination of drug therapy and behavior modification, it improves her sex life—not to mention the rest of her life as well," he says. To get a test for ADD, go to prevention.com/links.

REASON: SHE HAS TROUBLE REACHING ORGASM

Women typically blame this on psychological problems, but the reasons are often physical. Poor bloodflow to the genitals, for example, caused by cardiovascular conditions such as diabetes or heart disease, makes it harder to have an orgasm. Another common culprit: declining hormone levels due to perimenopause and menopause. Smoking can also disrupt bloodflow by constricting blood vessels. Here's how science can help.

THE AMINO ACID L-ARGININE: Like Viagra, this naturally occurring amino acid increases the production of nitric oxide, which is a chemical released by the genital nerves during arousal, sending much-needed blood to the area. Dr. Amen suggests taking 1,000 to 3,000 milligrams of an L-arginine supplement (available at drugstores) right before sex.

A NEW ANTIDEPRESSANT: The inability to experience orgasm is a common side effect of antidepressants called selective serotonin reuptake inhibitors (SSRIs). That's because the serotonin boost you get from these drugs decreases dopamine, which leads to sexual problems. Clayton often switches her patients to bupropion HCI, an antidepressant that doesn't affect serotonin levels, enhances dopamine function, and, in several studies of women, has boosted desire.

REASON: IT'S DRY DOWN BELOW

The lining of the vagina is extremely estrogen sensitive, and when hormone levels fluctuate during perimenopause, women produce less lubrication prior to and during intercourse. Hormone therapy is a solution for some women. But there are other alternatives. Here's how science can help.

A LUBRICANT THAT GOES STRAIGHT TO THE SOURCE: Whipple recommends Zestra (available at drugstores), a nonprescription feminine arousal fluid made from botanical oils, which stimulates nerves and blood vessels to increase arousal. Women who used Zestra five times in a 2- to 3-week period (many described a warm feeling in the genital area) boosted their sexual pleasure significantly, even if they were taking libido-dampening antidepressants or had sexual arousal disorder, according to a study of women ages 31 to 57 published in the *Journal of Sex & Marital Therapy.*

LOCALLY APPLIED ESTROGEN: This can significantly improve the lubrication situation—without the dangers (such as increased breast cancer) of oral hormone therapy. Whipple prefers insertable vaginal estrogen rings or tablets over vaginal estrogen creams.

REASON: SHE FEELS DISCONNECTED FROM YOU

The demands of family and work life can often make long-married couples feel like strangers in the bedroom. Here's how science can help.

AN OVULATION KIT: Oxytocin, often referred to as the bonding hormone, spikes right before ovulation, a time when most women are in the mood.

SLEEP YOUR WAY SEXY

Snoring can hurt your sex life Obstructive sleep apnea (OSA) could be an unrecognized cause of sexual dysfunction. In one 2006 study, researchers found that women's problems reaching orgasm increased with the severity of their OSA. Treating men and women for OSA (using continuous positive airway pressure, or CPAP) improved sex drive in all of them, according to another study. For tips on diagnosing and treating OSA, go to the National Sleep Foundation at sleepfoundation.org.

According to Dr. Amen, oxytocin also helps dull a person's memory of her partner's annoying traits (such as your dirty socks on the floor) enough to let her feel attracted to you. Chart her cycle and schedule "date night" right before she ovulates.

TWO LIBIDO-ENHANCING DRUGS

Ask her to ask her doc to keep an eye out for these higher-desire meds that are in the works.

LibiGel: The only prescription testosterone gel to boost sexual desire in women, this hormone treatment should receive FDA approval by 2011.

Bremelanotide nose spray: First in a new class of drugs called melanocortin agonists, this nasal spray—just click once and breathe through a small inhaler, 15 to 30 minutes before sex—increases bloodflow to the genitals. Unlike Viagra, it has no effect on the cardiovascular system. (It works via the central nervous system.) In clinical trials of both premenopausal and postmenopausal women with sexual dysfunction, it significantly increased desire and genital arousal. Expect FDA approval for women in 2011.

EXERCISE RESTRAINT

YOU'D LIKE A FRIEND WITH BENEFITS. BUT HAVE YOU CONSIDERED THE BENEFITS OF A FRIEND? THIS WOMAN SAYS YOU SHOULD. HERE'S WHY

BY LYNDA GOROV

The night Leo climbed on top of me and pleaded, "Come on, baby, please," I didn't know whether to be amused or offended. Granted, we'd been drinking. And I was in his bed, wearing a T-shirt and teeny panties. But we'd been friends for a decade. I was in town to catch up, not hook up. "Get off me, you idiot," I demanded.

In the morning, a contrite Leo was bedside, breakfast tray in hand. "I am such a pig," he said in his adorable Peruvian accent. "Forgive me. But I am a man."

Man. Pig. Whichever it was, Leo overcame what he swears was a one-time urge. He never touched me inappropriately again. Fortunately Leo and I moved past—way past—the awkward part of a male/female friendship. We're still pals to this day.

That's right. Men should be friends with women, even without the benefits. We need to expand the notion of what those benefits are. After all, inside information from your female friend can be put to good use. And that's hardly the only perk of remaining platonic.

YOU'LL SEE THINGS HER WAY. That is, you'll receive the female version of events. Over the years, I've commented on Leo's encounters with women of all types. Sound unpleasant? It's not. "Men ask questions, and they get answers," says Kathy Werking, PhD, author of *We're Just Good Friends: Women and Men in Nonromantic Relationships*. "That's good for them."

YOU CAN EMOTE FEARLESSLY. Talking with a female friend means there's usually no game to distract you and little chance of embarrassment if you bring up hidden thoughts. We love that stuff. Share. Compare. "The literature is really clear on this: Women gain from male/female relationships, but in terms of intimacy, sharing, and communication, men gain so much more," says Don O'Meara, professor of sociology at the University of Cincinnati, who published a benchmark study on cross-gender friendship in the journal *Sex Roles*. "It's to the man's advantage."

YOU'LL BECOME A MASTER LISTENER. And women love that. You'll experience intimacy without getting, you know, intimate. All her talking will train you in the invaluable art of listening, which—I can guarantee this—will coax the pants off some woman in your future.

Sure, there are obstacles to having a female friend. Turning a woman from, say, casual coworker into after-hours confidante can take time and effort—and often involves another sort of urge altogether.

As Jeff, a close chum since junior high school, explains, "You like her. She likes you. You get along great. You're both unattached. So why not take the next step?" How about because you can't take it back. Or because platonic love doesn't always work in the bedroom. And why the hell didn't Jeff kiss me in junior high?

"Men have a difficult time separating friendship from romance," says Werking. "They don't get the subtleties of relationships. I hope this is changing." (Werking's research shows that sex-free male/female friendships are more common among 20-year-olds than in older generations.)

Here's what she says men can do.

THINK THROUGH YOUR ATTRACTION. Is it physical? Intellectual? Emotional? All three? Might you actually love her (as a friend) rather than lust after her (as a sex partner)? Figure it out. You don't want to hurt her, or be hurt unexpectedly.

TALK IT OUT. That's what this is all about, right? Learning to use your words, not your body? If you can't move past your attraction—or you worry that she's attracted—bring up the subject. But be a good guy about it. That's how friends behave. Werking says, "I've interviewed a lot of people about their friendships that didn't last, and the primary reason was they didn't deal with the romantic undertone. . . . You just have to take a deep breath and broach the subject. You have to hit it head-on without worrying that it will ruin the relationship."

TEASE BUT DON'T TOUCH. Once you're both on the same relationship page, it's okay to flirt with her. Just don't feel her up. Don't risk what you have for one night of fun—unless, of course, your aim is to turn your friendship into something else altogether. Besides history, I mean.

TREAT HER LIKE A MAN. She can ask you to a movie. You can pay for dinner. No one needs to worry about mixed motives. "You don't have to be in control in a friendship relationship," says O'Meara, whose own best friend of 25 years is a woman, something almost unheard of among men his age (60). "It goes to the whole notion of what a friendship is, and the more intimate it is, the more real and the more equal it has to be."

KNOW WHAT SHE WANTS. Jan Yager, a sociologist and the author of *When Friendship Hurts: How to Deal with Friends Who Betray, Abandon, or Wound You*, advises that you make really certain your idea of friendship isn't her idea of sexual harassment, especially if you work together. Given clear signals, go for it.

And you're still not home free. Besides facing down family and friends who—wink, wink—are sure something hinky must be up between you and your buddy, there's a second woman to contend with: the one you're dating or the one who's your wife or the one you haven't met yet but hope to introduce to your friend one day. Let's call it the "girl friend" vs. the "girlfriend."

"In this society, there's an expectation that your spouse or romantic partner should be able to fulfill every need you have. Third-party jealousy is a huge problem," says Michael Monsour, an associate professor of communications at the University of Colorado and the author of *Women and Men as Friends: Relationships Across the Life Span in the 21st Century.*

But don't give up just yet. Wives and girlfriends can, and do, accept their men's female friends. It helps if those friendships have a history all their own, or if your leading lady is a friend of your friend, too. Again, it behooves you to behave in an up-front manner from the get-go. This means you have to introduce a new girlfriend to the "other woman" without delay. Make your friendship the opposite of extramarital. And while you're at it, don't talk her up too much—by her, I mean your friend. But don't ignore the subject either. This is a balancing act. Mystery arouses suspicion.

And finally, don't discuss your partner with your female buddy. Therein lies trouble. "Be careful not to use your friend to vent to or as a sounding board about your romantic partner," Yager says. "That's where I've seen platonic friendships head into trouble. It can lead to cheating, or leaving spouses."

For his part, my old friend Leo promises an introduction to the new woman in his life. He says he can't wait for us to meet. But he'd rather I keep quiet about the night he forgot we were only friends. After all, he'd like us to stay that way.

PEEK INSIDE HER HEAD

A STRONG BODY, TIME WITH YOUR KIDS (NOT YOU!), INFORMATION SHE TRUSTS...HERE'S WHAT (HEALTHY) WOMEN WANT

BY COURTNEY SMITH

How do women really feel about themselves—about their health and happiness, about how they look to the world and to themselves? Women responded to a huge survey, and their answers are enlightening.

WOMEN FEEL GOOOOD

Under age 40, women give their physical health high marks. After 40, their emotional health and mental health become more robust, peaking in their 60s. Their physical health then again gets better—proving, perhaps, that a sound mind helps you regain a sound body.

WOMEN'S TOP THREE PERSONAL CONCERNS

Women ranked how important 20 lifestyle issues are to their day-to-day lives. Here are their biggest priorities, which change with age. (They gave all at least an 8 on a scale of 1 to 10.) The following beat out body weight, heart health, and stress.

YOUNGER THAN 40

1. Happiness
2. Relationship with spouse
3. Finances

OLDER THAN 40

1. Happiness
2. Relationship with children
3. Memory

THEIR BIGGEST GOAL

Hands down, it's to lose weight. Based on their body mass index, 56 percent of women are overweight or obese. The average number of pounds a woman would like to lose is 41. Her biggest motivator is health (not looks). However, her number one reason for trying to lose weight is "I didn't feel good about myself anymore." What most women said was the payoff of slimming down: "Be healthier."

Although 86 percent of women who are dieting are doing it on their own, women report losing an extra 5 pounds when they diet with a friend or a support group.

WOMEN ARE FIRMLY IN CHARGE

No generation of women has ever had so much health information at its fingertips—through the Internet, PDA devices, TV, books, and magazines. They double-check what their doctors say and what their friends' doctors say and constantly seek new information—then they decide for themselves.

The Web has clearly allowed women to take their health into their own hands. When they have a health problem or question, their immediate first step is:

Check the Internet: 44 percent

Call their doctors: 23 percent

Call their mothers: 12 percent

Look at a reference book: 8 percent

Call a friend: 4 percent

Other or nothing: 9 percent

PERCENTAGE OF WOMEN WHO RANK HAPPINESS AS "ONE OF THE MOST IMPORTANT ASPECTS OF GOOD HEALTH"

WOMEN ARE SELF-STARTERS

What motivates women to change their lives? They said the biggest source of pressure to improve their health is:

Myself: 80 percent

Society: 37 percent

My doctor: 28 percent

When a woman goes to the doctor . . .

70 percent of them have already researched their symptoms and what they might mean online

50 percent of them take a list of questions to ask

71 percent of them look up the medications the doctor prescribed when they get home

59 percent of them ask about alternative health options

35 percent of them offer their own treatment suggestions

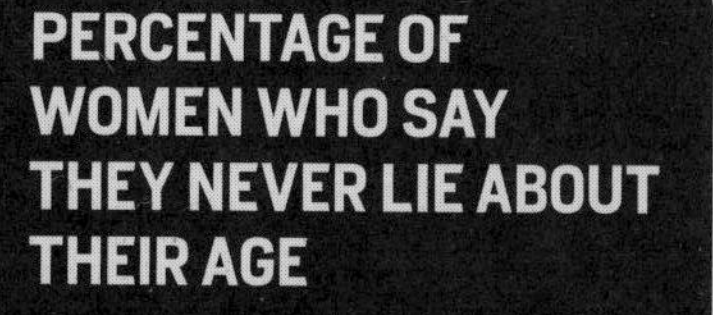

A PEEK AT THEIR FUTURES

Physically, women feel older than their age—until they turn 50. Then the tables turn, and they start to feel younger than their age. Mentally, however, most women feel about 40.

THEIR REAL AGE: 20–29

How old they feel mentally: 31.2

How old they feel physically: 32.2

Age they think they look: 24.0

THEIR REAL AGE: 30–39

How old they feel mentally: 39.1

How old they feel physically: 39.8

Age they think they look: 31.0

THEIR REAL AGE: 40–49

How old they feel mentally: 41.4

How old they feel physically: 48.6

Age they think they look: 40.3

PERCENTAGE OF WOMEN WHO WOULD OPT FOR $1 MILLION OVER BEING THEIR PERFECT WEIGHT FOREVER

74

SEX LIFE NOSEDIVE

After age 40, women's interest in sex dwindles. Only 24 percent of women older than 40 say sex is important to good health. Twice as many women under 40 say it is.

They get less stressed, more physical. By their 50s, they feel confident about their careers and families and can attend to physical concerns, such as heart health.

Prayer is in their future. Women start developing a more active spiritual life in their 30s, but they see it as integral to good health in their 50s and 60s.

Concern about memory skyrockets. Forty-five percent of women older than 40 consider memory to be one of the most important aspects of good health. Only 26 percent of women younger than 40 do.

HEALTH AND HUSBANDS

When women were asked what they most look forward to in their future, here's what they said.

Women under 40: "Spending more time with my spouse."

Women 40–49: "Spending more time with my spouse" (Close second: "Taking care of my physical health").

Women 50 and over: "Taking care of my physical health."

WOMEN'S REMEDIES OF CHOICE

Women embrace integrative care. When they're not feeling well, they would rather:

Use natural treatments: 23 percent

Take conventional remedies: 24 percent

Prefer a combination of the two: 50 percent

Use none of these: 3 percent

Women run hot and cold on doctors. When they have to make a difficult medical decision, most of them truly value their physician's advice: 69 percent of them agree that their doctors make all the right health care decisions for them.

However, when it comes to preventive care, women feel they're on their own: 50 percent of women say that their doctors do not help them stay informed about how to eat healthfully.

Only 24 percent of women say their doctors suggested they lose weight (even though more than half of them qualify as overweight or obese).

ASK THE GIRL NEXT DOOR

THE HONEST TRUTH ABOUT WOMEN FROM OUR LOVELY NEIGHBOR

Where are all the thirtysomething women hiding?

As far as I can tell, most women go into a self-improvement phase in their 30s. It's as if they've realized how much they want to accomplish while still young (and childless) and how little time they have to do it. When they're not working their butts off, they're at yoga class or playing squash. They're hiking in the mountains or taking cooking courses in foreign countries. They're learning to install cork flooring at Home Depot or heading up a grassroots charity. The good news is that meeting them is easy. Just sign up for any activity that doesn't take place at a bar.

What do I do when she cries for no reason?

Like the Florida panhandle, the female psyche is subject to random bouts of inclement weather. Instead of trying to stop her tears, treat them like the natural phenomenon they are. Hand her a box of tissues, put your arms around her, and wait out the storm.

Why do women wear heels so high they can barely walk in them?

Because they lengthen our calves, arch our backs, put a swing in our hips, and raise us 3½ inches—all of which equals a transformation from average woman to killer babe that's more than worth toe cramps and bloody blisters.

Is there a pick-up line that'll make a woman walking down the street stop for a conversation?

If there is, I've never heard it. Anything you say to a woman as she's strolling by is immediately categorized as a catcall. And any guy who catcalls women is immediately categorized as a meathead. There are a lot of places where it's perfectly acceptable to approach a woman cold—a bar, the beach, a coffee shop, a bookstore, even the supermarket—but the sidewalk isn't one of them.

What do I say when she asks if I think her hot friend is pretty?

Her hot friend is making your woman feel like chopped liver, so an honest "yes" will only kick her ego while it's down. Find a flaw in her friend's physique or personality—look hard, there has to be at least one—and claim that it turns you off. The proper response should be something like "Yeah, she'd be attractive if it wasn't for her squeaky voice/pointy chin/giant forehead/snotty attitude." It's a sweet little half-truth that will make hanging out with the hottie easier on everyone.

Guys fish, play softball, build stuff. How come so few women have hobbies?

They do have hobbies, they're just totally unrecognizable to your male sensibilities. All that time she spends on the phone with friends, shopping for shoes, and planning dinner? Those are hobbies. There's just no little wooden birdhouse at the end.

Her best friend is a straight guy. Should I care?

Yes. The problem with her opposite-sex buddy is that he can fill the same needs you do. It's like you're the Nike store and her male best friend is the Reebok shop next door. Yeah, she's brand loyal, but anytime you happen to be closed, all she has to do is mosey on over to Reebok to get her socks and sneakers. It's not sex you should worry about so much as emotional stuff. If she's going to him for comfort, protection, and connection, maybe you need to start paying more attention to her. Your other move is awkward but constructive. Subject his Reebok store to a friendly buyout: You have to buddy up with him, too.

My girlfriend keeps talking about this dude she works with. Is something going on there?

Nah. Cheating women are quiet women. If they were getting it on in the conference room, you never would have heard his name.

I have a friend who's very flirty. Is that just her style, or is she waiting for me to make a move?

To find out, arrange a situation in which you're (1) together at night, (2) in a sexy place like a bar or your couch, and (3) hovering within a foot of each other. Then watch how she acts: When a woman is flirting just for kicks, she'll freeze up when she feels at risk of being hit on for real. If she's just as smiley and touchy-feely as ever, she's waiting patiently for you to lunge for pay dirt.

A female friend told me she wasn't wearing underwear. She wants me, right?

Close. She wants you to want her.

My girlfriend takes forever in the bathroom. How can I get her to hurry up?

You can fib and say dinner is at 7:30 instead of 8. You can remind her (once, with a kiss) to start getting ready an hour and a half before your ETA. You can also shower and shave long before she locks herself in the bathroom. Beyond that, any attempt to speed up her beauty routine will only increase the odds that she'll poke herself in the eye with a mascara wand or tear a hole in her hose—either way, the blame will fall on you. Rather than worrying about being late, pop open a cold one, cue up an episode of *South Park*, and enjoy some rare uninterrupted time on the couch.

I need space to sleep, but a lot of women like to cuddle all night. What's a nice way to move her over?

On that first night, consider sucking it up. Most women feel vulnerable after getting it on with a new guy. Cuddling reassures her that there's some genuine affection underlying the rampant lust. If you want to increase the odds of a next time, let her pass out on your pecs. You can always nudge her off when she arrives in Neverland.

DECODE HER DIGS

Googling is passé. Sophisticated suitors should be able to figure a woman out without prying into her cyberpast. We've unleashed a team of psychologists to help you interpret her living space—without snooping, of course—using countertop and coffee-table clues to answer compatibility questions that affect every relationship.

WILL SHE SHUT ME OUT OR BARE HER SOUL?

YOUR CLUE: Her furniture. "A more private person will have the backs of chairs toward the entryway, and the traffic patterns may create a cozy, confined space," says Constance Forrest, PsyD, a design psychologist at Forrest-Painter Design, in Venice, California. Another clue: how she apportions space, particularly in a compact room. "Open, adventurous people often have cluttered, overflowing shelves and walls that are covered with art and photographs, and more-guarded people thrive on a high level of order," says Nicholas Martin, a personnel research psychologist in Washington, DC.

IS SHE FLEXIBLE OR CONTROLLING?

YOUR CLUE: Her bookshelf. "Look for an organizational pattern," says Samuel Gosling, a psychologist at the University of Texas. "Are books grouped by subject? Alphabetized by author?" A general orderliness may indicate someone who's responsible and secure, while a personalized Dewey decimal system may be a red flag for neuroticism, says Gary Aumiller, PhD, a police psychologist in New York City. Use variety, not quantity, to gauge her intellectual breadth. "Better to have 10 books on unrelated subjects than 100 on chemistry," says Gosling. A mix of new releases, classics, and other genres means she's an imaginative, curious woman.

IS SHE A DREAMER OR GROUNDED?

YOUR CLUE: Her art. Paintings or photos mean she's open and creative, but there's a big difference between having Ansel Adams and Andy Warhol hanging in her foyer. Women who collect Eastern art, such as Asian prints or Buddhist imagery, tend to be open, curious, and emotionally complex, says Gosling. Movie posters mean she's conservative and down-to-earth. And women who collect and display postcards, matchbooks, or ticket stubs are more adventurous and sensation-seeking.

PSYCHE SPECIFICS

Here are a few key things to check for.

1. Musical instruments signal an intellectual, worldly, and cultured woman.
2. Candles are more likely to appear in the homes of adventurous people.
3. A variety of textures and fabrics in pillows, couches, blankets, and rugs indicates an affectionate and sensual woman.
4. Fast clocks can mean she's conscientious or just high-strung; more than 10 minutes ahead spells trouble.
5. Celestial or international maps are more likely to hang in the homes of imaginative people.

WILL SHE GET ALONG WITH MY FRIENDS?

YOUR CLUE: Her photos. “Introverts tend to display more photos of nature, art, or objects, with muted backgrounds, while extroverts are drawn to pictures of people,” says Gosling. If her fridge is full of party shots, pay attention to the focus of each photograph: If she’s front and center—always—she could be narcissistic. Photos of animals usually reflect a woman who’s affectionate and sentimental, but beware of overkill. “She could be filling a maternal instinct,” says Aumiller.

READ BETWEEN HER LINES

One of life's great truths: Women often say one thing but mean another. Here's your translator.

"I'M BETWEEN RELATIONSHIPS"

"I'm interested, but I haven't made up my mind." She's put up a wall with an open window.

YOUR PLAY: Ask her—and her gal pals—to a BBQ. Winning over her friends will bump her off the fence and into your arms.

"I'VE BEEN DYING TO SEE THAT MOVIE"

"Ask me out." Any unsolicited desire she expresses about a movie or a new restaurant is often an invitation to ask her out.

YOUR PLAY: "Me, too! Want to go?" Then brandish your PDA and set the date.

"I HAVE A BOYFRIEND, BUT HE LIVES IN ROME"

"I'm taken, but I might consider a change." Her qualifier turns a typical brush-off into a possibility.

YOUR PLAY: Ask her to help you shop for a tie. She'll fill a void in her relationship by helping out with an errand. She may miss the mundane intimacy more than she misses Rome boy, and you'll be on deck.

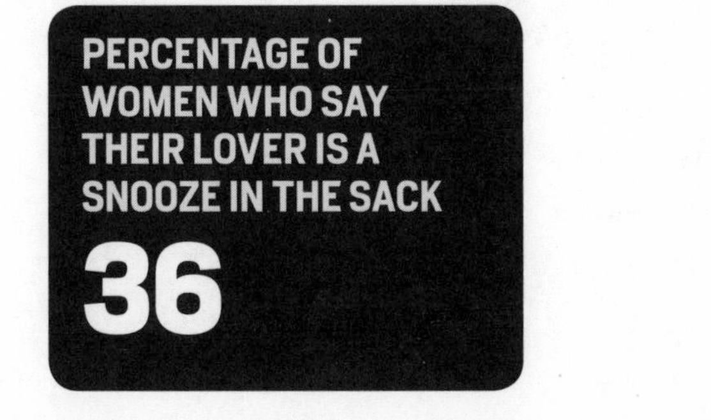

FERRET OUT A LIAR

When her brain thinks one thing and her mouth says another, her body gives up the telltale signs of lying. In *The Six Keys to Unlock and Empower Your Mind*, mentalist Marc Salem explores the fault lines between fact and fiction.

READ HER LIPS. The physiological stress of lying increases peristalsis, or the constriction of esophageal muscles involved in swallowing. Stress also slows saliva production, leaving a sudden dry mouth. Watch whether she compulsively licks her lips before speaking or swallows forcefully.

ASK FOR DETAILS. Most people resort to verbal gymnastics to avoid an outright lie. She might answer a question with a question to stall for time, or suddenly suffer selective memory. Once she's fibbed a little, she'll fib a lot, so press her for specifics and see whether she squirms.

LISTEN FOR FIBS. A moment of distortion in vocal tone can betray a lie. Listen for long midsentence pauses (as she tries to invent a story), a staccato burst of words, a sudden warble, or a rise or drop in pitch, caused by the trouble she'll have breathing normally when her nerves are in overdrive.

FIND HER HANDS. Her mitts express feelings in conversation, so a liar will hide her hands—either under her armpits or behind her back. But if she's thought through her lie in advance, she'll simply try to keep her hands still—unnaturally hanging at her sides or resting flat on a table.

FOLLOW HER GAZE. There's one lying cue even a practiced deceiver can't control. Check for dilated pupils. It's a biological by-product when the sympathetic nervous system—your fight-or-flight response—kicks in under duress. Those pools of darkness at the center of her eyes will spread as she utters the lie.

PERCENTAGE OF WOMEN WHO SAY THEY HAVE NEVER LIED TO THEIR HUSBAND OR BOYFRIEND

5

MANAGE ALL THE WOMEN IN YOUR LIFE

Jealousy on the part of your significant other can sabotage your best female friendships. Here's how to smooth over your relationship.

THE LEGGY COWORKER

WHY SHE'S WORRIED: Your sexy office gal pal has unfettered access to half of your weekday, and your girl fears this face time can spark a cubicle romance.

EASE HER FEARS: Play show and tell. Give your girl a guided tour of the office, introduce her to your coworkers—including Legs—and end at your desk, where she'll find a prominently displayed picture of herself. It's a talisman that wards off flirty office workers, says Dorian Solot, author of *I Love Female Orgasm*. "It shows her she's on your mind while you're on the clock."

THE COLLEGE COHORT

WHY SHE'S WORRIED: You spent 4 boozy, sexually charged years with this girl, who knows the secret handshake and dated half of your fraternity. What's more, unlike your girl, she has a standing invitation to game day and poker night.

EASE HER FEARS: Paint the friend as a mascot, not a romantic interest, says Susan F. Benjamin, author of *Perfect Phrases for Dealing with Difficult People*. And invite your gal to a few college game parties, so she'll see that the cutie sits squarely in your "like-a-sister" category.

THE MATRIARCH

WHY SHE'S WORRIED: Your woman feels resentful about her own need to impress your mom.

EASE HER FEARS: Ship your ladies off to a wine tasting together (find one in your city at localwineevents.com). Each wants to win the other's approval, which can lead to insecurities and false perceptions, says Gini Graham Scott, PhD, author of *Disagreements, Disputes and All-out War.* A retreat with some vino will melt away any hangups.

THE FACEBOOK FOX

WHY SHE'S WORRIED: You've dutifully declared you're "in a relationship" on your MySpace or Facebook profile. But she worries it means nothing to the harem of cybervixens on your friends list.

EASE HER FEARS: Let her plant a flag in your digital world. If they're not online too, girlfriends and wives place these sites just a notch above porn. Help her create her own page and bump her up to the top of your friends list.

THE GYM GODDESS

WHY SHE'S WORRIED: Your trainer is single and oozes sexuality from every pore. You may say her postworkout chats are harmless, but your girlfriend knows better (and so do you, playa).

EASE HER FEARS: Play matchmaker and set your trainer up with a friend, says Solot. Face it: You're taken, and she's a temptress. Best to try this underutilized brushoff, which will allow you two to still chat at the gym. The move takes her off your gal's worry list.

SATISFY HER CRAVINGS

Writer Mike Zimmerman chats with Dania Ramirez, new to the cast of Heroes, *about what women crave most in a relationship: honesty.*

I've known Dania Ramirez for 5 minutes, tops, and already she has me on a plane to the Dominican Republic, where she was born. She kicks off the virtual tour with lunch at a tiny Santo Domingo restaurant called Adrian Tropical. Then to the beach: Cap Cana, she says, is "8 miles of virgin white sand and coconut trees growing out of the water."

Virgins and beaches? Sounds perfect so far. Then Ramirez takes it over the line. "The best beer in the world is in the Dominican Republic: Presidente. There's more alcohol in it. You can get it colder than regular beer without freezing it. It's perfection."

Cap Cana. Virgins. Presidente. I got it. I'm ready to book my flight.

Ramirez, 28, who grew up in New Jersey after her family moved to the United States, loves talking about her home country, even though she doesn't have much time to visit. You see, her schedule is a bit packed.

She joined the cast of NBC's *Heroes* as the mysterious, powerful new character Maya. You probably know her better as Blanca, the single Latina mom who broke young Anthony Jr.'s heart in the final season of *The Sopranos.* And you probably saw her in tight black leather and tats in *X-Men: The Last Stand* as one of Magneto's right-hand gals. All these high-profile acting gigs tend to keep her from spending time in her beloved homeland.

We're meeting old-school-Hollywood style, at the Chateau Marmont, under the close supervision of John Belushi's ghost. I can see why he's paying attention. She's not slim. She's lithe. Her skin isn't brown. It's bronze. And luminous. Her voice resembles Demi Moore's, with a slight accent. Her laugh, which you hear often, is hearty. And her attitude is wide open. "I am not about the bullshit," she says. "I can't hide how I feel. People find that out about me fast. If I didn't like you, you'd get that side of me."

Then she gives me that hearty laugh, so I guess I'm all right.

"Honesty hurts people's feelings," she continues, warming to a favorite subject. "But it's the only way to be. I'd rather you be honest with me always, even if you make me angry with your honesty. I can still respect that you've been honest." (Got that, men? No more lies about the fat pants, when she asks.)

Ramirez's single days are behind her. She found an honest man in director Jessy Terrero, who recently proposed to her in a helicopter over the Dominican Republic. But in terms of what Terrero did to win her heart, Ramirez is, of course, honest. He didn't try to be a superhero—and this woman knows superheroes. He didn't try to impress her with feats of strength, physical or attitudinal. Instead, he played it straight.

"He treated me as an equal," she says, "which I think any woman—well, any intelligent woman—wants."

Ramirez has a few more honest suggestions on how to catch a lady's eye and her heart and, so as not to make it all about body parts, her spirit.

SHOW A LITTLE EMOTION. Ramirez wishes men would fight off their masculine stoicism every once in a while and show some heat. "Men don't realize that being so rational all the time only makes them feel cold. It creates a bigger problem: Now you have an emotional woman!" She laughs again, and this laugh is evil. "There's no rational way to deal with that."

Once in a while, show a lot of emotion. One time a guy totally broke down and bawled in front of Ramirez. She remembers it fondly. "Women deal with those emotions every day," she says. "It's normal. It's heartfelt." And, of course, the Dania capper: "It's honest."

NOTICE AND APPRECIATE. "Men forget about small gestures," she says. "I don't want to tell you to thank me. That pisses me off. But if you take the time and look at those little things, you would correct bigger problems. So notice. And appreciate."

GO FOR REALISM. "There's this ideal woman that men think up in their heads," Ramirez says. "It's the same for women—they think up Prince Charming. I want a relationship that's real. My fiancé always makes me feel like I can be myself, no matter how great or messed up that is. Good, bad, in between. It's all beautiful."

SOLVE THE SEX/MOOD MYSTERY

Quick, which comes first: Having sex or being in a good mood? Arizona State University researchers wanted to find out. They asked 58 middle-age women to record, every day for 9 months, both their emotions and how often they "got busy." The results? Feeling happy may make you more likely to have sex with your partner—but a romp under the sheets might also boost your mood, possibly making you want more affection the next day. Conclusion: You'll have to solve this age-old mystery of which one comes first yourself. Guess you'll just have to devise your own experiment.

GO AHEAD . . . SMILE!

You don't have to spend years in therapy to become happier. Studies have shown that these three strategies take just 1 week to make a real improvement, according to Martin E. P. Seligman, PhD, a pioneer of the positive psychology movement and a professor at the University of Pennsylvania.

Use your signature strengths in a new way. Researchers asked study participants about their top five strengths—generosity, for instance, or creativity—and then told them to use one of these strengths in a new and different way every day for 1 week. The result? The volunteers measurably increased their happiness for a full 6 months.

Write down the good things. Every day, a group of adults was asked to write down three things that had gone well and why they happened. And again, even though the experiment lasted only 1 week, participants reported feeling happier for 6 months afterward.

Pay a gratitude visit. People were given 1 week to write and then deliver a letter of gratitude in person to someone who had been especially kind to them, but whom they had never thanked properly. The happiness boost from this experiment lasted about 1 month.

TONING UP

It's not like you need another reason to slather on the SPF, but here's one anyway: The evenness of your skin tone influences how attractive you appear, according to a study in the journal *Evolution and Human Behavior*. Researchers photographed 169 women and fitted each face onto a standard digital model using special software. They erased features like wrinkles so skin tone was the only difference and then asked 198 male volunteers to rate the pictures. The men found the faces with the most even skin tones the healthiest and most attractive.

"Unevenness in skin color, like veins and redness, creates contrasts [that affect] our perception of beauty," says study coauthor Paul Matts, PhD. Protecting your skin is the best defense: Use a moisturizer with an SPF of at least 15 every day.

PERCENTAGE OF MARRIED WOMEN WHO SAY THEY LOVE TO FLIRT

39

MEAN GENE

Poor Ugly Betty. Maybe some bosses really can't help terrorizing their peons. A study presented at the American Psychosomatic Society's annual meeting suggests that some women might be angrier and more aggressive than others because of an altered gene. Researchers tracked 550 women and found that the angriest ones were most likely to have variations in a gene called HTR2C, which is a receptor for mood-regulating serotonin. They think HTR2C may also be linked to heart disease, which would make it no coincidence that stressed-out people can develop serious health problems—not to mention make those around them miserable. Next on tap: studying the gene in larger groups of women.

DRESSED TO CONCEIVE

Women dress better when they are most fertile, according to a study in the journal *Hormones and Behavior*. Researchers photographed 30 women twice: once in their most fertile phase (during ovulation) and once in their least fertile phase (the 2 weeks after ovulation). They then asked a group of people to pick the photo in which each woman was trying to look more attractive. The "fertile" photos won 60 percent of the time, perhaps because women unconsciously try to attract mates when they're most likely to get pregnant.

THE AROMA OF AMORE

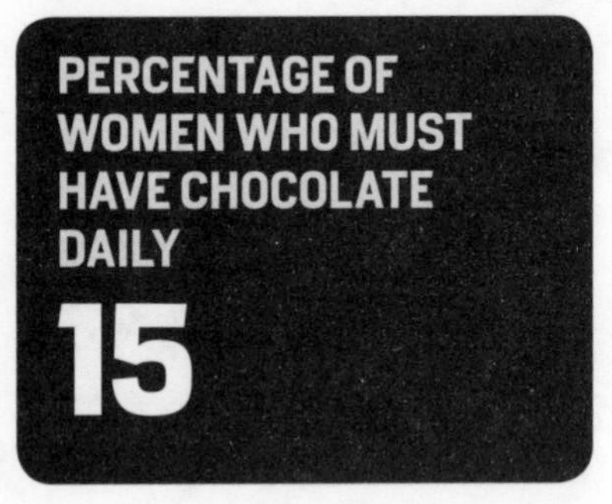

A potent aphrodisiac is just a jog away. Women are sexually aroused by the scent of male sweat, according to researchers at the University of California at Berkeley. When 48 female undergrads watched an erotic video after sniffing a control scent or androstadienone (a testosterone derivative in male sweat), the androstadienone inhalers experienced a 200 percent spike in sexual arousal. Androstadienone increased the women's levels of cortisol, a hormone that stimulates arousal, by almost 40 percent.

But watch the clock: You'll have only about 60 minutes before her cortisol surge wears off, according to study author Claire Wyart, PhD.

FOREPLAY FOOD

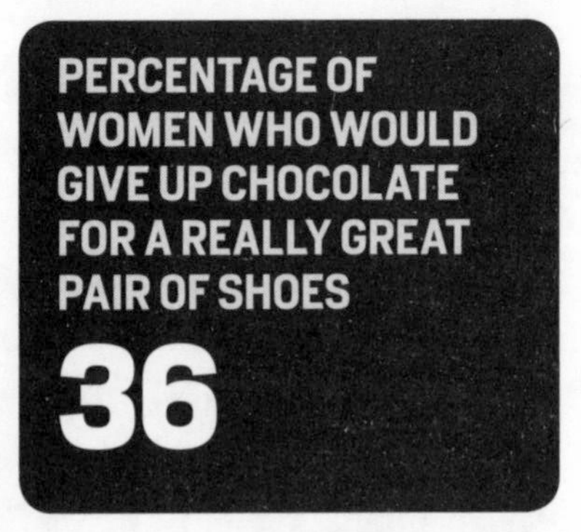

For a hot nightcap, give her Godiva. Women become more sexually aroused from eating dark chocolate than from kissing. British scientists monitored couples as they ate squares of dark chocolate and again as they kissed passionately. The finding: Women's heart rates rose 20 percent and their bodies released four times more endorphins when eating the cacao-rich chocolate. To ensure her arousal, opt for 65 percent cacao dark chocolate.

PICK-UP TRICKS

Don't keep your hands to yourself. Touching a woman's forearm will lower her guard. French researchers studied 120 women at a nightclub and found they were 50 percent more apt to accept a dance invitation if it was paired with gentle contact. Study author Nicolas Guéguen, PhD, notes that touching makes men seem strong and in control—sexually attractive traits.

RATIONALES FOR A ROLL IN THE HAY

Feeling hornier than a rhino? Chances are you don't need another excuse to knock boots. But researchers from the University of Texas at Austin surveyed nearly 2,000 people about why they have sex and found 237 reasons. Turns out, when it comes to jumping in the sack, men and women are more alike than you might think—and have plenty of oddball reasons for getting it on.

TOP FIVE SCREWY REASONS FOR DOING IT

1. Because of a bet
2. I wanted to get more than my friends got
3. My partner is a snore
4. I wanted to change the topic
5. It seemed like good exercise

TOP FIVE REASONS MEN DO IT

1. She was hot
2. I like how it feels
3. I wanted to feel good

4. It's fun
5. I like her

TOP 5 REASONS WOMEN DO IT

1. He was hot
2. I wanted to feel good
3. I like how it feels
4. I like him
5. I love him

PERCENTAGE OF THE AVERAGE WOMAN'S SALARY SHE SAYS GOES TO FASHION AND BEAUTY UPKEEP

about 10

CLOSETED DESIRES

Multiple choice: Gucci or guy? It might sound like no contest, but in a Unilever poll of 1,000 women, the dudes lost to the duds. Women on average said they'd give up 15 months of sex for a new wardrobe—and 2 percent would abstain for 3 years! Sixty-one percent said they'd grieve the loss of their favorite wardrobe item more than a month of sex. What's more, 48 percent of women said their most beloved article of clothing was more reliable than their guy for making them feel confident and sexy.

HIGH BLOOD PRESSURE HAVOC

Researchers have long known that for men, high blood pressure is like stray thoughts about Grandma: It can cause problems with sexual performance.

Now, a study presented at a recent American Society of Hypertension meeting has found that women with high blood pressure are more likely to suffer from sexual dysfunction, too. Researchers surveyed 417 women about their sex lives and found that hypertensive women are twice as likely to have low desire, pain during sex, and trouble reaching orgasm, probably because high blood pressure prevents enough blood from getting to the vagina to trigger arousal.

If your girl has hypertension and problems in the bedroom, urge her to see her doc: He can help her lower her blood pressure.

A SAD STATE

Girl feeling low? Get in line: Women aren't as happy as they used to be. In 1972 and 2006, University of Pennsylvania researchers asked 52,500 people how happy they were. In '72, 36 percent of women stated they were "very happy" with their lives, compared with 31 percent in '06. How come? One possibility is the "hottie theory," says study coauthor and economist Betsey Stevenson, PhD. Women experience enormous pressure to be attractive—and blame themselves if they come up short. Screw the image: Every day, urge her to do something she's great at, whether it's smoking a 5K, writing a letter, or slipping in a quickie.

» A MAN'S GUIDE POLL

Blonde vs. Brunette: The Grudge Match

Call it the Angelina Jolie effect. According to a recent sunsilk.com survey of more than 4,000 men, brunettes are the new sex kittens. (See the statistics for proof.) Sixty-three percent of men think blondes are airheads; only 2 percent consider brunettes to be ditzy. Redheads? Still a mystery.

Who has the hottest hair?

- 65 percent of men would rather drop cash on a dinner with a brunette than with a blonde. They get a better return on their investment, they say.
- 59 percent of men believe brunettes have more one-night stands than blondes do.
- 75 percent of men would rather wake up with a brunette than with a blonde.
- 13 percent of men say they have more intelligent conversations with blondes.
- 20 percent of men have mothers who prefer their sons date blondes.
- 29 percent of men plan to marry a blonde.

PART 3

DATE GREAT

PLAY WITH FIRE

HOW TO HANDLE THE (NEW) SEXUALLY EMPOWERED OVER-40 WOMAN

BY COLIN MCENROE

"I've been thinking that maybe we should not be having sex," I told a woman last year. "Maybe we should just be friends."

"I have no interest in a relationship with you that does not include sex," she told me.

So we went back to having sex. (I mean, what can you do?) The woman was in her late forties, a few years younger than myself. Unlike me, however, she was also incredibly hot, fit, agile, and inventive. We had a wonderful sex life, but I'll admit it: I was a little tired.

One woman, a cook who enjoyed working with me in the kitchen, said a few years back, "What do I want you for? Maybe I just want you for food and sex." Another, in a fit of pique about other deficits in our relationship, told me that we would not be cutting back on sex because "Sex is all you're good for." Both of those women were over 50, attractive, and—sexually speaking—generous and responsive.

There was a little bit of bluster in their statements. I mean, it turned out that most of these women also wanted, eventually, to share the richly textured joy of middle life, watch our various children grow up, and one day start playing with the grandchildren. But they sure didn't mind having a lot of hot sex first.

It's a supreme irony. Many of us men spent the first half of our lives trying to talk women into having sex with us. Now we occasionally try to talk them out of it. Okay, maybe not very often.

We live in a new culture of sexually empowered older women. If you don't believe me, visit a bookstore. The last two years have seen a rockslide of books both documenting and encouraging the sexual reblossoming of women age 40 and up.

The 2,000-pound gorilla is Gail Sheehy's *Sex and the Seasoned Woman*, published in 2007 by Random House. But standing in the shadow of Sheehy's book are other titles, such as *Better Than I Ever Expected: Straight Talk About Sex After Sixty*, by Joan Price (Seal Press), also published in 2007, and *Still Sexy After All These Years? The 9 Unspoken Truths About Women's Desire Beyond 50*, by Leah Kliger and Deborah Nedelman (Perigee/Penguin).

I could keep going, which is probably the name of yet another sex book for the older person, but I'll skip past some of the other titles and go straight to Jane Juska, who may have ignited this publishing trend in 2003 with *A Round-Heeled Woman: My Late-Life Adventures in Sex and Romance*. She published a sequel in 2007.

Juska famously ran a personal ad in the *New York Review of Books*: "Before I turn 67—next March—I would like to have a lot of sex with a man I like. If you want to talk first, Trollope works for me." By the time her book came out, she was 70 and happily juggling three lovers at once, one of them 33 years old. The book was kind of a Ms. Ulysses, documenting her lusty sail through a sea of men and her beachings on strange islands.

It wasn't always like this. I suppose it's quite possible that women of a certain age have always fancied more sex than they were having, but the larger cultural message said they should get interested in their grandchildren or art movies or something, while most of the men their age either ran off with younger things or just up and died.

My own experience has been that there is kind of a snooze alarm attached to the biological clock. It usually goes off when women are in their forties. They're all done having kids, and they start wondering what else they can do with that apparatus. Their husbands are becoming a little chunky, predictable, drunk, indifferent, whatever. And these women, many of whom are pretty fabulous, start singing that old Peggy Lee song: "Is That All There Is?"

Joan Price told me she wrote her sex-after-50 book partly because she couldn't find any books for people like her. Price is a fitness instructor from Northern California who found herself "in a new relationship and having the best sex of my life, but not without challenges."

She went looking for information and found "doom and gloom . . . you're gonna wither and dry up . . . give it up . . . sex is for the young."

Price wrote a book that is solution oriented. By that, I mean there's information about actual solutions you can rub on parts of you that aren't as damp as they used to be, and there's a chapter about sex toys, because Price believes that female orgasm, post-50, is "much more subtle and takes longer to get there . . . a lot of kissing and touching and maybe a sex toy."

Why should you, a guy, care about any of this?

Well, if you're married or in a long-term relationship, you may be under the false impression that your wife or girlfriend doesn't mind the way you're slowing down, doesn't mind the way sex plays a smaller role in your life now than, say, ESPN's SportsCenter does. She's probably relieved not to have to put out, right?

Wrong. A 2004 study of divorce cited by Sheehy and initiated by AARP found that two-thirds of all divorces involving couples over 40 are initiated by the woman. One-third of divorced or single women over 40 are dating a younger man. On an anecdotal level, I can think, without trying hard, of four women over 40 who left their husbands at least partly because the bedroom had become very cold. These women are friends of mine, and I know their stories because I'm divorced and in a position to chat with them. You know who doesn't know these stories? The male friends of the husbands. Guys tend not to share this kind of information with one another, even if it could save some other guy from making the same mistake.

The other group of people who should care are the men who aren't married or in a long-term relationship. If you're over 40 and trying to figure out which woman you should get with, you shouldn't assume that by choosing someone closer to your own age you're closing the door on high-volume, high-quality sex.

Sex is so many things. The best sex includes a kind of conversation, loaded with metaphors for how the two of you feel about each other. Older women are, generally, better conversationalists. They've lived more and thought more. I find that this spills over into bed. A woman older than 40 is more likely to linger over an interesting hip movement during intercourse, or slowly work to find the part of your neck that responds to her lips and teeth. (Jeez, I'm making myself hot.)

Women still complain to me that they have to list themselves as 45 or younger on Match.com if they want to generate any activity at all from men (at least, the ones who are looking for more than a nurse). Men tend to believe that if they want a lot of sex during their golden years, they should seek out a somewhat younger woman, partly because she's more likely to want a lot of sex, too.

Anthropologist Helen Fisher, PhD, a relationship expert and the author of *Why We Love,* says that's a cultural belief rather than a biological truth. "And it's going to crumble. It's crumbling already. You're writing about it, and we're talking about it. That's part of the crumbling process," she says.

For millions of years in the grasslands of Africa, women were the sexual and social equals of men, says Fisher. If you look at our biology, she says, it seems women are more wired for a steady diet of sex into old age than men are.

"Women tend to plateau sexually in middle age. About 10 percent report an increase in sexuality," says Fisher. "Men are actually more fragile, more apt to experience sexual problems and sharp falloffs."

The rise of agrarian society, which made it necessary to keep women, literally, down on the farm, created a whole matrix of cultural messages, one of which was the extinguishing of female sexuality with the onset of menopause, says Fisher, who covered this in *The First Sex: The Natural Talents of Women and How They Are Changing the World.*

"Women in their fifties and sixties used to go live with their kids and help raise the grandchildren. Now, they live independently and go on Internet dating sites. An animal has been set loose," says Fisher.

And who is going to have sex with that animal? I think there's an argument in all this for age-appropriate men and women getting together, instead of seeking younger partners, as well as a case for a more expansive idea of what sex is.

Yvonne Davis, 41, is recently divorced and works as a communications consultant in the Beltway and in Connecticut. She has been dating, and she finds she likes men her own age or a little older.

"I like older men. You can express your needs and wants to them, and they can accommodate you. Older men tend to be more patient and willing to get the job done," she says. "He may not have that six-pack, but he knows what his limitations are, and you just kind of roll with that—literally and figuratively."

Older women, she says, offer similar delights to men.

"I think an older woman can kind of hang more," says Davis. "She can be more explorative."

Men should understand, says Davis, that older women—best-selling books notwithstanding—have not really severed the connection between sex and emotions.

"I've met very few women who have come to the point where they can have sex and enjoy themselves and not expect more from the guy," she says. "I don't care if she is in her fifties and has money and is on her third career. I know I can't get there. Well, I can but I can't."

"What we want from men is not what they think we want," agrees Price. "Men think we want a raging erection and the Energizer bunny. We have always wanted foreplay. Now we want even more, so much that we don't even want to call it foreplay. I actually recommend that older couples schedule lovemaking. Schedule it at a time of day when you both have a lot of energy, which is usually not when you're falling asleep at night. There's a reason they call it 'afternoon delight.' And schedule at least two hours."

I can't even decide whether that makes me feel inspired or tired. It's certainly a larger time commitment than SportsCenter.

BRING SEXY BACK

ACHIEVING ROMANTIC BLISS WHILE TRAVELING REQUIRES A DELICATE BALANCE OF PLANNING AND SPONTANEITY. HERE'S HOW TO NAIL IT

BY BEN COURT

With a Cuban father, an Italian husband, and a career path that started at the Paris Conservatoire and has snaked all over the globe, British-born Sienna Guillory is the übercosmopolitan girl next door. Here the star of *Eragon, Helen of Troy*, and *Inkhart* dishes her tips on traveling smart.

BOOK A ROOM WITH A VIEW. "Boutique hotels are far more romantic than big chains. Always ask about the view: There's something sexy about waking up in a new environment."

OPEN THE HOTEL WINDOWS. "Travel is about losing yourself, so I never plug in my iPod. I like to hear the sounds and voices of a new place and breathe in its scent. It helps me sink into the right mood."

LOOK FOR ANTIQUE LINENS. "All women are suckers for good linens. My favorites are antique linens. Opulence always induces a delectable state of indulgence. I wouldn't want to sleep on satin sheets though—far too slimy."

LISTEN TO HER RHYTHMS. "Sometimes I wake up early and go for a quiet run with my husband. It's a great way to see a city's architecture before people and cars crowd the streets. Other times, I want to sleep in. Holidays have a different pace from workdays, and you should embrace that."

SHARE A PERFECT DAY IN PARIS. "I'd start with a late brunch at a café, followed by a stroll around the Rodin museum and a stop at the Frédéric Malle perfumerie. After that, I'd pop into Chloé, Sonia Rykiel, and Colette to find something wildly expensive. Then back to the hotel for a bath. I like to wear the clothes I buy in a new place, so I'd put on my new outfit and find a bistro in St. Germain."

DO YOUR RESEARCH. "There's nothing as uninspiring as being tied to a schedule. Yuck. That said, research is wildly impressive: Read up on the local history, find the fun neighborhoods, and know where to eat, drink, and shop."

FIND SPONTANEOUS ACTIVITIES. "Above all, spontaneity is what makes travel romantic. I often try whatever it is the locals are passionate about, whether it's dancing in Havana or watching soccer in Italy. You can't swim unless you get into the water."

INDULGE YOUR INNER SPY. "Sometimes in a new city, we will go to a popular neighborhood and follow a well-heeled local couple—discreetly, of course—to see where they are headed. Usually, they're going out for a cozy dinner and not something flashy. That's what I want."

BE GENEROUS. "Nothing impresses me like good manners. It's about generosity, with both your attitude to the moment and actions to local people. Small things are important, like being patient and tipping the concierge and maid well."

CREATE UNIQUE MEMORIES. "Traveling with a lover is about doing things you enjoy together and discovering things that only you know about. I've ended up collecting ridiculous T-shirts. In Cuba, I swapped the Chelsea soccer jersey I was wearing for a Cuba T-shirt a 10-year-old boy had on. When I wear it now, I'm instantly and constantly reminded of the excitement and warmth of the whole trip."

DATE DANGEROUSLY

FROM THE SHORT-SKIRTED SEDUCTRESS IN THE COPY ROOM TO YOUR BEST FRIEND AND FEMALE CONFIDANTE—YOU'RE SURROUNDED BY WOMEN YOU CAN'T HAVE. OR CAN YOU? WE POLLED WOMEN AND MEN, INCLUDING DOZENS OF EXPERTS, TO HELP YOU MAKE THAT HANDS-OFF HOTTIE YOURS

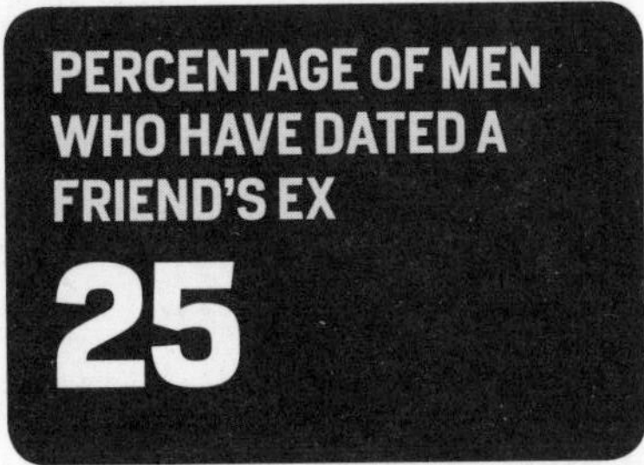

It's old news that we want what we can't have. But when it comes to dating, we're now getting it more than ever, according to our exclusive survey of 3,000 men and women. "Relationships once considered taboo are now some of the most successful, because you already know and like the person," says Ian Kerner, PhD, a relationship therapist and the author of *Date Scene Investigation*. That doesn't mean they're less perilous. We've created the ultimate guide to protecting yourself while pursuing the most passionate forbidden affairs.

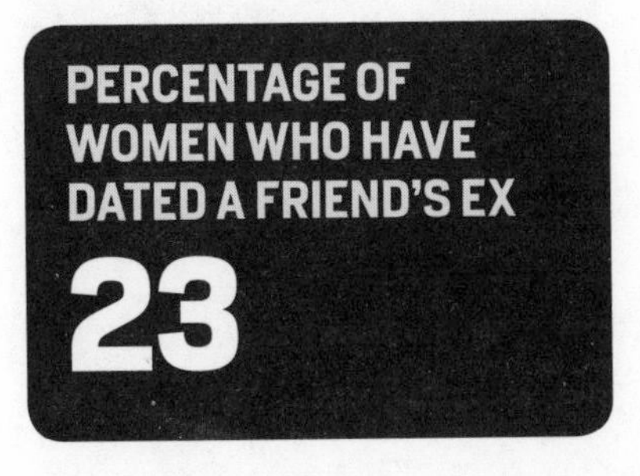

A FRIEND'S EX

Resist the urge; date her at your own risk.

WHY YOU WANT HER: Your buddy has extolled her virtues so relentlessly, she's become the woman of your dreams, too. "He's basically given you a sales pitch for his girlfriend," says Amy Bippus, PhD, a professor of communication studies at California State University at Long Beach.

WHAT TO CONSIDER: If the separation wasn't mutual, beware. "There's no bigger blow to a man's self-esteem than to be rejected in favor of a friend," says Judy Kuriansky, PhD, author of *The Complete Idiot's Guide to Dating*.

WHAT TO DO: If you must act, stay away until he has moved on to another love interest. "There's a psychological threshold that's crossed when a person takes up a new relationship," says Kerner. "Plus, you don't want to look like a scavenger."

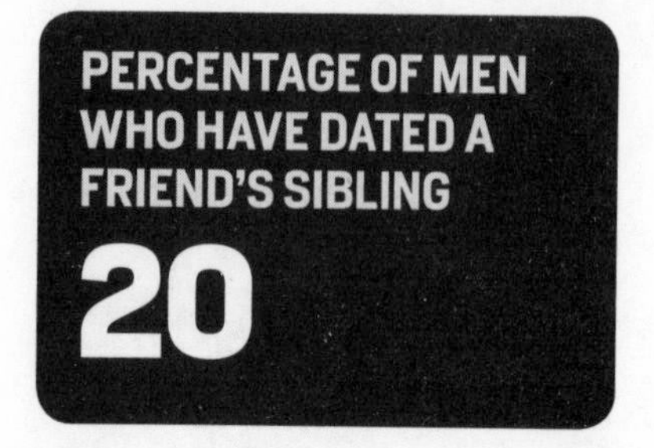

A FRIEND'S SIBLING

Proceed with caution; tread carefully while pursuing her.

WHY YOU WANT HER: She has your best friend's personality and Scarlett Johansson's curves, and she already knows your name. "You've crossed the toughest boundary in dating," says Logan Levkoff, a sex columnist.

WHAT TO CONSIDER: If the relationship sours, don't expect your friend to back you up. "Chances are, he'll protect his sister," says Levkoff. You'll also lose a sounding board for relationship troubles.

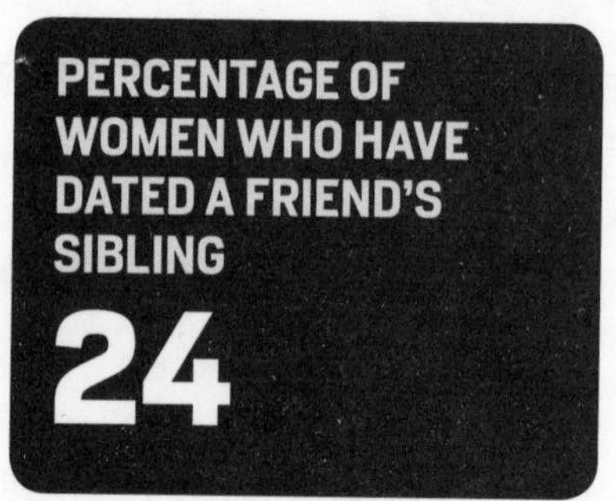

WHAT TO DO: Say this: "How would you feel if I said I was interested in your sister?" not "Dude, Susie is smoking hot. Can I date her?" "Ultimately, you want to give your buddy a chance to express himself, not deliver a thumbs-up or thumbs-down vote," says Kuriansky.

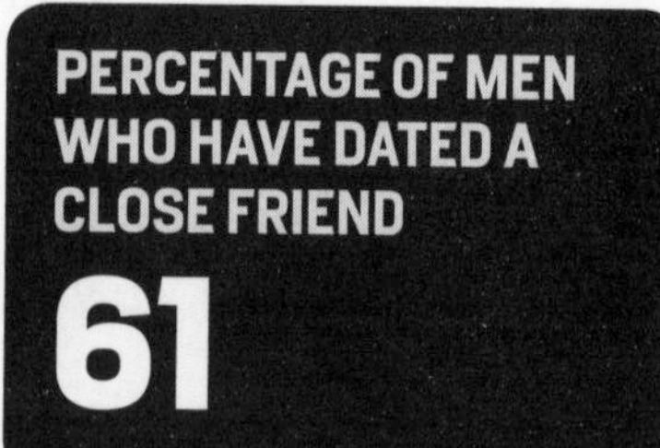

A CLOSE FRIEND

Make your move.

WHY YOU WANT HER: "She has the potential to be everything you need: the friend, the playmate, and the lover," says Levkoff.

WHAT TO CONSIDER: If you've been a confidant for her most lurid dating stories, chances are she's not open to an upgrade. But if, after hanging out, she starts referring to the two of you as "us," you're in.

WHAT TO DO: Choose your words wisely. "I've always loved you" could cheapen the friendship. "Women often feel betrayed if they find out you've been sexually interested all along," says Kerner. "Tell her she's great and ratchet up the intimacy a bit. It's better to let it happen naturally than to deliver a stump speech."

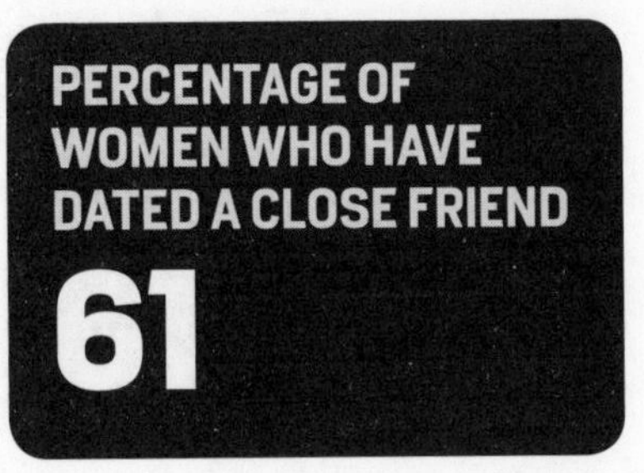

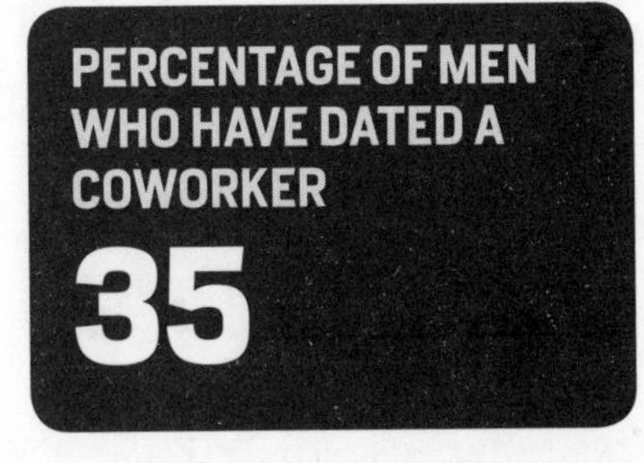

A COWORKER

Make your move.

WHY YOU WANT HER: "The workplace is a trove of attractive, like-minded people our own age who dress nicely," says Bippus. "It's deep intimacy with rigid barriers," adds anthropologist Helen Fisher, a relationship expert and the author of *Why We Love*. "That's a recipe for romantic love."

WHAT TO CONSIDER: Nothing kills a meeting—and your reputation—faster than puppy-dog eyes across a conference table. "Couples always think other people don't know, but they always do," says Marie McIntyre, PhD, author of *Secrets to Winning at Office Politics*. The obvious pitfall: You split and loathe each other, all under the eyes of the office gossips.

WHAT TO DO: You can have an office romance, as long as you keep the office and the romance separate. "You need to prove to your boss that your relationship status won't change the work environment," says McIntyre. A reassuring heads-up to your supervisor once you're exclusive could help reinforce your professional image. If a breakup comes, go ahead and have the screaming fight, but then settle how you'll deal in the office. Your jobs depend on it.

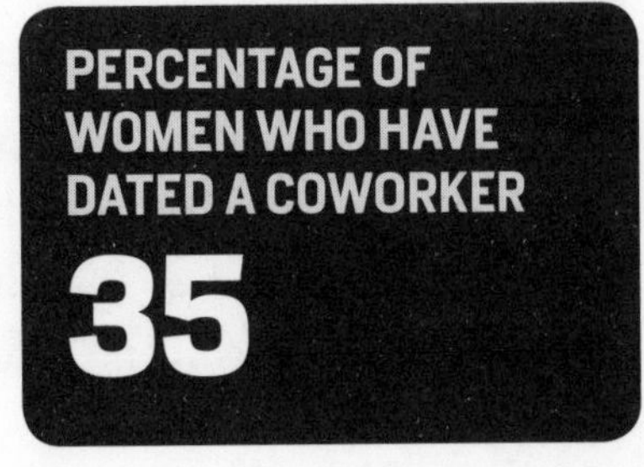

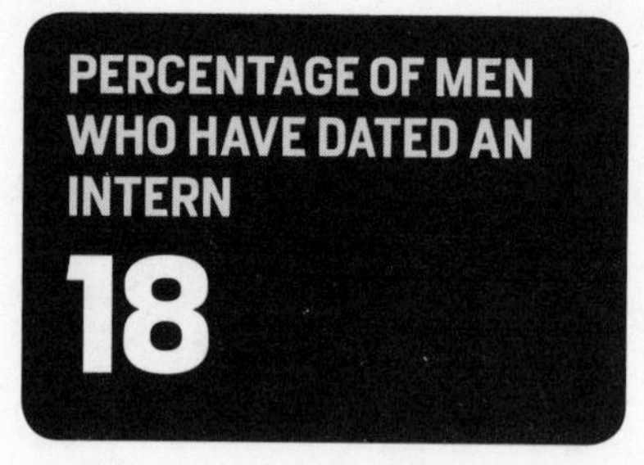

AN INTERN

Proceed with caution.

WHY YOU WANT HER: She's young, hot, well dressed, helpful, and somehow convinced that you're a lot better at your job than you actually are.

WHAT TO CONSIDER: Learn from Lewinsky: Nothing grabs attention—at the watercooler or the newsstand—like intern gossip. What's worse, she's a walking lawsuit. "Friendly advances can be mistaken as sexual harassment," warns McIntyre.

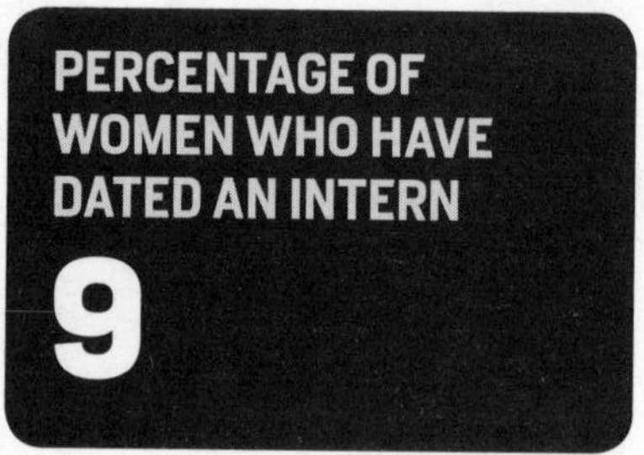

WHAT TO DO: Hold your horses. Even if she's interested. Even if you bump into her outside of work. Even if she's the one slurring come-ons at happy hour. "As soon as she's packed up her cubicle, you've got the green light," says McIntyre. Until then, let the tension build to a passion-packed payoff.

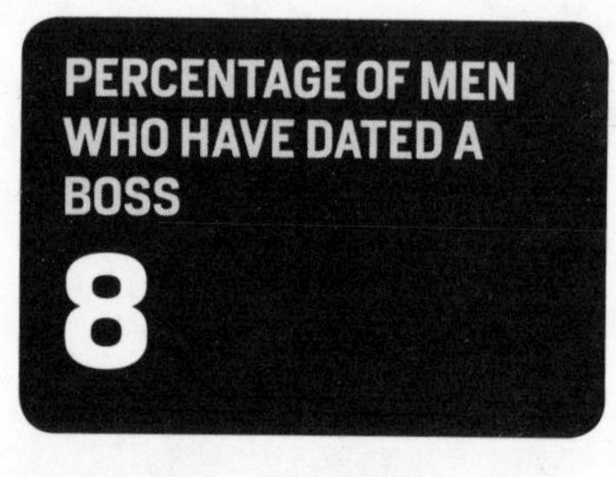

YOUR BOSS

Resist the urge; date her at your own risk.

WHY YOU WANT HER: She's great at telling you what to do. How might that boardroom attitude transfer to the bedroom? Another aphrodisiac: This relationship requires secrecy. That's sexy. At least until it becomes annoying.

WHAT TO CONSIDER: Remember how that one ex-girlfriend set your clothes on fire? Now imagine dumping your boss. Also, once coworkers get wind of the situation, they'll assume you're receiving unfair attention. Which you are.

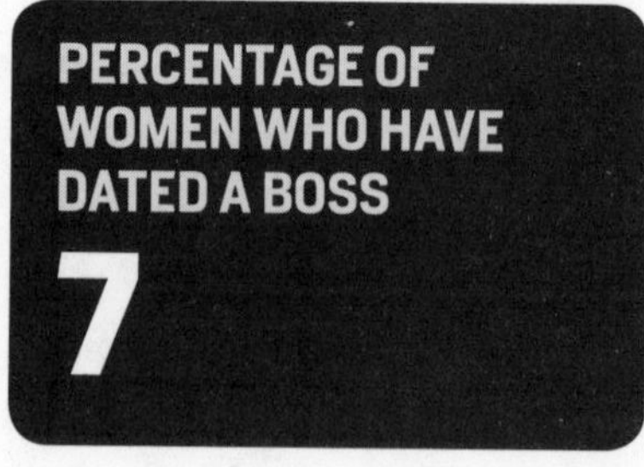

WHAT TO DO: Nothing. Simmering tension can work in your favor forever, if you leave it at that. If a relationship takes hold, you have another decision to make: Is the job or the relationship more replaceable? One way it can work: in sprawling workplaces with several supervisors, says Robyn DeVal, PhD, a marriage-and-family therapist. "There's less opportunity for overlap between your personal and professional lives."

YOUR SISTER'S FRIEND

Make your move.

PERCENTAGE OF MEN WHO HAVE DATED THEIR SISTERS' FRIENDS

13

WHY YOU WANT HER: She's the safe choice. "Meeting people is hard, and dating someone you know is easier and safer," says Norah Dunbar, PhD, a specialist in interpersonal communications at California State University at Long Beach.

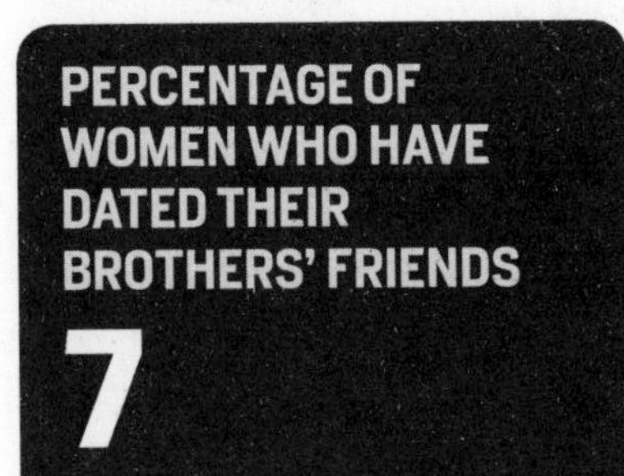

WHAT TO CONSIDER: "Some siblings aren't comfortable merging those worlds," says Kerner. "You run the risk of harming her relationship with a friend."

WHAT TO DO: You don't need your sister's blessing, but she could help you seal the deal. "Most siblings are willing to play matchmaker," says Kerner.

AN EX'S FRIEND

Resist the urge; date her at your own risk.

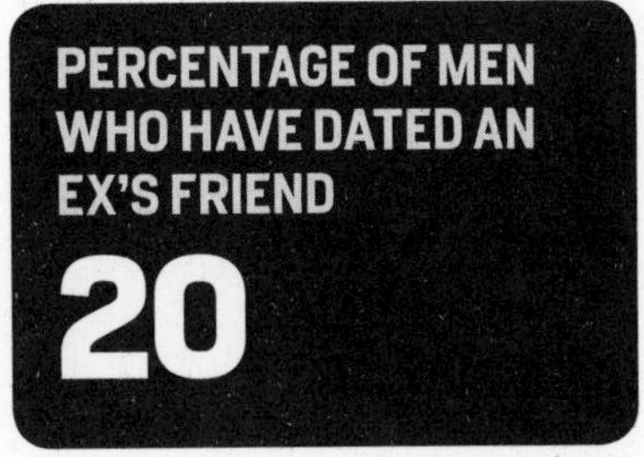

WHY YOU WANT HER: She's the Long Island iced tea of dating: a bunch of bad stuff mixed together that makes you feel good until the brutal hangover sets in. Even worse: You've just upped your creep quotient exponentially.

WHAT TO CONSIDER: "Women don't handle this situation as well as men do,"

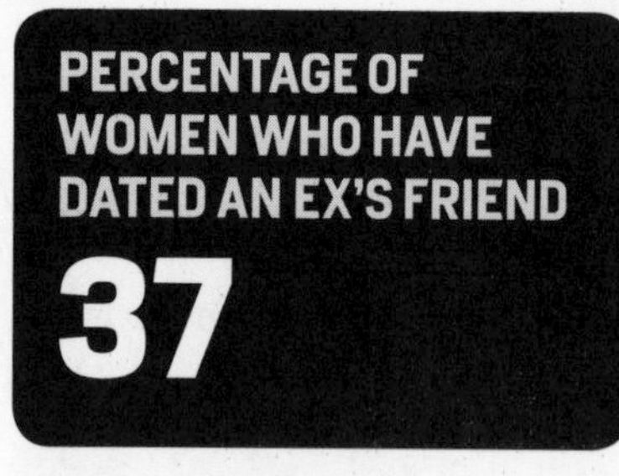

says Eve Marx, author of *Flirtspeak: The Sexy Language of Flirting.* "You have a 99 percent chance of losing her as a friend."

WHAT TO DO: Rein in your impulses. But if she's the predator, the burden is on her to bridge the gap with your ex.

YOUR OWN EX

Resist the urge; date her at your own risk.

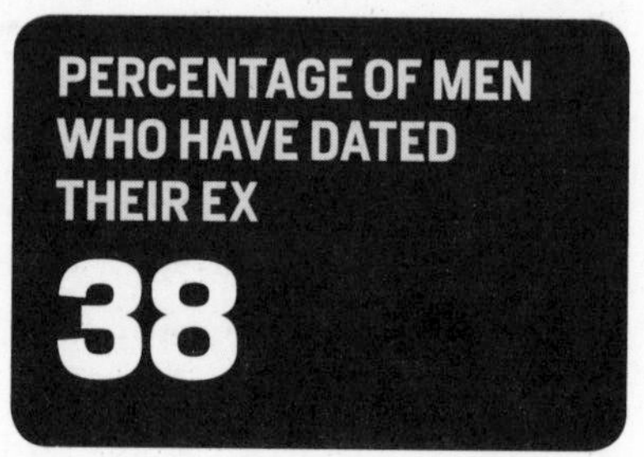

WHY YOU WANT HER: She's like mac and cheese. "It's all about comfort dating," says Kerner. You're hungry—for sex, for companionship—and she might be, too.

WHAT TO CONSIDER: Romantic tension grows until you start dating or hook up again, and then it fades immediately. "Most couples end up in a dangerous cycle," says Kerner. "No one is able to move on."

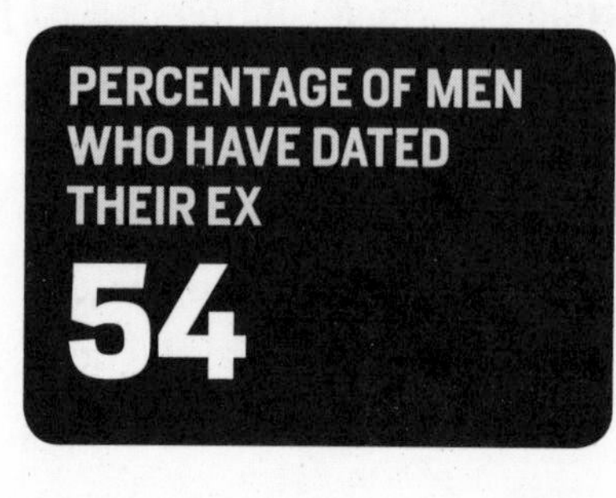

WHAT TO DO: Give yourself a grace period. You're trying to separate two bodies of water here. Every e-mail, text message, or face-to-face chat is a breach in the dam. Keep contact to a minimum.

He Said/She Said

Which of the following people have you lusted after—without ever making a move?

	HE	SHE
A close friend	59%	62%
An ex	26%	44%
A friend's ex	53%	41%
An ex's friend	34%	41%
A peer at work	42%	35%
A friend's sibling	50%	26%

ASK THE GIRL NEXT DOOR

THE HONEST TRUTH ABOUT WOMEN FROM OUR LOVELY NEIGHBOR

What's the easiest way to let her know I'm not interested?

Easiest? Don't call her back. Easiest while still being nice? Send an e-mail explaining that you enjoyed meeting her but get the sense that neither of you is feeling a spark.

I love slasher flicks, but my collection freaks women out. How do I explain?

What exactly is it that intrigues you about these movies? Is it the pacing and lighting? The concept of an überhuman villain? The paralyzing power of fear? Or is it the half-naked chicks being hacked to death with chain saws? If you can show your date that you're a thoughtful film critic, not a fan of random acts of violence, she'll be less likely to worry that you're hiding an ax under your bed.

I've been dating a woman for a month and haven't met any of her friends. Is she playing with me?

I doubt it. Actually it's a good sign that she hasn't paraded you in front of her friends yet. Women tend to do that when they're not sure about a guy and want a second and third opinion (usually delivered during group trips to the ladies' room). But if we're really into you, we keep you to ourselves at first. It's more romantic to get to know someone without other people's opinions and personalities figuring into the equation.

I'm sick of going to dinner with my girlfriend's boring friends. Can I just tell her that?

You know better than that. Sitting around with people you have absolutely no interest in is just one of the banes of being in a relationship. One thing you can do is suggest skipping the restaurant and meeting up with her crew at a billiards club or bowling alley so there's something obvious to talk about. Or lure them to an outdoor concert where you can sprawl out on a blanket and nod off when the going turns dull.

How soon can I date a girl who's friends with my ex?

To maintain your good-guy image with the woman, you have to wait 6 months to a year after the breakup. A long time, yes, but here's a work-around: If you think the feeling is mutual, confess your attraction to her, but acknowledge that it wouldn't be right if you rushed into anything. She'll respect your emotional intelligence. (Translation: You get to be a player without looking like one.) And who knows? Maybe the two of you can start discussing the fact that you shouldn't be dating over coffee, drinks, dinner . . .

If your boyfriend kissed a girl in a bar, would you want to know?

No. But thanks a heap for making me picture it, bud.

My girlfriend wants me to stop gambling. It's my money. What's the problem?

Maybe she's worried about your bank account, but there's probably more to it. Poker virgins stress about men who gamble, because they see it as a gateway vice. Her fear: First you risk cash to score a thrill; next you risk your relationship to hook up with Candy the cocktail waitress. To end the nagging, take her to the casino, set a limit, and stick to it. She'll see that you're having fun, not spinning out of control—unless you are.

Is it overkill to make a woman breakfast the morning after a casual hook-up?

In theory, being served blueberry pancakes after a night of appetite-stoking action sounds fantastic. But let's consider the realities. First, you barely know each other. Asking, "So, have you always lived in Des Moines?" over coffee will be kind of awkward when you've already seen each other naked. Second, the hook-up may have been a mistake. Hook-ups happen so fast that it takes a few days before you figure out whether the attraction was real. Do yourself a favor and say goodbye before you realize it wasn't.

I hate it when she uses my toothbrush. Can I tell her?

I can understand why it turns you off. Swapping bodily fluids is one thing, but swallowing bits of what she had for dinner is another. You could complain; the worst she'll do is call you anal. Or you could stash another brush under the sink or, even better, get a toothbrush sanitizer (violight.com). If she asks why you need it, remind her that when you flush, bacteria swirl up into the air and settle on the bristles. Yech.

How do I win my girlfriend's brother over?

Don't underestimate the power of saying little. As the quiet-but-polite guy who laughs at everyone's jokes but isn't trying too hard, there's no way you could come across as a loser, a wuss, or a jerk. As for winning him over, turn that idea upside down: Hold back your approval, and he'll feel compelled to make the friendly, let's-grab-a-beer overtures.

My female friends hate all the women I date. Does it mean something, or should I stop asking for their opinions?

As your instincts are no doubt telling you, your friends' feedback is totally unreliable. They care about you, yes, but the last thing any of them wants is for you to find Miss Right and suddenly stop providing a steady stream of nonthreatening flirtation and flattery. For your gal pals, the day you fall in love will feel like the day they close down Disneyland—another fun spot they never plan to visit, but hope will always be there for them.

TAKE HER AWAY

Romantic getaways are often anything but. Here's how to beat the four biggest vacation buzz kills.

SHE WANTS MAUI SUN; YOU'D RATHER EXPLORE ROMAN RUINS

THE FIX: "Find somewhere you'll both be thrilled to visit," says Reid Bramblett, founder of the trip-planning Web site reidsguides.com. (He suggests the Mayan Riviera as a solution to the duel above.) Trumping or caving in to her plans will create tension that can fester during the trip.

THE FINISHING TOUCH: Set aside time to enjoy day trips or events solo; recap over dinner.

YOU PLAN A 3-DAY VACATION; SHE PACKS FOR 2 WEEKS

THE FIX: Instead of complaining about her cargo, help her control the two biggest variables: weather and occasion. Provide her with a week's worth of forecasts and a list of activities, and she'll be less likely to overpack.

THE FINISHING TOUCH: Ship her luggage ahead using FedEx ground; you'll pay only $17 on a 20-pound bag. Lighten your own luggage with the checklist at reidsguides.com.

A FRENZIED DEPARTURE SCHEDULE THREATENS TO SOUR YOUR TAKEOFF

THE FIX: Polish off preparations at least 24 hours before your flight leaves. And avoid flights before 10 a.m., when traffic is worst, suggests Bramblett. Arrive at the airport at least 90 minutes early and kill time separately—by looking at magazines at a kiosk or getting lost in a book.

THE FINISHING TOUCH: Schedule a car or limo service for pick-up and arrival. You'll avoid the hefty long-term parking fees, and the driver's blaring horn makes for an effective backup alarm clock.

YOU'RE IN MEXICO. YOU'RE LOST. NO HABLAS ESPAÑOL

THE FIX: Forget Berlitz. "Just mention the biggest, most famous spot in town and slap a question mark at the end," says Bramblett. Or grab your hotel's business card when you head out for the day. Show it to a cabbie, and he'll get you home.

THE FINISHING TOUCH: Learn six phrases in the country's language: "Yes," "No," "Please," "Thank you," "Excuse me," and "Do you speak English?" Locals are much more likely to help if they see you're attempting their native tongue.

SAY IT WITH SEDUCTION

Words, wielded wisely, can be a powerful instrument of seduction. The key, however, is making your inferences subtle. Consider the four make-or-break romantic situations below.

YOU'RE ASKING HER OUT FOR THE FIRST TIME

DON'T SAY: "Want to go out to dinner on Friday night?"

TRY: "Want to go out for Thai food on Friday night?"

WHY IT WORKS: "You're creating an experience she can visualize," says Eve Marx, author of *Flirtspeak: The Sexy Language of Flirting*. Unlike a blank proposal, it engages and puts her in the moment.

YOUR ENTRÉES HAVE ARRIVED; YOU'D LIKE TO OFFER HER A PIECE OF YOUR MEAT

DON'T SAY: "Want some fillet?"

TRY: "Want a taste of my fillet?"

WHY IT WORKS: "Taste" is sexy, says Marx. "She could be thinking how you might taste each other later." Other triggers: "bite," "juicy," and "tender."

YOU WANT HER TO GO HOME WITH YOU

DON'T SAY: "Let's go back to my place."

TRY: "Let's go back to my place, because I have a great view."

WHY IT WORKS: The magic word: "because." "People comply 66 percent more often when they hear a phrase with 'because' in it," says Kevin Hogan, PsyD, author of *Irresistible Attraction*.

YOU WANT TO MOVE YOUR MAKE-OUT SESSION TO THE BEDROOM

DON'T SAY: "I really want to make love with you."

TRY: "Can you imagine how great it'd feel if we made love?"

WHY IT WORKS: Reframing your desire as a question forces her to think about it, says Hogan. The sensory word "imagine" reinforces the visual picture. If what she sees doesn't repulse her, you're in.

BE A GIFT-GIVING GURU

Just started dating? Here's the definitive gift-giving guide from *Men's Health*'s Girl Next Door, Nicole Beland, if your budding romance straddles the holidays.

2 WEEKS IN

No gift, no card. It's too soon to wear your heart on your sleeve. Take her out for a nice dinner and propose a toast: Tell her what a blast you've had with her the past couple of weeks.

4 WEEKS IN

Dinner and a small gift. A slickly designed museum gift will work (try moma.org). Alert: If you've been dating this long, ask her out for New Year's Eve; she'll be expecting it.

6 WEEKS IN

Is it love, or wait-and-see? If you're not sure, follow the 4-weeks-in tips. If it's love, spend $100 on a nice bracelet—thin and delicate if she's girly, bulky (like a cuff) if she's not.

WRAP IT UP

Great gifts come in great packages. Psych her up before she rips into it with inspired wrapping paper from whimsypress.com. (We like the Space Invaders pattern.)

TAKE HER BREATH AWAY

When shopping for the two dating standards, lingerie and flowers, there's a fine line between ca-pow and cliché. Here's how to choose right.

You can't expect a world-class ravioli if you're eating dinner at Olive Garden. So why would you go next door to Victoria's Secret and expect to find a handmade silk negligee worthy of brushing against your lover's skin? The finest lingerie money can buy comes from Trelise Cooper (trelisecooper.com) and her staff of seamstresses, who construct one-of-a-kind luxury undergarments in a tiny storefront studio in the town of Newmarket, New Zealand. Cooper starts with rare cottons and silks—found using her little black book of textile sources culled from 20 years in the fashion industry—and custom-made lace that is based on vintage pieces she finds at antiques markets in southern France and Spain and re-created by needlework specialists who use muted dyes to achieve a soft, classic look. The result is a seasonal limited collection of chemises, slips, and bustiers (available at Saks Fifth Avenue), inspired by an historical sex symbol or time period. Past inspirations have included Marilyn Monroe and Audrey Hepburn, but the new muse seems to be lifted from the pages of a kinky romance novel.

"I know what a woman wants to reveal and what she wants to hide," says Cooper, "but I always think from a man's perspective. I try to imagine what he'd want to see her in on their wedding night."

Flowers can be a bloomin' brilliant way to impress a woman. But the next time you're tempted to stop and smell the roses—or perhaps buy some for the woman you love—think again. "Many commercially available roses don't actually have any fragrance," reveals Amy Stewart, author of *Flower Confidential*. "They've had their scent bred out of them to make them more durable for their long trip from the flower farm to your doorstep. What you're really smelling at the flower shop is an aerosol spray that gives off an artificial rose fragrance." More evidence of the collapse of civilization, perhaps, but you're a civilized man who wouldn't dream of giving anything so inauthentic. So we've scoured the world to discover floral bouquets that make real scents.

PERSONALIZED BOUQUETS: B. Brooks, in San Francisco, is the Tiffany & Company of the online floral industry. They'll tailor a bouquet to your beloved's taste, after you answer a few questions about the occasion, her color preferences, and her personality. Next, the request is dispatched to one of 600 designers nationwide, who then scours local markets for unusual flowers, such as parrot tulips. From $75: bbrooks.com

RARE ORCHIDS: Beautiful Orchids imports its flowers from Asia, and its extensive offerings range from classics, such as the hardy Miltonia, to rarities like the Lilac Vuylstekeara—a hybrid created in Belgium in 1912. Plants generally last 4 to 5 weeks. From $65: beautifulorchids.com

WHOLESALE FLOWERS: The next time you throw a party for her, try filling the entire house with dozens and dozens of fresh-cut flowers. It's easier (and cheaper) than you'd ever think, if you cut out the middleman and buy directly from the growers. Grower's Box sources dozens of varieties of flowers, from snapdragons to sunflowers, from the best farms in Central and South America. From $200 for 250 roses: growersbox.com

SCIENCE OF SEX

TABLE FOR ONE

No sparkler to sport? You're in good company. The most recent census found that 97 million American adults (out of 220 million total) are single, and 46 percent of them are men. What's more, in a Pew Research poll, 38 percent of single women ages 18 to 29 said they aren't looking for a partner.

"Women [are] realizing that marriage is not the pot of gold at the end of the rainbow," says Jane Ganahl, former writer of the *San Francisco Chronicle* column "Single Minded." Women are more successful and independent than ever, she says, so ignore the hitch itch for a bit. The better you know yourself, the healthier your relationship will be when you do find Ms. Right.

THE PINOCCHIO PROFILE

Online daters, click with caution: A study in the *Proceedings of Computer/Human Interaction* says both men and women lie—a lot—about their looks and age in online dating profiles. The good news is that most of 'em aren't cheaters; relationship status was the least lied-about attribute. Here's how the numbers played out when Cornell University researchers weighed and measured 80 online daters from sites such as Match.com and Personals.yahoo.com.

LIED ABOUT	WOMEN	MEN
Height	42%	55%
Weight	59%	61%
Age	13%	24%

D**K FLICKS

No matter what you say about Rhett and Scarlett, a study in the journal *Media Psychology* found that men actually like romantic movies, too. Kansas State University researchers asked 124 men and 141 women to rate a "chick flick" such as *Titanic* or *Notting Hill* that they'd watched with a date. Then subjects guessed how both genders would score it. Most women thought men wouldn't like the movie, but surprisingly, most guys gave it a 4.8 out of 7. "Men are reluctant to be vocal about liking romance, but many of them do," says lead study author Richard Harris, PhD.

BLUES CLUES

When you gaze into her eyes, your subconscious may be looking for reassurance. Blue-eyed men are more attracted to blue-eyed women and are more likely to choose them as mates, apparently for evolutionary reasons, say researchers in Norway, home of lots of blue eyes. Using doctored photographs, scientists asked male and female subjects to rate attractiveness. Brown-eyed men and women and blue-eyed females showed no eye-color preference. But blue-eyed men found blue-eyed women more attractive. The likely reason? Because blue eyes are recessive, and brown are dominant—if both parents have blue eyes, their child will have blue eyes—increasing the man's confidence that he is the father, says study author Bruno Laeng, PhD, a psychology professor at the University of Tromsö, in Norway.

EASY TO PLEASE

First date? Be a little wary of your first impressions. Simply accepting a date makes a woman more attractive to the guy who asked her out. University of Minnesota researchers monitored the activity of the reward center in male volunteers' brains as they viewed photos of attractive women who had either accepted or rejected a date with them. Women who had accepted dates were rated the most attractive and triggered the most brain activity.

"This suggests that knowledge of another person's acceptance not only changes what we think about that person but also how we perceive their physical appearance," says researcher Chad Marsolek, PhD. Further research is needed to determine whether women react the same way.

PUCKER-UP PREFERENCES

When it comes to locking lips, do you and your girl like the short-and-sweet peck or the long, deep pre-shag smooch? Harris Interactive and Softlips recently polled 2,069 men and women about their kissing preferences. Here's the lowdown on the pucker-up:

LIKES KISSES THAT ARE . . .	WOMEN	MEN
Tender	48%	35%
Slow and wet	12%	23%
Forbidden	10%	14%
A PDA kiss	6%	5%
Lustful and passionate	35%	46%
Spontaneous	38%	31%
The first kiss	28%	24%

WATER WORKS

A sloppy first kiss can torpedo a new romance, say University at Albany researchers. They asked 122 women about smooching and found that two-thirds had ended a budding relationship because the guy tried to wet-vac their face. Why is it so hard for us to hold back? Men have weak sensory receptors, so we need wetter kisses to improve the exchange of pheromones contained in saliva.

FAST.COM

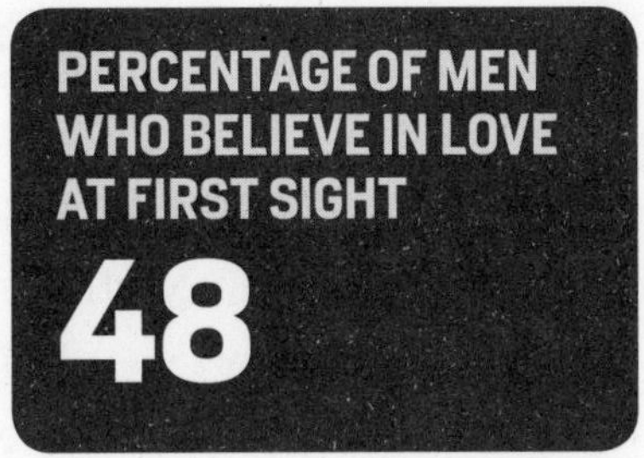

Laptop libido? Women who meet men online may be more likely to have first-date sex, reports a study in *Sexuality Research and Social Policy*. Researchers surveyed 568 women who said they'd hooked up with a man they'd met on the Internet. Thirty percent admitted to having vaginal sex on the first date and 27 percent to oral sex, while 77 percent went condom-free. People reveal more at an earlier stage when cyber-dating, says lead researcher Paige Padgett, PhD, MPH, so a first in-the-flesh encounter may feel more familiar. Play it safe: Have your "sex talk" online, before you meet up, and get all those embarrassing questions out of the way behind the screen.

LEAN CUISINE

Reserve a table for two: Dinner dates can make you thin. In a recent study, researchers at the State University of New York at Buffalo observed that men downed 35 percent fewer calories when eating with their significant others, compared with eating with their buddies.

"People tend to match their own intake to the amount their dining partners eat," says study author Sarah-Jeanne Salvy, PhD. "Women may be more cognizant of how gluttonous they appear to their partners." One way to avoid pigging out on guys' night: Choose an entrée for yourself and skip communal foods such as nachos, wings, and pizza, which encourage you to take eating cues from your porcine pals.

DAMPENED DESIRE

Ever walk into a bar and fall in lust with seven women at once? Easy, big fella. Researchers at Northwestern University studied speed-dating sessions and found that people who desired most or all of their potential dates were the least likely to find a match. People can pick up on indiscriminate desire, and it turns them off, says study coauthor Paul Eastwick, PhD(c). Conversely, when someone clearly desired one individual above all others, that individual was more likely to reciprocate. In normal dating scenarios, make the most of those opening minutes with a woman with a compliment tailored to her, Eastwick suggests. Refer to the real her (style or personality), not the superficial (jewelry or smile).

He Said/She Said

In a BBC survey of 200,000 people, women ranked humor the most desirable trait.
Men, on the other hand, want smarts.
What features do you consider most important in a partner?

	HE	SHE
Humor	42%	53%
Good Looks	43%	17%
Honesty	29%	39%
Kindness	28%	36%
Intelligence	49%	44%
Ambition	4%	8%

PART 4
ENHANCE SEX

SEDUCE HER, FAST AND EASY

WITH THIS SIMPLE GUIDE, SHE'LL BE READY FOR ANYTHING COME BEDTIME

BY IAN KERNER, PHD

Jack remembers the moment vividly. His fiancée, Tamara, pulled the sheet over her head, afraid to face him. She blurted it out: "Jack, I don't come when we do it."

His head spun. They'd been having sex for 2 years. She seemed, well, satisfied. To his—and her—credit, they talked about it; they didn't let this bombshell wreck their relationship. And they tried everything: vibrators, romantic weekends, oral sex—"until my jaw ached," Jack says.

After a month of effort, he came to my office, desperate and distraught, not sure what to try next.

"Maybe you have to stop trying so hard to turn her on," I said, "and learn how to turn her off."

Jack looked at me. Who was I, Yoda?

I switched from Zen-speak to sex-therapist mode, explaining that a woman's arousal depends on deep relaxation and an absence of anxiety. I've counseled countless women, and it's universal. When they're relaxed, it happens. There are brain scans to prove it.

FUN IN THE LAB

In the Netherlands, scientists used positron-emission tomography to peek at women's brains while their partners stimulated them to orgasm. They noticed that the amygdala, the area of the brain associated with stress and anxiety, was noticeably quiet prior to and during orgasm.

"It seems that letting go of stress and anxiety might be very important, and even necessary, for women to have an orgasm," says neuroscientist Gert Holstege, MD, PhD. This would explain why many women, alone with a vibrator, stress-free, can easily reach orgasm. It would also explain why Tamara, full of anxiety about having an orgasm, couldn't.

Eventually, Tamara was able to reach orgasm. Her breakthrough was partly because she learned she wasn't alone: It was a common problem. And once she relaxed, she could replicate the feeling. Jack, of course, played his role: chief of relaxation.

For Jack, and for you, the brain-deactivation sequence is best executed over the course of a full day. Remember, the more she enjoys sex, the more she'll want it.

EARLY MORNING

TELL HER HOW HOT HER SKIRT LOOKS. The scientific reality is that her androgen levels are high in the morning and low in the evening, which means her body is most ready for sex in the a.m. The reality-based reality: At 6 a.m. she's thinking about 9 a.m. meetings, the commute, and picking up the dry cleaning.

Your job is to make her think of you during her busy day, and that starts with brewing the coffee (teamwork), giving her a morning kiss (affection), complimenting her outfit (sex), and letting her take the lead sometimes during sex (empowerment). This is step one toward relaxation.

NOON

MAKE THE CALL OR SEND THE E-MAIL. Men respond most readily to external, visual triggers. Women usually respond to internal triggers—a thought or memory of something sexual or romantic. When you touch base with her at midday (you do that, right?) think relationship, not sex. You can do this.

I have a patient whose wife loves Italy. "Whenever I want to make her feel good," he says, "I e-mail her a photo from one of our trips, when we were really happy and connected, and let her know how much I love her." Bonus: If she's stressing at work, your call will let her start unloading her worries. That's another step toward relaxation.

RUSH HOUR

HUG HER WHEN YOU COME HOME. Don't let go. Don't always feel like cuddling after sex? Fine—get it out of the way now. The stress of her day produces cortisol, but what she really needs is oxytocin—the so-called cuddle hormone that counteracts stress and encourages bonding. Oxytocin production is stimulated after only 20 seconds of hugging. Yes, I know: You're stressed, too. But for us guys, stress can increase desire.

EVENING

DO SOME IMPROMPTU CLEANING. Remember Tamara, who couldn't reach orgasm? She was more receptive to stimulation if the house was clean. No, it wasn't a fetish for vinyl gloves; it was a typical female response. Women still do most of the housework. If it's already done? Instant relaxation.

Says Tamara, "I've noticed I'm much more likely to have sex on the days we have the housekeeper come. The house is clean, and I don't feel like I have a ton of chores to do."

NIGHT

SIP WINE AND SHARE. Turn off the TV. You don't need Wolf Blitzer detailing the carnage in Iraq. Conversation is pivotal to deactivation. "More than anything, I just need him to listen," Tamara says, "and I need to feel connected." (Tip: Pay attention.) Later, sure, watch something. I'd suggest laughing at *The Office* instead of watching Jack Bauer torture terrorists on *24*. Laughter means relaxation.

BEDTIME

HIT THE LIGHTS. One of the biggest reasons women can't relax during sex is body image. Keep the lights low. A candle? Perfect.

Some of the best foreplay is verbal. Quiet talk continues the unwinding process and helps you connect. Talk about the kids, the dog, upcoming events, anything that reinforces the notion of you as a team.

But encourage sexual talk, too. If she thought Jude Law looked hot in *The Holiday*, play with that thought. In a *Woman's Day* magazine/AOL survey, 76 percent of women said they'd fantasized about another man. Tell her that's fine; in fact, ask her to elaborate on her fantasies. Fantasy, a cousin of dreaming, helps her brain deactivate. It may be crucial for her to close her eyes and let her thoughts wander.

Lastly, remember that consistency is important. Think waves at the beach, which are hypnotically relaxing; again, that's the key. "Right when I'm close," Tamara told Jack, "you do something different." Unlike a man, a woman can lose an orgasm even as it's happening. As her brain is shutting down, any sort of change will wake her up again. Keep doing exactly what you're doing.

AFTERWARD

CUDDLE. You didn't really think you were getting out of this, did you?

»A MAN'S GUIDE POLL

We asked 225 women how often certain thoughts go through their minds during sex.

1 = Hardly ever   10 = Rather frequently

I'm really tired. 3	I'm the luckiest girl. 6
Just keep doing that. 8	He's the luckiest guy. 6
Come on, already. 4	He remembered what I like! 7
Oh, no—already? 5	Has he put on a few? 3
No—don't change position! 5	I could stay here forever. 7
Work is a drag lately. 2	Did I load the dryer? 2

TOY WITH IT

OUR RELATIONSHIP GUINEA PIG TEST-DRIVES THE LATEST SUBURBAN SEX TOY

BY T. EDWARD NICKENS

When I asked two of my best friends to introduce a sex toy into their marriage—for the purpose of journalistic research, of course—I was met with different versions of the same answer.

Dan took one wary look at the big cardboard box. "I don't know," he stammered. "Maybe if I slipped it into the bedroom along with a pair of airline tickets."

Matt was less equivocal. "Pass," he said. "Haven't I told you that I'm scared of my wife?"

"Come on, guys," I implored. "For crying out loud, you can buy these things at Walgreens."

Nothing doing. So now I have all three boxes in my bedroom closet. And I'm a very happy man.

Don't misunderstand my interest in sex toys. I don't want to rewrite the *Kama Sutra*. It's just that I—no, we—wanted to scratch a little 15-year marital itch without leaving the house. My wife and I have a lifestyle that would suck the sizzle out of Caligula: two jobs, two kids, no nearby parents to give us a night off, and a dog that licks our feet whenever we do wind up wound around each other. And the sex toy I'm talking about is as nonthreatening a device as you can imagine. There are no batteries required, no need to stress-test the wall studs behind your headboard. It's a pillow. But it's a pillow with a purpose, and sleep ain't it.

At first glance, the Wedge looks like something you'd prop your head on to watch TV in bed. It is 14 inches long and 7 inches tall, comes in five colors, and is cut to a precise 27-degree angle. Made of firm high-density polyurethane foam, the pillow is stain resistant and clad in a velvety washable microfiber cover.

But the geometry is what makes it a hip rest, not a headrest. That 27-degree angle, say its designers, raises a woman's pelvis just enough to bring man and G-spot consistently together. "Testers started at 45 degrees and worked their way down," explains Frank DeMarco, vice president of product design for Liberator, the manufacturer of the Wedge. "There was a lot of trial and error. But after a lot of sex, they figured it out." They also figured out that this seemingly innocuous hunk of upholstery performed well as the foundation for numerous sexual positions.

You can buy the Wedge as a stand-alone for $60 at large pharmacies and at liberator.com, or packaged with the Ramp, a larger pillow that comes in three sizes to "strategically lift your lover's hips" to the appropriate rear-entry altitude, according to the instructions. The pillows have been lauded by physical therapists for people with disabilities; they relieve lower-back pain, according to many users; and they have been profiled positively in that subversive kinky-sex journal *Arthritis Today.*

So enough background. Is the sex that much better when going Wedgey? In short, yes. There are more possibilities afforded by a firm 27-degree angle than we ever would have imagined. I haven't given geometry this much thought since eighth-grade math. But besides the physical payoff, it offers a surprising amount of psychic connection. At one point during our research, my wife furrowed her brow and muttered, "Hmm. It's not really working so well this way." But the point was, we were exploring a new way—literally and figuratively—and actually communicating about what worked and what didn't. Which, we ultimately decided, meant it was working very well indeed.

I'm fortunate enough to have a wife who's willing to help her self-employed husband with his assignment, but there are lots of guys, like Dan and Matt, who can't imagine showing up in the bedroom with a sex toy, even if it does look like a reading aid. "People equate sex toys with an act," says sex educator Lou Paget, author of *The Great Lover Playbook*, "but in many relationships, they are really about communication. Using something as nonthreatening as the Wedge allows a couple to focus on themselves. Which is what most couples don't often do."

If a soft touch is required for you to introduce a sex toy into your bedroom (whether it's a ceiling-mounted swing harness or merely a pillow with a higher purpose), follow these five tips.

PURCHASE ONLINE. Thankfully for the uninitiated, sex shops have moved online so that you can shop from the privacy of your own home. Paget suggests that you let her do the navigating and choose a product based on her feedback. The Liberator Web site is a good place to start. "It's playful, appealing to both the shy and the adventurous," says Paget. "And there's enough on there that anyone might say, 'Hmm, yeah, that does look like fun.'"

THINK US INSTEAD OF ME. Focus on sex toys that are pleasurable and fun for both of you. Selfish requests only backfire and are, well, unsexy. Paget suggests using phrases like "I could imagine the two of us doing this" and "I think this would be fun to try with you."

BE POSITIVE. This isn't about what's wrong with the sex. It's about making what's right even better. "Be clear that your intention is to have fun and build on what's already working with your sexual relationship," says Paget.

DELAY THE GRATIFICATION. "Boosting anticipation is always a great idea," says Paget. Say, "Not tonight, but this weekend." It will give both of you time to think about it and get excited.

TURN A NO INTO A YES. Some women can be shier about sex toys than men are, so there's a chance she might say no at first. But that doesn't mean you should give up on the idea. "Just because she wasn't interested in trying it today," says Paget, "doesn't mean she won't be interested in a little while, when she's more comfortable with the idea."

SEDUCE ANY WOMAN

IT'S OFFICIAL: FOREIGN MEN HAVE MORE SEX, WITH MORE WOMEN, THAN AMERICAN GUYS. WE TRAVELED THE GLOBE TO FIND OUT HOW THEY DO IT (AND NO, IT'S NOT THEIR ACCENTS)

BY LAUREN MURROW

Sorry, dude, but guys in other countries are having more sex than you. Way more. We know, it doesn't make sense. Pop culture and the Internet would have us believe that American men are the most oversexed stallions on the entire planet, that every girl is 20, tanked, and topless. Plus, we have George Clooney and Matthew McConaughey. And has anyone tallied Tommy Lee's numbers?

Yet, there are the stats. According to a *Men's Health* magazine survey of 40,000 readers worldwide, foreign men have sex up to 70 more times a year than you do. So much for our superpower status. But don't worry—we have a plan. We took a trip around the world to find out what makes men from other countries so attractive to the women they pursue. We also enlisted the help of sex experts around the globe to save you from another sexless night. Master their tips and soon you'll simply be able to say "G'day" and mate.

ENGLAND: TAKE HER, OUTSIDE

Hugh Grant has typecast British men as meek and bumbling. But according to a 2005 Durex survey of 317,000 people in 41 countries, these blokes are so irresistible, their partners can't even wait to get back to the flat. Twice as many Brits as Americans report having had sex on public transportation and in alleyways and gardens. "Many a chap has fallen in love in the checkout line at the supermarket," says Vicki Ford, a British psychosexual therapist and the author of *Overcoming Sexual Problems*. And apparently they consummate it on the way home.

HOW TO DO IT: Arouse her temptation. Pull her into a side alley or a dark doorway and plant one while gently stroking her neck, suggests Emily Dubberley, a British sex expert and the author of *Brief Encounters*. "Fear of being caught stimulates her fight-or-flight response," explains Ford. "Adrenaline floods her system, making everything feel much more intense."

AUSTRALIA: DRIVE HER WILD

We Americans love our cars, but Australians love *in* their cars. Almost 75 percent of Aussies have had sex on the road, according to Durex. "We can always find a private space to get it on," says Jan Hall, PhD, an Australian sex therapist. The car provides the ideal cover: "Sneaking away for a surreptitious shag or fondle says, 'I can't wait,'" states Gabrielle Morrissey, PhD, Australian author of *A Year of Spicy Sex*.

HOW TO DO IT: Heading to a party is the perfect opportunity to lure her over to the driver's side. The mood is up, and you're dressed to the nines. Playfully graze her inner thigh with your fingertips. Suggest that it's proper to be fashionably late—how should we fill the time?—and park on a secluded street for a quickie. "It's like sharing a secret all night," Morrissey says, "especially if you've promised each other an encore."

ROMANIA: PLAY IT STRAIGHT

Meeting women is easy, if you're not sidetracked by insecurity ("Is she looking at me?"), coy games ("Have our waitress ask her waitress what she's drinking"), or body-language interpretation ("Dude, her eyes say no, but the angle of her feet says olé!"). When Romanian men want a woman, they tell her. "The men here have a lot of self-confidence," says Felicia Abaza, sex editor of *Men's Health* Romania. "And the women are tuned to respond to it."

HOW TO DO IT: Tired come-ons will fall flat. Instead, lean in unexpectedly and whisper in her ear, "I just had to be near you." Be mindful of your tone. Brash: bad. Calm: good. "Caress her with your voice," says Patricia Cihodaru, MsC, a Romanian psychologist and sex expert. And when you've become friendly enough that you won't get a punch in the chops, "say she looks beautiful and tell her how much you want her," says Cihodaru. "Hearing your desire is the strongest aphrodisiac."

CHINA: BUILD TENSION WITH TECHNOLOGY

Forget the 3-day rule. In China, men follow up the day after a successful date—by e-mail. "Technology plays a big role in relationships here," says Yoyoo Chow, sex editor of *Men's Health* China. "Most couples meet over the Internet. So if a man doesn't take the initiative, she'll find someone else pretty quickly."

HOW TO DO IT: Send a short, suggestive note, says Chow. Something as simple as "Last night . . . wow! When can I see you again?" will incite her interest. If she feels the same way, she'll respond accordingly. As the sexual tension builds, resist the temptation to pour out your soul or create a list of your top 10 fantasies. At this early stage, short equals sexy—always. And remember: Use of emoticons will ensure that you spend the night alone.

ITALY: SEDUCE HER WITH FOOD

It's no secret that good food, wine, and conversation lead to great sex. "Italian men flock to dinner parties to meet women," says Adriana Amedei, sex editor of *Men's Health* Italy. "There's no crowd, no noise; it's relaxed. All you have to do is share your opinions . . . at least to start." The real mating game, says Amedei, begins at the table. Flirting overtly over a meal (or discreetly under the table) builds tension that will spill over later. "Food and sex are intimately connected, because they tap into the senses," says Martha Hopkins, author of *InterCourses: An Aphrodisiac Cookbook*.

HOW TO DO IT: "Listen attentively to her, make eye contact, and seek out a common interest," says Hopkins. "Then, while eating, conjure up the same sounds that accompany passionate sex: mmm, oooh, aahh." You're creating a mood and a fantasy. Be subtle about it, however. You don't want the host to say, "Um, Fred, do you mind? We're eating."

INDIA: PROLONG YOUR PLEASURE

Indian men know that the journey is almost always more interesting than the destination. "Sexual pleasure is linked to the gradual process of seduction, which includes courtship, touching, and kissing," says Sanjay Srivastava, PhD, author of *Passionate Modernity*. "Focusing on the finish misses the point."

HOW TO DO IT: Practice a technique called karezza, in which the man remains inside the woman for at least 10 minutes, moving only when necessary to maintain an erection. Penetrate her slowly and gently. Match your breathing and maintain eye contact to focus on your emotional connection, not the physical act. "Conventional sex can be very limiting," says Kenneth Ray Stubbs, PhD, author of *The Essential Tantra*. "This results in a larger climax for both partners."

NETHERLANDS: PLAY WITH POSITIONS

Lovers in the Netherlands know what they want—and how to ask for it. Sixty-four percent of Dutch men and women are confident asserting their needs during sex, compared with less than half of Americans, according to the Durex survey. "In bars, men are picked up as often as they approach women themselves, and both are willing to experiment in bed," says Achsa Vissel, a Dutch sex psychologist. Being forward with your compliments—and desires—will pave the way for pleasure.

HOW TO DO IT: "Dutch men pay attention to places that seem less erotic, like the inner arms, back, and shoulders," says Vissel. Shaking up the routine leads to more sex: Sixty-three percent of the Dutch are satisfied with the amount of sex they're having, compared with 55 percent of Americans. When your partner is ready to move past the missionary position, try moves that allow you to stroke her clitoris during sex, such as doggy-style or cowgirl.

GREECE: DON'T BE SO UPTIGHT

Americans are bombarded with sexual imagery all day, yet we're closemouthed about sex. Not in Greece. "We talk about sex all the time—in the office, with our friends, with our partners," says Nikki Hayia, sex editor of *Men's Health* Greece. "A Greek man can talk dirty to his woman in front of 10 people, and it doesn't bother him to kiss and touch her in public." Simple public displays of affection can work for you, too: A study by the Berman Center in Chicago found that couples who kiss often in nonsexual situations are eight times more likely to be sexually satisfied.

HOW TO DO IT: Hint at what's to come, says Hayia: Subtly stroke her thigh or lower back during dinner; run your fingers up her leg; steal a lingering kiss on her bare shoulder at a crowded bar. "American men are too uptight," Hayia says. "Relax, guys. Have sex like there's no tomorrow."

HOW MANY TIMES A YEAR DO YOU HAVE SEX?

Romania: 232
Korea: 228
Greece: 224
Czech Republic: 222
Portugal: 222
Brazil: 219
Philippines: 217
Italy: 198
Russia: 193
Hungary: 188
United Kingdom: 182
Indonesia: 177
South Africa: 176
Poland: 175
Mexico: 174
Netherlands: 168
United States: 161
Spain: 159
Germany: 148

HAVE SEX WITH SOMEONE NEW—EVERY NIGHT

ONCE YOU'RE PAST THE AWKWARDNESS, ROLE PLAYING CAN LEAD TO THE BEST SEX OF YOUR LIFE. BUT YOU HAVE TO ASK

BY DOUGLAS DANOFF

The beautiful young French woman was soaking wet—but alive, thanks to my fast action. Moments earlier, I'd pulled her from icy Patagonian rapids. In the faint starlight, I could make out her lovely face, her lustrous red hair, and the form of her breasts straining against her wet shirt.

She was whispering, and I brought my ear close to her full lips. "Only one thing can warm me up," she said in a heavy accent. "You must make love to me." She began unbuttoning her top.

Okay, this wasn't Sylvie, the French backpacker, and I wasn't Carlos, the Chilean ranger. The water was a trickling shower in a tiny apartment. The stars were candles propped on the bathroom sink.

My girlfriend, Ivy, and I were role playing. Go ahead and laugh. Back in my tent—er, bedroom—the sex was phenomenal, as Ivy/Sylvie's body slowly warmed, then became charged with new vigor.

Weird, right? That's what I thought at first. It's not. Pretending to be someone else is fun. It's exciting. It's hot. Trust me—I'm a PhD with seven published papers on the female orgasm.

Okay, I'm not. (That was last Thursday.) But listen to this guy: "Part of enjoying tantalizing sex is experiencing a level of escape," says Scott Haltzman, MD, a clinical assistant professor of psychiatry at Brown University and the author of *The Secrets of Happily Married Women*. "Role playing interweaves well with the natural tendency to dissociate from the daily demands of life. It helps your woman experience more liberation under the covers, because she can put herself mentally in a different, more exciting place."

In other words, men, if role playing helps her find new excitement, do whatever makes her happy. Is that too much to ask for an endless string of wild nights?

A few months earlier, Ivy and I had reached a point of mild desperation: Our sex life had grown, well, boring. Dr. Haltzman reassures me now that this is normal, "probably because dopamine levels [in the brain] diminish as you're exposed to something repeatedly." We humans are lucky, he says. We have imagination. "And exposure to anything novel stimulates feelings of excitement and attraction." Try role playing. You have nothing to lose except your identity for a couple of hours—and some of your inhibitions.

STARTING OUT

Our adventure began when a friend of mine told me over lunch about a recent round of toe-curling sex, with him dressed as a pilot and his wife as a flight attendant. My buddy spoke freely; I was inwardly petrified. I couldn't possibly share my fantasies with Ivy, much less act them out. What would she think? My basic ideas—doctor and nurse; professor and student—were embarrassing enough, but my darker ones about rough sex frightened even me.

But I was normal. Nearly everyone has fantasies, and most of us are reluctant to explore them, says Brian Zamboni, PhD, a clinical psychologist and sex therapist at the University of Minnesota medical school. "We're simply embarrassed to disclose information—sexual, personal information—we normally don't share. We're afraid of being laughed at."

A couple of weeks after that lunch, Ivy and I were on my couch. We'd had a bottle of wine and were laughing easily, and I was in a courageous mood. I decided to bring up the idea of role playing. My heart raced, but the nervousness and adrenaline made me all the more excited to have this discussion.

After some hemming and hawing, I stammered something about playing a game. She said yes. "Can I blindfold you?" Again, yes. I found a scarf, tied it over her eyes, and we were off. I did my best Mickey Rourke with Kim Basinger in *9½ Weeks*, using honey and apricot preserves (wasn't much in the fridge). That was it. But it was fun, and a start.

Later we talked about it, and it turned out Ivy was relieved I'd brought it up. "And since we were in a long-term relationship," she says now, "role playing seemed like a natural extension of the trust we'd built."

You may have already role-played without knowing it: "Talking dirty or baby talk can be a type of role playing," Zamboni says.

THE GUIDELINES

Apparently I'd done pretty well for a rookie. When I talked to Brian Mustanski, PhD, a sex researcher at the University of Illinois at Chicago and formerly at the Kinsey Institute, he offered a few suggestions.

TIMING: Raise the idea in context. Play off a movie you've watched—say, *The Graduate*. Wonder aloud what it would be like to sleep with Mrs. Robinson. "The best thing is if you get her to see the scenario as her idea," Dr. Haltzman says. Lift a line: "Mrs. Robinson, you're trying to seduce me!" Then see what happens.

FLATTERY: Start with "something positive and complimentary, like 'I think you're really sexy,'" Mustanski says. "Then say, maybe, 'I've been having this fantasy lately. How would you feel about trying it?'" Never mention boredom!

PACING: Don't be in a hurry. "Start off slowly," Zamboni says, "giving each person permission to laugh. Pretend. You may not be dressing up like a doctor, but you can talk like a doctor and go in and out of the role. Be spontaneous. Explore. Remember, there's no right way to do it. Have fun and a sense of humor."

TECHNOLOGY: "A few years ago," says a friend, Anna, 23, "I wasn't quite ready to role-play in real life. So I started out by doing some online role playing. It was the perfect way to go, because I could explore my own preferences anonymously and without any pressure."

Anna says she and her boyfriend have used role playing from the start. "Maybe the first date isn't the time or place to bring up ball gags," she says, "but I started hinting as soon as we began taking our relationship to a sexual level. I wouldn't want to find out years into a relationship that my boyfriend had been wanting to role-play all along."

Ivy and I proceeded gradually. Usually we'd begin with a story and only move into the role playing several sessions later. "We took baby steps," Ivy says. "And I enjoyed every little hurdle. Taking another step, pushing it a little—that's the best part."

Butterflies can be a good thing; being nervous makes the role playing even better.

THE SCENARIOS

What is your partner like? "If she's very conservative, she may be more interested in a mild, better-accepted scenario," Dr. Haltzman says. Some common ones: victim and rescuer, teacher and student, nurse and patient, French maid and baron.

But keep this in mind: "Most people's fantasies aren't really safe," he says. "One of the biggest fallacies about sex and relationships is that they have to be fuzzy and comfortable. Sometimes it's important for them to be just slightly uncomfortable."

So say goodbye to yourself for a night, and let an alter ego have some fun. "Role playing is a comfortable way for couples to explore their sexuality from behind masks. Often the roles people enjoy most are the ones that are the most different from their normal lives," says Mustanski.

Ivy, for example, has a corporate job in a button-down firm but is into playing the slut with me. "I really liked the time I was a drugged-out whore wearing this tiny pink leather miniskirt with silver sparkles, with mascara down my cheek," she says. "It turns me on to become someone else for a little while."

Dr. Haltzman recalls one woman's post on his Web site: "I'll let my husband sleep with whatever woman he wants, so long as she has my Social Security number."

A woman I know, Suzanne, 29, has tried many classic scenarios: voyeurism, exhibitionism, playing a slut. "I like exhibitionism, because I know I'm hot, and it feels powerful to rub it in sometimes," she says with a wicked laugh. "And violent sex is great if you trust your partner."

»A MAN'S GUIDE POLL

We asked 4,000 women and men which role-playing scenarios they'd consider trying.

1 = No way 10 = That'd be hot

	WOMEN	MEN
Athlete and cheerleader	6.5	8
Sailor and hooker	4.5	3.5
Professor and coed	7	8.5
Rich man and French maid	7.5	9
Strangers in a bar	9	8.5
Pilot and flight attendant	8	8
Producer and actress	3	4.5
Nurse and wounded soldier	6.5	6.5
Employee and female boss	6.5	9.5
Boss and secretary	7	8
Lifeguard and swimmer	6.5	7
Han Solo and Princess Leia	3	2

Rough sex is a common female fantasy. "That doesn't mean rape, but it does involve the man's using a certain amount of force," Zamboni says. Combine assertiveness with tenderness. And have a code word that means, "Stop. Too much."

THE PAYOFF

Ivy was grateful for my suggestion that we role-play. "I saw it as being for my enjoyment, as well," she says.

Fulfilling a fantasy is not kinky; it's intimate. "You're learning more—and discovering something new and deep—about your partner," Zamboni says. "So this can be an opportunity to build intimacy."

A warning: You may see each other in a different light, Mustanski says. Tell her you won't be offended by anything her character does, and ask for similar assurance from her. Consider a mild start: Our *Men's Health* magazine poll shows that both men and women would love to try the simple "strangers in a bar" scenario. No costumes necessary.

If you're investing in a wardrobe, you do the shopping—"and drop the coin, too," says Ivy. There's a big difference between a $40 geisha wig and a $10 wig. ("One looks like the real deal; the other looks like roadkill.") And don't expect sex on the spot, Ivy warns. "I needed about a week to come to grips with the Mary Magdalene outfit."

We're having fun. As Ivy says, "If role playing comes from a place of love and trust, there's really no downside to it. You just end up with a better sex life and maybe even a new little Angelina Jolie dominatrix outfit—which is nice, because you can get him to clean the dishes before having sex!"

Okay, I've got to go now. The sink is full. But dessert is waiting. . .

FIRE IT UP

YES, THE SEXUAL FLAME WILL START TO FLICKER. HERE'S HOW TO FAN IT BACK INTO A BONFIRE

BY JAMYE WAXMAN

If you were to scribble a postcard to your sex life, would it say, "Wish you were here"?

Whether your relationship is 5 months or 5 years old, your sex life is constantly evolving—and not always for the better. Hot and heavy becomes warm and comfortable, which, before you know it, morphs into chilly and awkward. "These changes start between 2 months and 2 years," says Maurice Taylor, a licensed marriage therapist and coauthor of *What's the State of Your Union?* "That's when you start seeing the hidden sides of your partner. She's angry, pouty, or bossy. These displays of anger can kill your sexual chemistry."

A lot of men would assume at this point that the relationship is doomed. But it doesn't have to be, once you understand that change isn't a death knell; it's opportunity knocking. Here are five ways to bust a rut and resume rutting.

TRY DAMN NEAR ANYTHING ONCE

You'd think the sexual repertoire of couples would broaden over time, but it actually tends to narrow as comfort sets in. That's why Lex and Leslie have a pact: Nothing is off limits. "The last new position we tried was where Leslie was on her back with her legs curled up so her ankles were near her head, and I was positioned above her," says Lex. "We joked about her being a contortionist, but she really liked the intense eye contact it provided."

Novelty ignites passion by increasing your brain's levels of dopamine, a neurotransmitter linked to romance and sex drive, says anthropologist Helen Fisher, PhD, a relationship expert and the author of *Why We Love*. Fisher has been studying relationship biology for more than two decades. "So if you keep doing things that are new and different, you have a better chance of sustaining the romance," she says.

Okay, but how do you get your partner to don a Catwoman suit and purr? "Just ask," says Lex. "Make sure she knows you don't expect her to do it ever again. And be willing to do anything for her, too. Once."

ARNOLD WAS RIGHT ABOUT THE PUMP AND ORGASMS

Exercise works wonders not only on your body, but also on your woman. "Exercising together fuels our passion," says Melinda, who, along with her husband, Stephen, redefines the term "pump you up."

"Vigorous activities, such as jogging and spinning, release endorphins that improve your mood and relax you," says American Council on Exercise spokesman Gregory Florez. "In the hours following 30 to 40 minutes of cardio, skin temperature is elevated and your sense of touch is heightened. It's a great time for intimacy."

Melinda and Stephen, who've been together for 5 years, work out at home in their underwear—"more visual stimulation and extra motivation," says Stephen. Foreplay includes pushups and chest presses. "Sometimes we do exercises that bring us really close, but we don't actually touch," he says. "I'll do pushups while Melinda's on the floor doing chest presses. Or she stands up doing curls while I'm underneath her doing situps. We get hot, sweaty, and turned on, and then it's time for another workout—this time in the bedroom."

Don't hold back, either. "Sweat is an aphrodisiac," says Florez, who is also the CEO of FitAdvisor.com. "The smell of perspiration from a clean person is arousing. Postexercise, your brain is in a state of hyperarousal, and your body may be as well."

GIVE HER A TOKEN FOR SEX

Remember those innocent teen games, such as truth or dare and spin the bottle? Embracing them now, only not so innocently this time, can reignite your fire.

Jon and Susanna, a couple for 10 years, have sex with Parker Brothers all the time. It's not as kinky as it sounds—they trade Scrabble points for 3-minute sexual favors. "It can be a massage, kissing, oral sex, talking dirty, a dance, whatever we want," Susanna says. "Last time we played, Jon asked me for a striptease. I made him think I was going all the way—but I stopped when I was down to my panties.

"The game is all about the tease. Scrabble kicks up our ETS—estimated time for sex. The game disintegrates slowly, usually when one of our trysts becomes about getting the other person off."

Psychiatrist and sex therapist Barbara Bartlik, MD, explains why silly games lead to crazy sex: "Bringing an item into the bedroom, like a board game, forces you to think about how you're going to use this item to make the experience different. Whoever dreamed up the idea feels triumphant, while the other person feels well attended to. These positive experiences feed our relationships and make love last."

Whether it's Scrabble or Battleship doesn't really matter. "The best thing is, it takes the guesswork out of communication," says Jon. "It gives us structure, and it's fun to have a built-in forum to ask for what we want sexually."

BECOME A MARATHON MAN

Better sex will lead to more sex, says Dr. Bartlik. So forget the quickies, and love each other longtime. Consider making an appointment that neither of you is allowed to cancel: Lie in bed together for 1 hour on a weekend morning. You might just chat, or you might rock the sheets like porn stars. Either way, you're connecting.

Let's say you're like Brian and his wife, Mary—you don't necessarily have the luxury of a lazy Saturday morning. "When we first met, we had sex every day," says Mary. "But we're parents now and don't have as much time. Now it's just once a week. But with an hour or two of actual intercourse, it's always amazing and meaningful."

Having been together for 10 years, the couple lets the anticipation build with extended foreplay that can last as long as an hour. "We start slowly—

mostly just hands, bodies, and mouths everywhere," Mary says. "Eventually, we move into all types of sex—fast, slow, gentle. Brian tries to hold out an hour before we explode."

More of a 5-minute man than a marathon man? Try these stamina boosters from Barbara Carrellas, author of *Urban Tantra*.

"Stop stroking or thrusting your penis for 10 to 20 seconds. Relax completely, take your focus away from your genitals, and instead focus more on your breathing."

"Lie on your back. Gravity will draw blood away from your erection. If you are already on your back, lift your hips."

"The best way of all to avoid premature ejaculation: Relax, breathe deeply, and slow down. This is easier in a passive, receptive mode, so let her be on top. Ask her to stop or slow down before you reach climax. She can continue to touch and stroke you all over your body—except for your penis, that is."

PLAN A SEX EXCURSION

For Lesley and Tim, sex isn't just part of a vacation: It's the very reason for the getaway. Travel is usually the most draining aspect of time away, but this couple actually plans trips around where and how they might have sex along the way. Recent exploits for the couple, together for 4 years, included oral sex on a flight to Aruba, and sex under a blanket on another flight—this one to

>>A MAN'S GUIDE POLL

215 women tell us which PDAs are their favorites.

1 = Big no-no   10 = Very classy

Hand-holding = 9	Hand in my back pocket = 5.5
Peck on the cheek = 8.5	Movie makeout session = 6.5
Hug as greeting = 9	Shoulder rub = 6.5
Kiss as greeting = 8.5	Playful butt slap = 6
Big kiss as greeting = 7	Arm-in-arm walk = 8
Arm around me at party = 8	Hand on my back = 9

Bermuda. “There was nobody around, and we tried to stay inconspicuous,” Tim recalls. Rather than dampening sex drive, the possibility of getting caught can send sexual desire into overdrive. It’s why the Mile High Club is such a nonexclusive fraternity.

Luckily, you don’t have to fly to a far-flung land to take your sexual satisfaction to new altitudes. “Surprise your partner on a random Monday or Tuesday,” suggests Megan Andelloux, director of the Miko Learning and Resource Center, in Providence, Rhode Island. “At dusk, blindfold her and lead her to the car. As you drive to a remote location, her excitement will build. When you arrive, take off her blindfold and spend lots of time making out in your car before relocating to the backseat.

“Even if you end up just 2 blocks from home, the sex will be worlds away.”

BE THE BEST IN BED

LOCK THE DOOR AND FLUFF YOUR PILLOWS: THE FIRST ANNUAL SEX AWARDS ARE HERE!

BY JAMYE WAXMAN

We've given a "Best in Bed" Award to the sauciest, silliest, most satisfying products in the sexual universe. Each winner had to meet more than one of our strict criteria: be solidly constructed, get the job done well, make us feel good about sex, and not look the tiniest bit trashy. Plus, we tested 'em all—yeah, yeah, it's a tough job—so we can guarantee you won't be disappointed. Clear out a spot on your bedside table, because your sex life is about to become fully accessorized.

LIQUID LOVE

A little lubrication is sure to whet your appetite for action, and we're not just talking about splitting a bottle of red wine. From products that keep your erogenous zones slick to bubbles that take you from stressed to sensual, here are four bottles to add to your shopping cart pronto.

BEST FOR MARATHON BOOTY: Light, moisturizing, and unscented, K-Y Intrigue is a condom-friendly formula that uses pharmaceutical-grade silicone to keep things friction-free during extra-long carnal relations. It even stays slick underwater. And its pearly white plastic bottle won't break when it rolls off the bed. $18 for 2.75 oz, drugstore.com

BEST FOR NATURAL WETNESS: Water-based products come closest to feeling like the lubrication your body produces. The downside is that they tend to dissolve quickly, requiring many reapplications. Fragrance-free Moist beats out every other water-based lube we tried for long-lasting slipperiness. And if you do need more, the one-handed pump makes it easy. $7 for 4 oz, greatpleasures.com

BEST FOR THE BATH: Regular old bubbles just aren't sexy enough. Which is why we love the pink, translucent orbs created by Naughty Bubbles.

BEST FOR MASSAGE: Trade full-body rubdowns with Babeland Honey Apricot Body Massage Oil. It smells deliciously edible, but it's subtle enough that you won't feel queasy after 2 hours of sweaty fun. $15 for 5.25 oz, babeland.com

SEXESSORIES

In our search for the naughtiest playthings to outfit your bedroom, we bypassed the stuff that seemed too uncomfortable and nutty (nipple clamps, vinyl underpants, sex swings) and the stuff that clearly wasn't worth the money (why buy chocolate body paint or flavored pixie dust when you can use Hershey's syrup and cinnamon sugar?). The winners: edgy items that staffers were fighting to take home and try.

BEST FOR NERVE TINGLING: A light tickle is a highly underrated source of erotic sensation. Give each other goose bumps all over with the Decadent Ostrich Feather Crop. Our tester swears that just holding it in her hand will make her feel like a vixen. $49, erosboutique.com

WHAT WE (ALL) WANT IN BED

Men and women want similar things from their sexual partners, though not the qualities you might think, according to an Australian survey. An interesting finding worth noting? Well, let's just say you can stop sucking in your stomach now . . .

Women want a partner who . . .

1. Cares about her
2. Enjoys sex
3. Is fun to be with
4. Is someone she loves
5. Is interesting
6. Is willing to have sex
7. Is intelligent
8. Gives good orgasms
9. Is physically attractive
10. Has lots of money

Men want a partner who . . .

1. Enjoys sex
2. Is fun to be with
3. Cares about him
4. Is interesting
5. Is someone he loves
6. Is willing to have sex
7. Is intelligent
8. Is physically attractive
9. Gives good orgasms
10. Has lots of money

BEST FOR "BONDING": Keep your partner right where you want her with All Tied Up Bonding Tape. It holds tight but comes undone in a jiffy—and won't stick to body hair, our tester says. $20, bootyparlor.com

GET IN THE GAME

Most sex games for couples are hokier than a *Love Boat* episode, and every box we found that had the words "great for parties" scrawled across it involved ridiculous dares ("Show a stranger your thong!") that made us cringe. But these three, we're happy to say, are fun, creative, and guaranteed to lead to an inspired night of naked coed wrestling.

BEST FOR STRUTTING YOUR STUFF: Okay, so this isn't actually a game, but it'll definitely make you want to play. The Striptease Kit packs pasties, body glitter, a sheer scarf, and illustrated instructions on how your partner can give you a variety of old-school stripteases. We doubt you'll put on the pasties, but there's absolutely no reason why you can't strip for her, too. $25, goodvibes.com

BEST FOR EMOTIONAL BONDING: If you're looking for something softer, slower, and more romantic and don't mind a little "cosmic energy" talk, the Tantric Lovers game by sex educator Ava Cadell is perfect for getting your om on. Bonus prize: Practicing tantra is said to lead to greater intimacy and prolonged orgasms. $30, avacadell.com

BEST FOR SEXPERIMENTATION: Way wilder than strip poker, Nookii takes card playing to a whole new level. You simply take turns picking a card and following the extremely racy, step-by-step instructions. It's a brilliant way to orchestrate super-satisfying foreplay. $30, mypleasure.com

BURNING BOOKS

Barnes & Noble is brimming with sex tomes, but most are filled with half-baked information or are so clinical or raunchy, you can't bear to read beyond the first paragraph. These four titles are exceptionally smart, practical, and entertaining—well worth stacking within reach of the bed.

BEST HOW-TO: If you're going to own just one instructional book about sex, this is the one. As funny, hip, and informative as an episode of *The Daily Show*, the 800-plus-page *Guide to Getting It On* by Paul Joannides is written for generations X and Y. Having already sold 500,000 copies, it's packed with specific advice about what to put where and covers every topic a couple could possibly be curious about. $20, goofyfootpress.com

BEST HISTORICAL: To excel at something, it's crucial to know your subject inside and out. Sex is no exception. For true enthusiasts, *The Collected Erotica* compiles images of more than 400 historical—and salacious—works of art from around the world. Accompanied by erotic literature from the likes of Anaïs Nin, Henry Miller, and Oscar Wilde, this paperback is an affordable, compact classic. $19, amazon.com

BEST INTELLECTUAL: It's an unfortunate truth that the very things we love about domesticity—familiarity, comfort, closeness—can dull even the most ravenous mutual attraction. In *Mating in Captivity*, Esther Perel makes a convincing case for maintaining autonomy, not always talking about your feelings, and pushing the sexual envelope to keep desire at its sweaty peak forever. $25, amazon.com

BEST SELF-HELP: Laura Berman promises better sex in 10 weeks in the soft-cover edition of her top-selling *The Passion Prescription*. And if anyone can deliver, it's sex therapist Berman, the director of the Berman Center in Chicago. She's right on target with her smart, realistic, weekly to-do lists that include such tasks as "masturbate at least two times this week," plus a men's at-a-glance guide to each chapter. $15, amazon.com

FEEL THE VIBE

If your wife or girlfriend doesn't own a vibrator, she's missing out on the single most useful tool for female pleasure. Bear in mind that vibes are not penis replacements: They're titillating toys she can use alone or with you. Hold one against your frenulum—the spot where the chin strap would be if the tip of your Johnson were a helmet—and you'll see what we mean.

BEST MINI: The petite but powerful Nea tops our mini-vibe category. Its delicate floral design makes it fit for a geisha, and its sleek curves hug all the essential girl parts. Just 3 inches long, it has a rechargeable ion battery that delivers up to 7 hours of bliss. Tester says: "It works like a charm, and no one would guess it's a vibrator." $98, lelo.com

BEST MAX: Some multispeed vibes sound like Air Force One prepping for takeoff. But for whisper-quiet, battery-operated fun, the Doc Johnson Lucid Dream No. 14 is top gun. Control the buzz level with a quick turn of the dial; no wires to get tangled up in. Made of bendy jelly rubber, it provides Mary Lou Retton–esque flexibility to target every hot spot. Tester says: "The tilted motorized tip hits the G-spot like nobody's business." $25, drugstore.com

BEST RING: We think the disposable buzzing ring is the best thing to happen to sex since Dr. Ruth. But not all are created equal. The Screaming O vibrating ring turns your penis into her favorite vibe with a textured nub that also hits you in just the right spot. And, best of all, the rubber gel ring stays put on your penis—but is still comfy—and lasts for up to 30 minutes, so it won't fizzle before you reach the finish line. $7.50, thescreamingo.com

ASSUME THIS POSITION

The best carnal configuration of all time hits all the right spots. When it comes to sex positions, we'll take them all. But our go-to is the clitoris-pleasing cowgirl. When she's on top, facing you, she controls the angle and depth of penetration, and she's free to grind her hips whichever way works best at any given moment. Bonus: Because she's more likely to move back and forth than up and down (which stimulates your penis more intensely), you will last longer.

1. You lie on your back, enjoying the view of her gorgeous bod and engaging in romantic eye contact.

2. She rocks or slides her hips back and forth to drum up some delicious clitoral friction.

3. She can tilt her pelvis forward to maximize contact between her clitoris and your abdomen.

4. She can make your night by reaching behind herself and stroking your testicles.

5. Give her a breast massage or place your hands on her hips or butt. The more erogenous zones that are being stimulated, the bigger the orgasm she's likely to have.

6. She should lean back, resting her hands on your upper thighs, to bring the tip of your penis in contact with her G-spot.

7. Place a pillow under your bum for deeper penetration.

UNDERCOVER LOVER

The latest sex toys come brilliantly disguised. Adult accessories are starting to look more and more like innocent household objects.

1. Topco for Grrl Toyz Incognito tickling dust brush with Tasty Berry body powder: You could use this blush brush on your face, but it was designed for your other cheeks. Plus, it vibrates. $16, vibrator.com

2. Berman Lina vibrating pen with silicone sleeve: Score some O's with a vibrating pen that also writes. $17, holisticwisdom.com

3. African Treasures 20" rainstick: We like a wand that makes us wet, but this baby is just a run-of-the-mill rainstick. $19, africantreasures.com

4. Logitech PlayGear Stealth earbuds: Unless you're a techno-perv, these are just boring PSP earphones. $20, logitech.com

5. I Rub My Penguin by Big Teaze Toys: Send this vibrating penguin to your South Pole. $36, bigteazetoys.com

6. Emitations Caine's Handcuff necklace: Sorry! It's just a necklace—not an S&M accessory. $20, emitations.com

7. Heaven Essence Pouring Passion massage oil candle: When the wax in this gravy boat melts, it turns into massage oil. $35, heavenessence.biz

8. Liptrick by Booty Parlor: This lipstick vibrator won't tint your kisser, but it will shake her thing. $26, bootyparlor.com

BECOME HER SEX MACHINE

A PEEK INSIDE HER TOP DRAWER OFFERS SOME SURPRISING INSIGHTS

Her sex toys help you unlock the secrets to pleasing her every time.

THE CLASSIC DILDO

Unlike porn actresses, most women first focus these male stand-ins on their clitoris, penetrating only as climax nears, says Lisa Lawless, PhD, cofounder of the National Association for Sexual Awareness and Empowerment.

THE LESSON: Your penis isn't just for penetration. Use it to stroke her outer labia and clitoris during foreplay, says Vivienne Cass, PhD, author of *The Elusive Orgasm*. Gyrating along these pleasure points while steadily increasing pressure will push her desire to the tipping point, so once you penetrate, you'll deliver orgasm-inducing thrusts.

THE G-SPOT STIMULATOR

These instruments of pleasure target the spongy, sensitive area in her upper vaginal wall, 2 inches from the opening.

THE LESSON: G-spot (as opposed to clitoral) orgasms come from strategic pressure, not size. "Those huge, manmade members aren't what she's hiding under the mattress," says Lawless. To put pressure on this sensitive area with each thrust, you should enter her when she's on her back, with her knees resting on her chest.

THE RABBIT

With two vibrating petals shaped like a set of hare's ears, this Bugs-inspired toy rubs both sides of her clitoris.

THE LESSON: Stimulate (gently) the clitoris from all sides. First, use your index and ring fingers to rub the sides. After she warms up, simultaneously stroke the top of her clitoris with your middle finger, completing the chorus that will send her over the edge.

THE DUAL-ACTION DEVICE

This device massages her clitoris and G-spot in tandem so she's flushed with sensation in the two areas that trigger an orgasm.

THE LESSON: Good things come in pairs. If you're licking her clitoris, finger her G-spot. If she's in the cowgirl position, rub her clitoris. "At any given time, either the G-spot or the clitoris should receive attention," says Dorian Solot, author of *I Love Female Orgasm*.

THE CLASSIC VIBRATOR

This multispeed "massager" lets her focus on her most nerve-rich erogenous spot, the clitoris, as she slowly increases the intensity.

THE LESSON: A little change is good; too much can capsize an orgasm. Always start slow, with gentle, broad strokes of your finger or tongue. Build toward a climax, instead of rapidly changing techniques and intensity. Hum while you lick and you'll cause the same sensation as her pocket rocket.

SUPER FREAKS

Hard to say whether it's rainy-day boredom or just the perpetual coffee buzz, but on average, people in Washington State are the kinkiest in the country, according to online dating site OKCupid.com. The poll of 704,000 men and women measured the kink factor with questions about fetishes, bondage, and other sexual interests. Here's the state of S&M in the U.S. for men and for women.

Kinkiest Women

1. New York
2. Washington
3. Oregon
4. Nevada
5. Florida
6. Colorado
7. New Mexico
8. Massachusetts
9. Kentucky
10. Arizona

Kinkiest Men

1. Florida
2. Washington
3. New York
4. West Virginia
5. Arizona
6. California
7. Texas
8. New Jersey
9. Massachusetts
10. Virginia

WORLDLY AFFAIRS

Americans are early to mate, but late to marry.

Australia

Average age at which men lose their virginity: 18

Percentage of men who "lose it" before age 15: 13

Average man's age at marriage: 29

Brazil

Average age at which men lose their virginity: 17

Percentage of men who "lose it" before age 15: 30

Average man's age at marriage: 24

Great Britain

Average age at which men lose their virginity: 17

Percentage of men who "lose it" before age 15: 13

Average man's age at marriage: 24

Kazakhstan

Average age at which men lose their virginity: 21

Percentage of men who "lose it" before age 15: 4

Average man's age at marriage: 23

Kenya

Average age at which men lose their virginity: 17

Percentage of men who "lose it" before age 15: 26

Average man's age at marriage: 25

Philippines

Average age at which men lose their virginity: 21

Percentage of men who "lose it" before age 15: 3

Average man's age at marriage: 24

USA

Average age at which men lose their virginity: 17

Percentage of men who "lose it" before age 15: 18

Average man's age at marriage: 28

Zimbabwe

Average age at which men lose their virginity: 20

Percentage of men who "lose it" before age 15: 6

Average man's age at marriage: 24

ASK THE GIRL NEXT DOOR

THE HONEST TRUTH ABOUT WOMEN FROM OUR LOVELY NEIGHBOR

She wants me to be more "tender" in bed. What does that mean?

It's like brain surgery: Slow down, pay attention, and make small, careful movements. Brush her hair out of her eyes, trace her collarbone lightly with your finger, spend a full minute gently licking each nipple. Find a part of her body you haven't touched in a long time and kiss it a minimum of three times. And two things that aren't brain surgery: Say her name, and tell her you love her.

My girlfriend is wild in bed when she's been drinking. Can she be that way when she's sober?

Find ways to act goofy together, like trying to learn kung fu from a DVD. Most women don't let it all hang out in the bedroom because they're afraid the guy will be turned off. If she realizes that she can let loose with you, she'll do it when she's naked and sober.

She kisses as if she's trying to suck my face off. Can I change that?

Yes, and there are two ways to go about it. If she has a sense of humor and thick skin, you can crack a few jokes about how she smooches like a Dyson or is clearly trying to make out with the wall behind you. But such women are few and far between. For the rest, praise what you enjoy and stay silent about what you don't. Tell her you love when she kisses you softly or gently slides her tongue into your mouth. Never mind that she's never actually done either of those things. She'll get the point and appreciate your sensitivity.

A woman asked me to bite her nipples. Do most women like that?

The general consensus seems to be no. But, personally, I think a nipple nibble hits the spot if the moment is right. As with spanking, nasty talk, and sloppy tongue thrusts, it's a move you save for sex that's frantic and raw. If she's clawing your back and gnawing on your neck, bite back. Even then, your teeth should register but not hurt. Controlled aggression is sexy. Actual pain is just wrong.

Why do women seem so reluctant to engage in manual stimulation?

Most women remember hand jobs as acts of sexual charity. We'd pump our fist robotically and think of something else until our college boyfriend finished up and dozed off. If you want her to polish your knob with passion, give her a challenge. Suggest a "hands-only" night—no kissing or coitus allowed. Explore her body from head to toe with your digits, spending 20 minutes or more on her vaginal area. Then let her have a turn. Just be sure to anoint your tool with lube. Slipperiness will help her hands flow smoother and faster.

She says it hurts when I stimulate her manually. What am I doing wrong?

Even at its hardest, your penis is crowned by a soft, smooth head for a very good reason: No matter how vigorously you thrust, the thick, spongy tip massages the inside of her vagina in all the right ways. Your smaller, nail-tipped fingers aren't anywhere near as forgiving, so you need to be gentle. Given that the densest nerve concentration in the vagina is right around the opening, slowly inserting your fingers up to the knuckles and wiggling them is all it takes to make her moan. There's no need to go poking around unless your partner requests it.

I'm going down on a girl and she doesn't taste or smell like roses. Is there a polite way to back out?

Hold your breath and very slowly redirect your attention: Kiss your way up past her navel to her breasts. Give each of her nipples a swirl with your tongue, then kiss her shoulders, collarbone, and neck. She'll think you were going for the all-over body smooch from the get-go.

I'd love her to vary her action down there. Any suggestions?

Lure her into a hot shower by offering to wash her hair. (We lo-o-ove that.) After giving the rest of her body—especially her nether regions—an erotically slow scrubdown, hand her the soap. As she slides a sudsy hand into your nooks and around your crannies, let her know what feels good by dropping big fat hints like "Oooh, that's a good spot" and "You need to rub there more often." Then, if necessary, remind her of her amazing shower moves the next time you're getting dirty.

She never lets loose when she's on top. What can I do?

To make a girl go primal, you need to short-circuit her inner critic, help her let go of self-consciousness, and just do what feels good. A bottle of champagne is always encouraged but optional. What you really need is a dark room (so she won't worry about jiggling thighs) and her favorite music turned up loud (to drown out the sound of skin slapping against skin). And you need to cheer her on by telling her that she's incredibly sexy and that you love it when she sweats and moans and moves hard and fast. Keep saying it, and it'll slowly start to sink in.

Outdoor sex is one of my fantasies. How can I make camping more romantic?

Start with food: Put a stockpot full of water and a skillet on the fire. Sauté garlic, onions, and olive oil in the skillet, then add tomatoes, basil, and red wine. (Don't forget the corkscrew.) Let the mixture simmer for half an hour while you drink the rest of the wine in front of the fire. Boil and drain some linguine, add the sauce, and serve it on biodegradable bamboo plates. Now the bed: Use a plush sleeping bag as a base, cover it with a sheet, and top it all with a blanket and portable inflatable pillows. She'll be well fed and more than happy to spread out naked under the stars.

Most of the time I can't hold out long enough for her to orgasm. How can I speed her up?

Why not make it a nonissue by ringing her bell before your train enters the station? A little lube and a lot of manual stimulation will work wonders. (Spend at least 10 minutes giving her clitoris light, slow attention.) If you can't wait, wear a Trojan vibrating-ring condom (trojancondoms.com) to stimulate her at twice the speed.

OVERCOME OBSTACLES

We polled 1,000 women to find out how to conquer bedroom challenges.

ENDLESS BICKERING: Fighting over serious issues is normal, but bickering can cramp your sex life, says Valerie Davis Raskin, MD, author of *Great Sex for Moms*. Unless compromise is easy, "it's often better to put minor disputes aside," she says. "You shouldn't talk over everything endlessly." In our survey, the most trivial quarrels were about the house. Avoid them by playing to each other's strengths. Then divvy up the decisions accordingly.

A HOUSEFUL OF KIDS: If tantrums and diapers are polluting your passion, ditch the kids (for a night). "It's all about creating opportunity," Dr. Raskin says. "Spontaneity is enviable, but planned sex can be great, too." Particularly if you're not getting enough. You know that couple next door? They're probably in a similar situation, so propose a kid swap. You take theirs on Friday, they take yours on Saturday.

If the neighbors are freaks, go home when the kids aren't: lunchtime. Nearly 40 percent of women would be willing to get busy at noon.

PERCENTAGE OF WOMEN WHO WISH THEY WERE HAVING MORE SEX

60

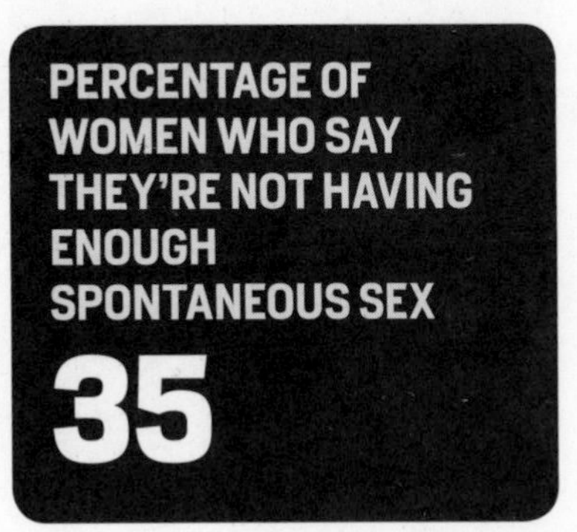

LATE-NIGHT TV: Here's a disturbing set of statistics: Italian researchers found that having a TV in the bedroom halves your sex tally, yet 64 percent of couples keep a set in the boudoir.

"Getting it on is about putting the brain and body in a passionate state. TV does the opposite," says Heidi Raykeil, author of *Confessions of a Naughty Mommy*. Can't quit? Buy a DVR and watch your favorite shows on weekends.

CONFLICTING SCHEDULES: Sixty-hour workweeks plus social plans can leave her too tired to tangle. But pumping up the passion at the beginning of your week sets the tone for days to come. Go to the gym together on Monday or Tuesday: Studies show both sexes experience a surge of libido-boosting testosterone 30 minutes after a workout. Shower and then hit the bedroom. "It'll zap stress and the sexual momentum will last through the weekend," says Michael Breus, PhD, author of *Good Night*.

AN EXTRA SLICE OF PIE: Hoovering down a romantic dinner can backfire. Share an entrée to eat less and spark a passionate interaction, says Bunny Crumpacker, author of *The Sex Life of Food*. "Choosing a meal together and sharing the dish can boost your sense of cooperation," she says. Your best bet: Whip up a dish at home—66 percent of the women we surveyed said they'd be more likely to have sex after a home-cooked meal.

PUSH HER BUTTONS

Slow down: Women want the lip-lock to last twice as long as you do, according to a MensHealth.com poll. Maximize your extended playtime by pinpointing her five pleasure points.

HER LIPS: Target the philtrum, the central ridge of her upper lip and an area the ancient Greeks called the most erogenous zone on the body. Two major cranial nerves are close to the surface here, says Cameron Clokie, MD, an oral surgeon at Mt. Sinai Hospital in Toronto. Gently nibble this pouty point to release oxytocin, the same hormone unleashed during her orgasm, says anthropologist Helen Fisher, PhD, a relationship expert and the author of *Why We Love.*

HER JAW: A sortie around her neck and jawline amps up her pleasure. One twist: Hum softly as you plant kisses along her jaw. You'll send a chorus of euphoric vibrations along the bone and into her inner ear. This audioerotic move also stimulates the skin's Pacinian corpuscles, which release calming endorphins, says Thomas Swift, MD, president of the American Academy of Neurology.

HER TONGUE: Tongue helicopters are for high schoolers. Help her leave the launchpad by teasing the nerve-dense tip of her tongue. Nerves there release the arousal-inducing neurotransmitters serotonin and dopamine, says Dr. Clokie. Vary your lingual caresses with light, lips-only clenches of her tongue tip.

HER NECK: Massaging her hairline at the nape, moving from her hair to her bare neck, doubles her pleasure. You're stroking the junction of two different tissue types, says Dr. Clokie. Working this border region sets off two separate sensations that meld into a single, mind-blowing message to her brain: more.

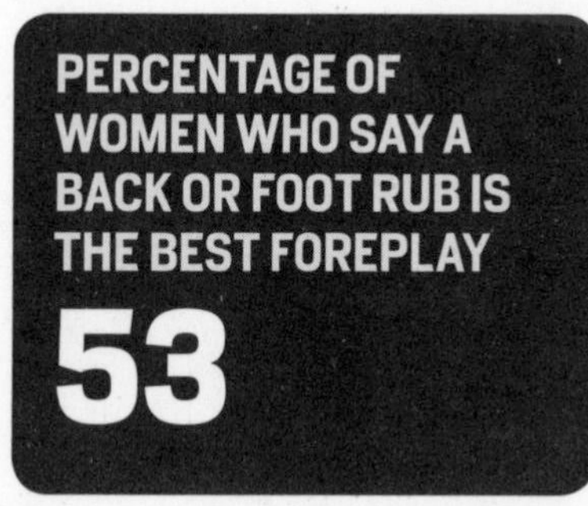

HER CLAVICLE: Canoodling her collarbone is a classic move. But most guys focus on the outer regions and miss the passion-laced center. "The densest nerve region is where her clavicle connects to her sternum," says Dr. Swift. Slowly kiss your way to this nerve center to produce a progressive passion buildup.

A DAB'LL DO YA

Entice by Babeland is our latest bedside must-have. The lube's glass bottle looks innocent and sleek, while the purified-water-based formula helps you maneuver without glycerin, fragrances, or other unnatural stuff getting up in her bod. ($15 for 4 oz, babeland.com)

DODGE BEDROOM BLOOPERS

No matter how many boots you've knocked in your day, switching from one sex position to another can be tricky—and nothing kills a mood like an elbow to the groin. So we asked Yvonne K. Fulbright, PhD, author of *Touch Me There!*, to pass on a few slick tips. Here's how to bang without getting bonked.

SEXY SWITCH: From standing in the cold to standing under the showerhead

THE TRICK: Position yourself under the showerhead and behind the water stream, then reach around to soap her girl parts. To switch, take one step forward together, so now she's under the stream. Look at that! No swiveling, shoving, or shuffling necessary.

SEXY SWITCH: From missionary to her on top

THE TRICK: With her lying on her back, have her wrap her legs around your waist. Push yourself up and rock her toward you until she's upright. Have her move her feet out of the way as you lie back. Gallop home, cowgirl.

SEXY SWITCH: From standing up to comfortably lying on the bed

THE TRICK: Stand facing each other. Wrap your arms around her waist, lift her up, and lay her gently on the mattress. Now here's the twist: Keep both of her legs locked around your waist as you lift and move her farther back onto the bed. That wasn't so hard, was it?

SEXY SWITCH: From her facing your head to facing your feet

THE TRICK: Have her sit up. Grab her left calf, lift it, and use it to spin her clockwise across your body to avoid a kick to your face. Her right leg will follow. (For this one, proceed with caution—and lots of lube.)

SEXY SWITCH: From facing each other on your sides to 69 with her on top

THE TRICK: Have her sit up so that she's on her knees with her legs tucked beneath her. Have her place a hand on either side of your hips, then pass her leg over your face. Now her pelvis is over your chest. Have her slowly lower herself back and down. Together at last!

BUILD A BETTER ORGASM

To seduce her right, engage her five senses.

HEARING: A woman's sexuality is socially influenced—that is, she heats up by discovering what turns her partner on, says Emily Nagoski, PhD, a sexuality educator at West Chester University.

YOUR MOVE: Be vocal. Moan when she hits the right spots during oral sex, gasp when you enter her. These sound effects will cue her feedback loop and rev up her arousal.

SIGHT: Just like you, she can be turned on by a fleeting glance. "Women tend to respond genitally when they see anything sexual," says Nagoski.

YOUR MOVE: Porn is great if she's game, but catch her when she's in front of a mirror. Kiss the back of her neck and move your hands across her front. You'll heighten her sense of both sight and touch—a surefire route to a mind-blowing orgasm.

SMELL: The brain regions that control smell, memory, and sexual arousal are tightly linked, says Linda Banner, PhD, the author of *Advanced Sexual Techniques*.

YOUR MOVE: You may have moved on to a new cologne, but spray some of the old stuff across your bed. When she hits the pillow, it'll trigger steamy, tension-busting memories of those romps from your early dating days.

TASTE: Sweet treats on her tongue ring her brain's reward bells, making her ripe for arousal, according to a study from the University of Pittsburgh.

YOUR MOVE: Seduce her by hand-feeding her fruits with curious textures, such as pomegranates or lychees. The sugar and unique feel of the fruit on her lips and tongue can serve up an arousing double shot of pleasure.

TOUCH: You know the hot zones. But are you doing enough to stimulate the cool ones?

PERCENTAGE OF MEN WHO REGRET NOT TAKING ACTION IN A SEXUAL SITUATION

71

"Most men forget about temperature," says Nagoski.

YOUR MOVE: Hold an ice cube in your palm and as it melts, drip it down her abdomen. To touch off a heat wave, place a piece of candied ginger in your mouth and lick her inner thigh. Bonus: A foot massage can trigger the nerves that connect with her genitals.

PERCENTAGE OF WOMEN WHO REGRET NOT TAKING ACTION IN A SEXUAL SITUATION

47

BUST OUT OF YOUR ROMANCE RUT

Jumpstart your sex life by breaking these six relationship routines.

SEX IS A RACE

BREAK IT: Explore her. Focus on her thighs and lower belly. Make a mental circle 2 inches around the outside of her vagina, and don't cross the line while you kiss, lick, and caress, says Gloria Brame, PhD, author of *Different Loving*. You'll ignite her nerve endings and bring her close to her red zone. It makes sex about discovery, not some destination. "Goal-oriented sex isn't sexy," Brame says.

SAME TIME, SAME PLACE

BREAK IT: Relive the past. Take her to the garage and reclaim the space you long ago ceded: Seduce her in the backseat of the car. It feels a little public, it's steeped in testosterone, and there's a throwback, high-school quality to it. Make it a quickie, which has its place in the sexual diet; having lots of sex begets more sex, because you stay connected, says Laura Berman, PhD, director of the Berman Center in Chicago.

PREDICTABLE FOREPLAY

BREAK IT: Work out together. Think of it as fat-burning foreplay. It will raise her dopamine levels, easing her anxieties. "She'll feel the sex is about her and not some random need she has to accommodate," says Pepper Schwartz, PhD, a professor of sociology at Washington University. Bonus: Your post-run sweat has androstadienone, a testosterone derivative that spikes her arousal when she smells it.

LOPSIDED FIRST MOVES

BREAK IT: Tie her hands. It's now up to her to figure out how to remove your shirt, tie, cuff links, and pants. You'll share a few laughs and marvel at her ingenuity. Whether you tie her up or she binds you, the game will break your predictable, first-move habits. The bonus: "It acts as an automatic foreplay extender," says Berman.

TV, THEN SEX

BREAK IT: Read to her. It doesn't have to be erotica. It's an intimate activity that makes her focus on your voice. The deeper, the better. Low voices are a sign of high testosterone, which ups her attraction to you, according to a Scottish study. Read lying in bed with your head up, to dip an octave; it forces you to push air with your diaphragm instead of your lungs.

HABITUAL HAND-HOLDING

BREAK IT: Caress her neck. Sure, holding hands can work as an aphrodisiac: It shows her you're devoted and proud to tell the world. But after a while, its poignancy wanes. A stepped-up PDA will deepen her connection to you, so she'll be more willing to really give herself to you in the bedroom, says Schwartz.

HAVE SEX FOR DESSERT

What fuels great sex? The clichéd stimulants, such as oysters and avocados, "aren't necessarily valid aphrodisiacs," says Barry Swanson, PhD, a professor of food science at Washington State University. Follow our menu for a libido-lifting, energy-boosting three-course meal that will guarantee she stays for breakfast. Bon appétit!

DRINK: A GLASS OF RED WINE

Grape skins contain the antioxidant resveratrol, the closest thing we have to an actual aphrodisiac. It increases estrogen production, say Northwestern University researchers, and that heightens sexual appetite and makes lubrication easier for her later in the evening.

Red wines from muscadine grapes have a higher resveratrol content than other reds do, say researchers at Mississippi State University.

Caution: Too much vino in too little time forces the body to absorb the alcohol quickly, causing drowsiness.

APPETIZER: SHRIMP COCKTAIL

The zinc-dense shrimp increase sperm levels and make orgasms more powerful, according to a study in *Fertility and Sterility*. They also contain a stress-reducing amino acid and the feel-good hormone serotonin.

ENTRÉE: FILET MIGNON AU POIVRE (6 OZ)

High-protein foods boost production of dopamine and norepinephrine, hormones that increase alertness and assertiveness.

Eating too much (and this goes for everything on the menu) can trigger your body to release cytokines—hormones that induce sleep.

Black pepper aids digestion, according to an *Indian Journal of Medical Research* study—helpful for any energetic activities after dinner.

SIDE: BAKED SWEET POTATO

It's high in potassium, which helps reduce stress—a great way to curb performance anxiety later that night. "The thing to avoid is dumping on a lot of salt, because the sodium can inhibit the potato's potassium," says Swanson.

Top the potato with a dollop of sour cream, another source of libido-friendly protein.

SIDE: SPINACH SALAD

Spinach is a potent source of magnesium, which helps dilate blood vessels, ensuring the smooth bloodflow that's crucial for strong erections, according to Japanese researchers.

RECIPE FOR SEDUCTION

Seal the deal with these three dinner moves.

Strategize your seating. Arrange the table so she'll sit with her back to the wall. "She'll feel like all your attention is focused on her instead of wandering about the room," says Joy Davidson, PhD, a New York City sex therapist and the host of the online video series *The Joy Spot*.

Don't hurry to the table. Meeting her at your front door with the food already on the table can be awkward. Instead, greet her with a glass of wine, give her a quick tour, and then seat her near the counter to watch you prep.

Skip the movie. "Rushing isn't sexy," says April Masini, author of *Date Out of Your League*. Time-sensitive activities, such as going to the movies, are better for when you're not tied to a stove.

DESSERT: FRESH RASPBERRIES DRIZZLED WITH MELTED DARK CHOCOLATE

British scientists have discovered that women release four times more endorphins after eating chocolate than they do after making out. The caffeine in chocolate also increases your alertness for what's to come after dessert.

Try using Chocolove's Extra Strong Dark Chocolate (77 percent cacao) on the raspberries, and pair them with a glass of port. You'll get a double dose of polyphenols—antioxidants that increase your HDL (good) cholesterol.

BASIC INSTINCTS

You can thank Mother Nature for her sexual proclivities. According to the journal *Evolution and Human Behavior*, women's menstrual cycles influence their perception of unusual sex acts.

Scientists asked 307 women ages 18 to 45 to rate statements about bestiality, incest, and sex with 80-year-olds. They discovered that women who were likely ovulating—and thus most fertile—when they took the survey found the suggestions more disgusting.

Lead researcher Daniel M. T. Fessler, PhD, says that because those sexual behaviors are less likely to result in healthy kids, thanks to evolution women find them more off-putting when the chances of pregnancy are higher.

SCORE KEEPING

Nature's got your back: Australian researchers say that the more sexual acts she performs on you, the more of your pheromones (libido-increasing chemicals) she'll be exposed to. Meaning, if you return the favor, she'll be primed for an "Oh."

How to increase her chance of reaching orgasm:

Intercourse alone = 49%
+ you stimulate her = 59%
+ she stimulates you = 72%
+ you perform cunnilingus = 81%
+ she performs fellatio = 89%

IN YOUR DREAMS

Does your wife or girlfriend know just how much action you're enjoying on the side? Men have sex in about one of every 12 dreams, states a Canadian study. And surprisingly, that same rate applies to women, too. The survey of 173 people (and 3,500 of their dreams) reveals that 8 percent of our midnight musings involve sex. The subjects of those nightscapes? The deed itself, followed by sexual propositions, kissing, fantasies, and masturbation. Big shocker—men were twice as likely to dream of multiple sex partners. Here's a closer look at what else is going bump in the night.

DURING SEXUAL DREAMS, WHO IS YOUR PARTNER?
Men: A stranger, usually more than one at a time
Women: A celebrity hunk, or a current or past partner

WHO INITIATES THE ROMP?
Men: She starts it.
Women: I take control.

WHERE ARE YOU GETTING IT ON?
Men: In a public place
Women: In a familiar, private bedroom

DO BOTH OF YOU CLIMAX?
Men: No. I do my thing, but she doesn't.
Women: Yes. We both have an orgasm.

PERCENTAGE OF MEN WHO FEEL AT FAULT AFTER HAVING SEXUAL DREAMS
56

SEXUAL DREAMS IN WHICH A CURRENT OR PAST PARTNER APPEARED

Men: 14%

Women: 20%

REPORTED HAVING AN ORGASM IN THEIR DREAMS

Men: 4%

Women: 4%

SAID THEIR SEX-DREAM PARTNER EXPERIENCED ORGASM IN THEIR DREAM

Men: 0%

Women: 4%

SEX DREAMS IN WHICH A CELEBRITY APPEARED

Men: 5%

Women: 9%

THE SPERMINATOR

The long-awaited male contraceptive pill is getting closer. British scientists are developing one that men can pop 2 to 4 hours before sex. It prevents sperm from exiting the penis but doesn't affect the intensity or sensation of climax, creating a "dry orgasm." Fertility returns to normal within hours of taking the pill. Researchers expect it to hit the market in the next 5 years.

GREEN VIBRATIONS

Sure, your car can run greener, but so can her rabbit: You can now buy vibrators and dildos made from toxin-free synthetics. Pleasure props that hit you with a plastic-y smell when first opened or that have a fleshlike feel may contain a compound called polyvinyl chloride (PVC). Plus, that wondrous wand could have a bonus group of plastic compounds called phthalates. Some studies have shown that PVC and phthalates potentially cause a range of ailments, from cancer to obesity.

To feel good about getting off: Visit goodvibes.com for new lines of toys made from nonporous metal, glass, wood, ceramic, or silicone.

HEALTH BLOW

Researchers have discovered a link between oral sex and throat cancer. A study of 300 people published in the *New England Journal of Medicine* found that those who'd had more than six oral-sex partners in their lifetime were almost nine times more likely to develop throat cancer as those who had none. Researchers speculate that going down may orally transmit the human papillomavirus (HPV). Both sexes can get HPV, and many people have no symptoms. Certain strains can lead to oral, cervical, and penile cancers. But don't despair. Throat cancer is rare: Tonsil and throat cancers affect about two in every 100,000 adults in the United States.

TEST TIME

Okay, fine—no one actually wants to take an HIV test. But avoiding it is not smart: More than 250,000 Americans are positive but don't know it. To help reduce the 40,000 new HIV infections that occur each year, the Centers for

Disease Control has updated recommendations for HIV testing. The new guidelines call for testing everyone ages 13 to 64 seen in a doctor's office or emergency room, unless the patient refuses. "We want to remove the stigma and anxiety surrounding HIV testing by making it part of your routine health care," explains Jennifer Ruth, a spokesperson for the CDC's National Center for HIV, STD, and TB Prevention. You should get tested every time you change partners or have unprotected sex with someone who hasn't been tested. Visit hivtest.org for more info and to find a testing site near you.

PART 5
GET BETTER

SURVIVE PROSTATITIS

HALF OF ALL MEN WILL SUFFER FROM PROSTATITIS. MANY WILL EXPERIENCE A PELVIC PAIN SO EXCRUCIATING THAT SITTING, SLEEPING, AND EVEN HAVING SEX WILL BECOME IMPOSSIBLE. MOST DOCTORS ARE HELPLESS TO STOP IT. MEET THE FEW WHO KNOW HOW

BY STEPHEN RAE

Deep in a redwood forest, at the end of a quiet country lane in California's Sonoma County, 12 men in their thirties and forties lie on mats in a carpeted room on the second floor of a seven-gabled, cedar-shingled lodge. Each is wearing headphones and eye pillows.

"Your pain is not your enemy. If you know how to listen to it, it will help you," David Wise, a 60-year-old clinical psychologist, intones into a microphone. Wise is leading a workshop, training participants in what is called paradoxical relaxation. "The more you are afraid of your pain, the more it will hurt," he says. "Fearing pain makes you more anxious and causes you to tighten up, which raises the level of electrical activity in your muscles and makes the pain worse, which causes more tightening, more anxiety, and more pain."

But the pain he describes is one from which any man would cower. This isn't a gathering of weekend athletes with strained hamstrings or high-powered execs with cluster headaches. These men suffer from prostatitis, a motley array of sexual, urinary, and pelvic-floor pains and dysfunctions that make daily life agony and orgasms feel like electric shock. Each has paid $3,800 for this 6-day treatment, called the Stanford Protocol. Most would have paid twice that. "I was walking down the street one day when suddenly, out of nowhere, I got this ferocious pain in the tip of my penis, as if a ferret had clamped down and wouldn't let go," says a 47-year-old lawyer from Portland, Oregon. A 35-year-old actuary from Sacramento, California, wound up in the fetal position in the emergency room with testicular pain that felt "like I'd been kicked in the nuts."

Little known and poorly understood, prostatitis is men's big secret, the third most common reason we go to urologists—number one for men under 50. Because the disease is only now being seriously studied, there are no solid numbers on how many men suffer nationwide. One recent study showed that 11 percent of the men in one county in Minnesota had been diagnosed with prostatitis in recent years. A Canadian study found that 6 percent of men in two Canadian provinces had reported moderate to severe pain from prostatitis in the prior week. Four percent of Finns have it. "Half of all men will have a prostatitis experience sometime in their lives," says Rodney Anderson, MD, codeveloper, with Wise, of the Stanford Protocol. Not all will become as sick as the men in the lodge, whose bizarre pains take severe tolls on relationships, careers, and lives.

It is a phenomenon I've come to know all too well.

When prostatitis hits, it instantly becomes the most important thing in your life. On Tuesday, I ran 5 miles. On Wednesday, a stabbing pain in my butt kept me from sitting down. And no one seemed to know how to help me.

As I would come to learn, my nightmare was all too typical. I was told an inadequately treated urinary tract infection had spread to my prostate. The stabbing pain was mercifully intermittent, but the intense bladder pressure was constant. Think of a time when you really, really had to go, maybe after six beers. Imagine feeling that way all the time. Imagine trying to fall asleep. The boor who was my first urologist said, "Look at you! You need a psychiatrist!" as I sat in his office distraught after three sleepless nights. He insisted on strict celibacy during weeks-long courses of antibiotics, but his office dispensed a flyer on the illness recommending frequent sex. Rightly perceiving me on the verge of collapse, my G.P. slapped me on Xanax, a cousin of Valium in the benzodiazepine family, which seemed to quiet the nerves that were firing abnormally in a way painkillers couldn't touch. It allowed me a few hours of sleep.

I saw another urologist, the head of the prostate center at a major New York City hospital. He put my blood, urine, prostatic fluid, and semen under the microscope, looking for leukocytes and other things of proven irrelevance, and he put me on expensive antibiotics, anti-inflammatories, alpha blockers, and Elavil, an antidepressant given in low doses for chronic pain syndromes. The only certainty was bankruptcy: Prostatitis, he said, was a "frustrating" disease to treat. A third of patients get well, a third show no change, a third get worse.

If women had prostatitis, they'd go on *Oprah*. But men don't like to talk about what goes wrong between their legs. "Guys think there's a stigma," says Mike Hennenfent, president of the Prostatitis Foundation, a patient advocacy group. It's often the wives who contact him. "A minister's wife told me, 'Our congregation wouldn't understand this.'"

Men's silence is reflected in federal spending on the disease, which, until 1995, was practically zero. Prostatitis was the Rodney Dangerfield of urologic conditions, a research backwater and "a wastebasket of clinical ignorance," as one doctor put it. It was thought to be a bacterial infection of the prostate gland, resulting in inflammation. Doctors gave antibiotics, anti-inflammatories, and, beginning in the 1990s, alpha blockers, which help relax the prostate. When this failed, they gave more antibiotics. "My doctor kept upping the dosage to the point where my pharmacist was freaking out," says the Portland lawyer.

"The patient will be given anything that gets him out of the office," says

Richard Alexander, MD, a professor of surgery and urology at the University of Maryland. "That's how the disease is managed."

Hennenfent was a 67-year-old Angus cattle breeder from Illinois who had suffered for 35 years when he helped start the Prostatitis Foundation in 1995 to press for research and serve as an information clearinghouse. Patients organized on its Web site (prostatitis.org) and lobbied Congress, which authorized the National Institutes of Health to fund research. Eleven North American academic centers, including Stanford's esteemed urology department, were chosen to conduct research, recruit patients, and run clinical trials. The results are in:

Prostatitis patients have less bacteria in their semen than do men in control groups.

There is no correlation between the presence or absence of inflammation and symptoms.

No drug in the pipeline holds promise.

None of the standard treatments work.

Which is why men end up lying on their backs and learning about paradoxical relaxation.

Wise, a man of modest height and crinkly eyes, with a long-standing Zen meditation practice, spent 22 years in pain from what felt like a golf ball lodged in his rectum, frequent and urgent urination, and a variety of other distressing, perplexing, and painful symptoms. In 1998, he left San Francisco for Sonoma County, where he lives amid deer and wild turkeys on 11 hilly acres punctuated with a gazebo and nine profusely carved buildings built with his own hands. Wise came to understand that prostatitis is not a disease of the prostate but a kind of ongoing charley horse in the pelvic-floor muscles that surround it—a neuromuscular disorder that strikes men who chronically hold tension in their pelvis much the way TMJ pain strikes those who hold tension in their jaws. For a variety of reasons—anxiety, pelvic trauma, compulsive masturbation or sexual activity, even traumatic toilet training—some men add to the burden of their hardworking pelvic muscles by chronically clenching them. In such predisposed, usually type-A men, Wise believes, a period of intense physical or mental stress can be the final straw, triggering the muscles to constrict. This chronic tension takes on a life of its own, continuing long after any injury or stress abates.

Wise spent a decade learning how to stop the unconscious tightening of his pelvic muscles, eliminating his pain through paradoxical relaxation, certain yogalike stretches, and an eyebrow-raising form of physical therapy based on the concept of trigger-point release. Trigger points are taut bands within muscles, formed through stress, tension, or injury, which radiate pain but can be neutralized by applying pressure. Tim Sawyer, an expert in trigger-point release and a physical therapist, mapped trigger points inside, outside, and around the pelvis that are associated with prostatitis symptoms.

Wise took his program to Dr. Anderson, a neurourologist at Stanford who was frustrated by his inability to do more for his prostatitis patients. "This is all such a black hole of medicine," says Dr. Anderson. "The doctors just don't get it." The Wise program, he added, is "the best treatment I've seen in more than 25 years of doing this stuff. I have so many patients who say 'Once I started doing this, things just got better.'" In 1995, Wise joined Stanford's urology department as a visiting scholar, and Wise, Dr. Anderson, and Sawyer began seeing patients. Wise and Dr. Anderson published a book in 2003, *A Headache in the Pelvis*, and refined their treatment into the 6-day protocol Wise now leads.

Patients finally found relief. "We've gone from a time during which we saw virtually no success stories, to having success stories and recoveries become almost routine," says Mark Meeker, founder of ChronicProstatitis.com. "This is a sea change." In the past 18 months, the treatment's credibility has been enhanced with the publication of two papers in the *Journal of Urology*, the field's leading journal, documenting the protocol's success. The *Urology* articles "really gave hope," says the Portland lawyer, "and a legitimacy the medical community needed."

Back in the lodge, one by one, the men are summoned to an outbuilding for their daily hour of physical therapy, called intrapelvic trigger-point release. With strong fingers, Sawyer works the kinks out of the patient's rectal walls from the inside. Patients' spouses—about half bring theirs—are present during treatment and learn to perform it; the whole point is to teach patients to treat themselves. A tough sell, you'd think, in a culture that dreads digital rectal exams, but these men are desperate and have tried everything from downing boiled broccoli broth morning, noon, and night, to flying to pricey Philippine clinics.

It wasn't until I read *A Headache in the Pelvis* that I fully understood how incompetent my doctors had been. Of course the antibiotics they had given me didn't work; I no longer had an infection. (Patients report that stress worsens symptoms, impossible with an infection.) Indeed, the problem with prostatitis is that we don't know whether the prostate is involved at all. (If it were, then why doesn't taking it out—as some men have done, along with hav-

THE PROSTATITIS ACTION PLAN

How do you know whether you have prostatitis? The most common sign is severe pain in your privates, whether it's the penis, the rectum, or elsewhere in the neighborhood. Some men have climaxes that feel like a leg cramp; others feel as if they have a constant need to urinate. The condition can strike at any age, but most victims are in their thirties or forties, probably because stress appears to contribute to the disorder. While the disease remains poorly understood, here's what you should do, based on the latest and best research.

See a doctor immediately. Some experts believe prostatitis can be triggered by urinary tract infections, in which case treating the infection promptly may be key to recovery. Make sure the doctor cultures your urine; that's the only way to know for sure what you're dealing with.

In some instances, antibiotics will even cure the prostatitis itself, but a large number of prostatitis cases are nonbacterial and must be treated with a variety of options, including alpha-blocker prescriptions and dietary supplements such as quercetin or Prosta-Q.

ing colostomies, anal canals injected with Botox, pelvic nerves dissected, and testicles and bladders removed—cure it?) Benzodiazepines, on the other hand, are designed to treat anxiety and have a second use as muscle relaxants. The other things that helped me—massage and hot baths, which doctors do recommend—soothed sore muscles, not sick glands.

I called Wise, who referred me to Marilyn Freedman, a physical therapist in Great Neck, New York, who specializes in pelvic-floor myofascial trigger-point work. With her South African accent and disarming manner ("I'm very comfortable with rectums!"), she defused the tension inherent in a stranger sticking a finger up your bum.

The days after I saw Freedman were hell. Despite enough Xanax to stun a horse, my symptoms raged uncontrollably for 48 hours. But this was followed,

---

If you do have an infection and your doctor prescribes an antibiotic, question him thoroughly as to how long you should remain on the drug. If you don't eradicate the infection completely, it could spread and worsen the symptoms. Also ask about muscle relaxants.

Ask for a referral to a urologist, and make sure he's up-to-date on the latest research and treatments for prostatitis. One way to tell: If he doesn't give you the National Institutes of Health patient questionnaire or the Stanford Protocol, he probably isn't on the cutting edge.

Find a physical therapist trained in male pelvic-floor work. One surprising source is the women's health section of the American Physical Therapy Association. Women's doctors have more experience in pelvic-floor work. A list is available at womenshealthapta.org.

For more information, go to pelvicpainhelp.com (the Stanford Protocol), urologyhealth.org, chronicprostatitis.com, or prostatitis.org.

astonishingly, by complete remission—total normalcy for the first time in 6 months. This faded, alas, after a couple of days, but the flare-up that followed my next treatment was shorter and the state of normalcy lasted longer. Physical therapy released the stress I was carrying around in my pelvis, and I became healthy again.

Nine months later, I was a victim of identity theft, and my symptoms returned. Freedman fixed me in one visit.

Hurdles remain to mainstream acceptance. "Unfortunately, many urologists and pelvic-pain physicians regard trigger points with little more credibility than a Ouiji board," says Wise. Even open-minded doctors face the challenge of administering it in the standard brief office visit, notes Jeannette Potts, MD, of the Cleveland Clinic, who reached many of the same conclusions as Wise independently and uses trigger-point-release therapy with her pelvic-pain patients.

To doctors taught that prostatitis is a prostate disease, the neuromuscular model could represent a paradigm shift. In this new paradigm, the doctor is a team player: After a physical exam to rule out cancer and other pathologies, the Stanford Protocol integrates physical therapists with the urologists. "It doesn't go over well when a big organization loses a disorder," Leroy Nyberg, PhD, the urologist in charge of urology research at the National Institutes of Health, told the audience at a recent NIH-sponsored pelvic-pain conference. Left unsaid was any dread over the loss of 8 percent of urologists' incomes.

Still, the Stanford pedigree, the *Urology* publications, the uselessness of other treatments, and, above all, patient demand are having an impact. These days, physical therapists are nearly as likely as doctors to attend pelvic-pain conferences. Large teaching hospitals have begun using biofeedback for pelvic-muscle relaxation. And the NIH is considering multicenter clinical trials of pelvic-floor physical therapy.

"There has been a groundswell of interest," says Dr. Anderson, who for the first time can offer his patients an improved therapy. "It's a whole new ball game."

SOUND OUT PROSTATE CANCER

MORE AND MORE MEN ARE FACING A MEDICAL CONUNDRUM: EITHER RISK LOSING YOUR SEX LIFE FOREVER, OR TRAVEL ABROAD FOR A $20,000 PROCEDURE THAT THE FDA HASN'T APPROVED YET

BY JOHN BRANT

Jack Barkin, MD, picks up a scalpel and cuts a quarter-inch incision below the navel of patient Mike Bowman, a 54-year-old medical-equipment salesman from North Carolina. Bowman lies with a spinal anesthetic in a semiconscious sprawl, his legs spread in a stirrup chair similar to those used by obstetricians. Through the incision Dr. Barkin guides a suprapubic catheter into Bowman's bladder, which will remain in place for a few days after this morning's procedure until the swelling in the prostate area has subsided. Before this, Dr. Barkin ran a Foley catheter up Bowman's penis to flush water through the prostate region and to fill the bladder. "For better visibility," explains Dr. Barkin. "Water is good and air is bad for conducting ultrasound."

Then Dr. Barkin slides a lubricated probe, which is connected to a Sonablate 500 acoustic ablation device, 8 inches up Bowman's rectum. Turning away from his patient—he will not touch Bowman again during the ensuing 2-hour procedure—he clicks the mouse of the Sonablate's computer, firing up the R2-D2–size machine. Deep inside Bowman, the probe shoots out three beams of high-intensity focused ultrasound (HIFU), an energy source similar to what doctors use to dissolve kidney stones. The beams triangulate Bowman's cancerous prostate, which appears as a fan-shaped gray mass on the computer's monitor. "This doesn't look so bad," says Dr. Barkin. "The cancer is small enough that we can treat it in two sections instead of three."

Indeed, Bowman's prostate is in such relatively good shape (meaning that its tumors are well defined, threatening neither to invade surrounding tissue nor metastasize to distant parts of his body) that if it were 20 years ago, he may not have known he had prostate cancer until it was too late. It wasn't until 1985 that the FDA approved PSA screening, a test that measures levels of prostate-specific antigen in the blood; an elevated score—from 4 to 10 ng/mL—suggests the presence of cancer. In the absence of early symptoms and timely diagnosis, he may very well have become one of the nearly 30,000 American men who die annually from the disease, the most common cancer among males.

Today, however, patients like Bowman—fit, affluent, sexually active men in their forties, fifties, and sixties with early-stage prostate cancer—are Dr. Barkin's prime customers. They're living the short-straw end of the statistics that show that, in North America, men are 35 percent more likely to develop prostate cancer than women are to develop breast cancer; by 2015, the number of newly diagnosed prostate-cancer cases will jump to 300,000 a year—a 50 percent increase from today. These medical early adopters have considered every treatment option covered by insurance in the United States—scalpel surgery, radiation, cryotherapy, and brachytherapy—and have chosen instead to pay $20,000 out of pocket to come here, the Can-Am HIFU clinic in Toronto, where Dr. Barkin uses ultrasound to heat their prostate tumors to 212°F, destroying them in less than 3 seconds. "Basically," says Dr. Barkin, rather matter-of-factly, "we're cooking the prostate."

The speed of the procedure, however, isn't what will draw an estimated 700 American men across the border to Canada or to clinics in Central America to pay for a treatment that has yet to gain FDA approval. Rather, it's HIFU's astonishingly low rate of erectile dysfunction. "I do every kind of prostatectomy, from scalpel to robotics," says Dr. Barkin, "and the rate of erectile dysfunction with all other treatments, no matter how skilled the surgeon, is around 50 percent. With HIFU, it's less than 10 percent. Plus, you can't beat the recovery time."

At Dr. Barkin's clinic, which he runs as a sideline to his standard urology practice at Toronto's Humber River Regional Hospital, men are treated as outpatients on Saturday. On Sunday, most feel well enough to go sightseeing.

The operating room is small, brightly lit, and oddly cheerful, seeming more like a dentist's office than a place of life-or-death stakes. Content that the procedure is proceeding smoothly, Dr. Barkin, an inveterate teacher, launches into a quick lecture on the walnut-shaped gland that is the prostate. The first spurt of an ejaculation comes from the prostate, he explains, whose evolutionary function is to secrete enzymes that protect sperm from acids in the vagina. All male mammals possess a prostate. In humans, it sits at the crossroads of several crucial organs: the rectum, anus, bladder, urethra, and seminal vesicles. Two razor-thin bundles of nerves run vertically along both sides of the prostate and are largely responsible for stimulating and preserving erections. "Here you can see them plain as day," says Dr. Barkin, pointing out two faint dark lines on the monitor. I fix my eyes on the glowing computer screen, which shows sonic beams systematically zapping Bowman's tumors into benign scar tissue, which possesses an eerie resemblance to cooked popcorn.

Bowman's long journey to this fifth-floor cancer clinic—marked only by a hastily word-processed sign next to the elevator—began three months earlier, in July, on the day that his prostate biopsy returned positive. "My first thought was, I'm going to die," recalls Bowman. "My second was, Why me?" After the initial shock and subsequent pulse of anger, Bowman confronted his first fateful choice: treat or not treat? Take out the gland that delivers a man so much pleasure during the first half of his life, and so much anxiety later, or proceed with watchful waiting?

The concept of watchful waiting, in which a physician closely monitors an untreated prostate-cancer patient for spiking PSA levels or other signs that the malignancy threatens to spread, never appealed to Bowman. At 54, he was in his prime, in good shape, and with many good years ahead of him—years, reckoned Bowman, that could allow his cancer to spread insidiously into other organs, his liver perhaps. Or maybe the cancer would beeline for his colon before heading north to his lungs.

Many physicians would argue that Bowman's concern was for naught. In the great majority of cases, prostate cancer is so slow-growing that Thomas Stamey, MD, the Stanford University urologist who pioneered PSA screening, has been reported as saying that up to 90 percent of the prostatectomies performed during the last decade were unnecessary. Indeed, only one in four men with latent prostate cancer will ever show symptoms, even if left untreated, and there is a less than 20 percent chance that men ages 50 to 54 with early-stage prostate cancer will die from it. Moreover, no long-term studies have proved definitively that treating prostate cancer increases longevity. Mountains of data, by contrast, attest to treatment's bleak side effects, the most prominent being the likelihood of erectile dysfunction and urinary incontinence.

What bothered Bowman, however, was that despite intense ongoing research, there's no reliable way to predict the nature of a prostate tumor—whether it's among the aggressive 25 percent that kills, or the more benign 75 percent that rarely produces symptoms. "I can understand the statistical argument, but from a personal survival standpoint, the whole idea of 'watchful waiting' seems absurd," says Bowman. "Wait for what? For the tumors to magically dry up and go away, like warts? Or for the cancer to invade my spine and liver, and then decide it's time to treat it?"

As recently as a decade ago, scalpel prostatectomy, which was pioneered in the 1940s, was the standard treatment for prostate cancer, and excising the malignancy—nerve bundles and all—was the surgeon's primary, and often sole, concern. In their defense, surgeons had little choice in the matter. Most men seeking treatment back then had reached stage II of the disease, and because their cancer had already spread, saving their lives almost always entailed removing the gland. Today, however, with PSA screening standard for men older than 50 and early diagnoses increasingly common, the effort to save those delicate nerve bundles—through techniques such as nerve-sparing radical prostatectomy, robotic surgery, and now HIFU—has blossomed into a multibillion-dollar industry. In short, men with prostate cancer finally have a say regarding the preservation of their sex gland.

"One guy might say, 'This cancer freaks me out. Cut it out with a knife and damn the consequences,'" says Dr. Barkin. "A second man might want every precaution taken to preserve the nerves and erections by being less aggressive, but if the moment comes, err on the side of killing the cancer. A third man might say he'd rather die than live with erectile dysfunction. And men do die for that reason. You'd be surprised how many."

The sheer number of available prostate-cancer treatments—there are six mainstream options—initially bewildered Bowman (see "The Prostate Cancer Conundrum" on page 232), and, like many newly diagnosed men, he spent weeks studying the voluminous and contentious literature on the subject. "I worked day and night," he recalls, "but I never seemed to get tired. I felt like I was in a war, fighting for my life. And just like war, there was the fog: too much information." He obsessively surfed Web sites, interviewed a range of urologists, and discovered that, invariably, each one recommended his own pet procedure.

This was due partly to the confidence each physician had in his craft, but it would be naive to assume that none of them had an eye on financial gain. National spending for prostate-cancer treatment, after all, is about $8 billion annually. And the more patients a physician treats, the bigger his piece of the prostate-cancer pie. What was once an unglamorous medical specialty has, in the past 20 years, developed into one of the most lucrative.

Although none of the six standard treatment options are guaranteed to cure prostate cancer, all are effective. A study in the *New England Journal of Medicine*, for example, showed that prostate-cancer patients who underwent surgery were 44 percent less likely to die from the disease than men treated by watchful waiting. But life expectancy wasn't Bowman's chief concern. "I just didn't want to lose my potency, and no conventional treatment could offer the successful statistical outcome I wanted in that regard," says Bowman. "In fact, having prostate cancer brought home the degree to which sexuality permeates everything I think and do. Your sex is who you are, to a certain extent. And I never quite realized that until I was in danger of losing it."

(continued on page 236)

THE PROSTATE CANCER CONUNDRUM

Today's prostate-cancer patient has more treatment options than ever before. Here's how to decide which one is right for you.

The American Cancer Society recommends that all men have a PSA screening and digital rectal exam annually starting at age 50. Men at higher risk—African-Americans and those with a family history—should begin at age 40. For more information about prostate cancer, visit prostatecancerfoundation.org.

TREATMENT	WHO IT IS FOR	WHAT IT IS	PROS	CONS
Active surveillance (or watchful waiting)	Men who choose not to undergo more aggressive treatments because of a slow-growing tumor or other medical conditions	The patient makes frequent trips to the urologist for PSA tests and digital rectal exams.	No surgery	Cancer could spread; heightened anxiety from having an untreated cancer
Radical prostatectomy	Men with aggressive stage I or II cancer who are more concerned with survival than side effects	An incision is made in the abdomen and the prostate is cut out from behind the pubic bone.	Surgeons are most experienced with this method. It offers the best chance of eliminating the cancer.	Most invasive treatment; highest risk of impotence and incontinence
Nerve-sparing prostatectomy	Men with aggressive cancer who are very concerned about side effects such as impotence and incontinence	The surgeon cuts carefully to the edge of the prostate, sparing the outlying nerves that are critical to sexual functioning.	With a skilled surgeon, there is a high cure rate and a low risk of side effects.	Malignancies in surrounding tissue might be missed and cancer could spread.

TREATMENT	WHO IT IS FOR	WHAT IT IS	PROS	CONS
Laproscopic surgery (or robotic surgery)	Younger men with stage I cancer who are concerned about side effects	The surgeon cuts several small holes in the abdomen, through which he inserts robotic tools that he controls remotely by computer.	It's much less invasive than scalpel surgery, with less blood loss and a shorter hospital stay.	More challenging than traditional surgery; relies heavily on surgeon's skill
External radiation therapy	Younger men with stage I cancer who are concerned about side effects	Very high doses of x-rays are delivered to the tumor cells five times a week for 7 to 8 weeks as an outpatient.	It's less invasive than scalpel or laproscopic surgery, and it has a lower risk of side effects.	Too much can damage surrounding organs; too little can result in relapse.
Brachytherapy (or radiation seed implantation)	Younger men with stage I cancer who are very concerned about side effects	The surgeon inserts tiny metal pellets containing radioactive iodine or palladium. The cancer is killed as the radioactive material degrades.	Doesn't require daily visits to the treatment center	Relies heavily on the surgeon's skill
Cryotherapy	Younger men with stage I cancer who are very concerned about side effects	Argon gas is delivered to the prostate via probes through the perineum, freezing the cancer.	Minimally invasive, little blood loss; short hospital stay	High rates of impotence; scarce data on cure rates

A SYBARITE'S GUIDE TO CANCER PREVENTION

Wine, dine, and exercise your way to a healthier sex gland.

Sip red wine. Oenophiles appreciate its spicy nose, ruby color, and sweet earthy taste, but urologists appreciate vino rojo for a different reason: its ability to sweep cancer-causing free radicals from the body. Research at Seattle's Fred Hutchinson Cancer Research Center found that drinking one glass of red wine a day can cut your risk of prostate cancer by more than half. Tippling more than three glasses has the opposite effect. In a study of nearly 48,000 men at the Johns Hopkins Bloomberg School of Public Health, researchers found that knocking back more than eight drinks during a weekend binge increased the risk of prostate cancer by 64 percent.

Eat like an Italian. Despite a spate of small studies questioning the cancer-blasting power of tomatoes, the evidence still tilts in favor of the red fruit. In fact, Harvard researchers found that men who consumed just two servings of tomato sauce a week reduced their risk of prostate cancer by 23 percent. Eat whole tomatoes or tomato products rather than taking a lycopene supplement.

Fire the presidential staff. Now you can add hard science to foreplay, sex toys, and any other persuasive techniques you employ between the sheets. The more often you ejaculate, the less likely you are to develop prostate cancer, say researchers at the Cancer Council Victoria, in Australia. Their study of 2,338 men found that those who ejaculated more than five times a week were 33 percent less likely to develop the disease than those who ejaculated less frequently.

Catch the day's catch. A diet rich in omega-3 fish is not only good for your heart, but also helps slow (and even prevent) the progression of prostate cancer, according to a study at Wake Forest University, in North Carolina. Oily fish such as wild salmon and herring (i.e., those dense with desirable "long chain" omega-3 fatty acids) work best, say researchers. Shoot for at least two servings a week. Don't like fish? Pop a daily 1,000 milligram omega-3 capsule.

Work out more often. Score another hit for the benefits of regular exercise: It can help armor-plate your prostate. In a study of 29,000 men in the International Journal of Cancer, researchers found that participants who worked out for an hour a week cut their risk of prostate cancer by 31 percent. Thirty minutes resulted in a 16 percent drop.

Use solar power. Basking in sunlight—which stimulates your production of vitamin D receptors—can benefit your body where the sun don't shine, say researchers at the Northern California Cancer Center. Their study of 900 men found that those with the highest amount of sun exposure had a 50 percent lower risk of developing prostate cancer than their less exposed peers. Ten minutes a day will do the trick. Leave your arms and legs exposed, but wear sunscreen on your face, ears, and neck to reduce your risk of skin cancer.

Supplement in moderation. Call it multivitamin inflation: Manufacturers looking to sway consumers often pack their pills with hundreds of times the RDA of minerals and vitamins. Not wise, according to researchers at the National Cancer Institute, who found that men who pop more than seven multivitamins a week increase their risk of prostate cancer by 30 percent. So stick to one low-dose multi a day. If it contains more than the RDA of any one vitamin or mineral, find another brand.

Go light on dairy. Researchers at the Fred Hutchinson Cancer Research Center advise drinking less milk for the same reason the National Dairy Council suggests drinking more: calcium. In their study of 3,341 men, the researchers found that taking 1,200 mg of calcium daily—through supplements or three 8-ounce glasses of milk—can mask blood levels of prostate-specific antigen, complicating the early diagnosis of prostate cancer.

Bowman first learned about HIFU while researching on the Web. The more he learned about it, the better it sounded. HIFU technology was first used to treat prostate-cancer patients in France in the 1990s, and it was refined by researchers at the Indiana University School of Medicine, who developed the first version of the Sonablate machine. To date, HIFU has been used on more than 20,000 patients worldwide, and the Sonablate 500 scored a success rate of 94 percent in patients with low-grade localized cancer, according to recent research by Toyoaki Uchida, MD, of Japan's Tokai University.

"In the course of my sales work," says Bowman, "I've sat in on a lot of surgical procedures and seen things I'd like to forget. For my own surgery, I wanted the least invasive, most controllable procedure possible." But Bowman quickly learned that this favorite treatment of aging rock stars, airline pilots, and, intriguingly, American physicians, comes with a significant catch: It's not offered in the United States (nor is it covered by U.S. insurers, for that matter). To receive it, one must travel to Europe, Japan, Mexico, or Canada and pay a fortune in medical expenses.

Bowman's plight raises an important question: Why isn't HIFU available in the United States? "The FDA is very rigorous when it comes to clinical trials for cancer treatment," explains Naren Sanghvi, who helped develop the Sonablate machine. "In the case of the Sonablate 500, studies must prove unequivocally that it resolves prostate cancer. Then researchers must follow the trial participants for years to determine that the cancer doesn't recur." In the United States, such data has been slow in coming. The Canadian government approved the procedure in 2004, but it is not covered by national health insurance because Health Canada is still waiting on 10-year results. It pays for the other treatments that are currently as effective.

In the summer of 2006, the Sonablate 500 passed the first round of testing in the United States, which deemed it safe for clinical trials. In the spring of 2007, clinical trials began at two clinics in Tennessee and one in Texas. (To enroll, visit focus-surgery.com.) According to Sanghvi, test data will be gathered and evaluated over the next several years, and if all goes well, FDA approval will follow within the next decade. "Every American urologist who looks at HIFU is intrigued," says Ian Thompson, MD, chair of the urology department at the University of Texas Health Science Center at San Antonio. "But the big question, and the greatest hurdle for FDA approval, is whether HIFU can be proved to cure prostate cancer. And that takes time."

Once the procedure is complete, it takes Bowman several minutes to shake off the anesthesia. He emerges groggily, feeling his way back into reality bit by bit, almost at the pace it took the Sonablate to cook his prostate. News that the procedure was a success takes a while to sink in. He is reluctant to sit up in bed, let alone take his first steps down the hallway toward the recovery room, but once he gets his legs under him, he feels a surge of relief and energy. He vows that when he returns to Charlotte he will mount the soapbox about prostate cancer.

"The week before the Komen Foundation's Race for the Cure, you couldn't turn on the television or walk down the street without hearing about breast cancer," he says. "Well, September is National Prostate Cancer Awareness Month in the United States. Are you aware of that fact? I didn't think so."

Then, in midafternoon, almost exactly 7 hours after Mike Bowman entered the clinic, Dr. Barkin gives him the okay to leave. Bowman accepts a nurse's arm in the elevator, but once out on the sidewalk and tasting the cool autumn air, he lets go. The nurse urges him to move cautiously, to cross Bay Street at the traffic light, but Bowman, declaring that he's ravenous, is eager to get back to his hotel.

"Hell, let's jaywalk," he says, stepping lightly off the curb.

Three days later, back home in Charlotte, Bowman's bladder function returns to normal and a doctor removes his catheter. The next night, his greatest fear regarding prostate-cancer surgery is laid to rest.

GET YOUR MOJO BACK

CROSS YOUR LEGS, MEN. A PHENOMENON CALLED XENOBIOTIC ATTACK IS MEDDLING WITH YOUR MANHOOD, AND YOUR FAMILY JEWELS MAY NEVER HANG THE SAME WAY AGAIN

BY RICHARD CONNIFF

In 2003 professional golfer Shaun Micheel took his game to a new level. He won the PGA Championship on the 72nd hole with his 21st birdie of the tournament. Then everything seemed to fall apart.

"I lost my drive. I didn't enjoy practicing anymore. If I made a couple of bogeys, I just wanted to go home," he said at the time. It was more than a slump. He barely even showed up on the professional circuit the following year. At first he thought it was depression. "I seemed to be tired all the time, and irritable. I wasn't myself."

But in April 2005, a blood test showed that, at the age of 36, Micheel had the testosterone level of a 70-year-old. His doctor had him rub a hormone-replacement gel onto his biceps each morning. By September his testosterone level was back to normal.

It wasn't a miracle cure. He still hasn't won another major tournament, though he did manage a second-place finish last year. But Micheel is working his way back up the list of money winners. More important, both he and his wife say testosterone has given him back his old, upbeat personality.

Good news for him, but what about the rest of us? Some scientists now wonder whether a lot of other "walking, talking, normalish guys," as one urologist put it, are also experiencing a fading of the hormonal basis of masculinity, leaving them feeling less like the men they used to be, less than their fathers were in their time.

Most men can expect their testosterone levels to drop by about 1 percent a year beginning in their fifties. So a man in his seventies might have only half

MISSING MANHOOD

Rock-solid evidence that testosterone is tumbling is still limited to studies on men in Denmark and Finland. But other indicators—such as the global fall of sperm counts—seem to point to a downward trend worldwide. Shanna Swan, PhD, an epidemiologist at the University of Rochester, reviewed sperm concentrations from men in 61 countries between 1934 and 1996 and discovered a strong downward slope: "It's dropping by about 1 percent per year, but the trend is strongest in Western Europe and the United States."

Sperm Specifics

United States: –68% (1938–1988)
Brazil: –45% (1979–1990)
U.K.: –40% (1949–1993)
Israel: –34% (1984–2003)
Hong Kong: –30% (1980–1987)
France: –26% (1983–1991)
Denmark: –20% (1944–1996)
Nigeria: –10% (1980–1991)
Finland: +8% (1979–1987)
Sweden: +15% (1971–1983)
Germany: +16% (1971–1993)

the testosterone he had when he was 25. But researchers behind the Massachusetts Male Aging Study—which has been tracking behavioral and physiological traits of 1,709 men born between 1916 and 1945—noticed something strange. Men born more recently had T levels that were surprisingly low. The 60-year-old in 2003 had about 15 percent less testosterone than the 60-year-old in 1988, according to Thomas G. Travison, PhD, lead author of the testosterone study. Sixty was looking like the new 70. Had something happened? Could we be in the middle of some broad biological or environmental change affecting all men simultaneously?

No one was suggesting that men rush out to get their testosterone levels checked (though, okay, I did), much less consider testosterone therapy (and, yes, I am considering it). As one endocrinologist put it, "You need to see more than one study from more than one laboratory before you start waving your arms and shouting alarm."

But the Massachusetts results marked a turning point: Testosterone is no longer just a hot topic for misguided weight lifters or baby boomers with delusions of eternal youth. It's something the average aging male will need to think about, starting with a few testosterone basics.

Testosterone is literally what makes us men. Delivery of the right amount at the critical moment shifts development of a fetus away from the basic human blueprint, which is female, and onto the path to masculinity. A surge in testosterone (from the testes—hence the name) in adolescence boosts us into manhood. And for the rest of our lives, testosterone, or the lack of it, seems to play a key role in muscle strength, lean body mass, bone density,

IS IT TIME FOR T?

Testosterone levels follow a predictable course over a man's lifetime, but you can buck the decline with the right health, exercise, and eating strategies.

The Jock

Age: 27; Weight: 165; Score: 192

Men in their twenties tend to be swimming in testosterone, and our tester's habit of lifting weights three times a week sent his score to well-above-average levels. In addition, he avoids two testosterone saboteurs that affect men in their twenties: booze and junk food.

He eats plenty of meat, including beef, buffalo, and pork, which studies have found to be essential for high T.

The Working Dad

Age: 37; Weight: 220; Score: 131

After a man turns 30, a new set of stressors tends to emerge: family, a mortgage,

mental sharpness, and sex drive—the things that often make us feel best about who we are.

Despite testosterone's explosive reputation, there's no solid evidence that it causes aggression or violence. On the contrary, heightened testosterone is often associated with self-confidence and social success. Testosterone levels typically increase to ready us for a challenge, whether it's a football game or a chess match. Testosterone also rises after a victory, causing an increase in confidence that often leads to even more victories, the so-called winner effect. Who would want less of a hormone like that?

And yet the quantity of the stuff, even in healthy young men, is astoundingly small. Most doctors measure total testosterone as the starting point, and for American men under the age of 40, the normal range is 300 to 1,000 nanograms per deciliter of blood. (That's what "ng/dl" means on your medical laboratory report.) A nanogram is a billionth of a gram, and a deciliter is a 10th of a liter. Or, to put it in layman's terms, not bloody much. If you

---

and rising job responsibilities, to name a few. And sure enough, our tester's levels of the stress hormone cortisol were the highest of the bunch. Cortisol can actually blunt the body's production of T and cause your gut to grow. Our family man sweats away stress by jogging 16 miles a week, which is probably why his T levels remain on the high end of normal.

The Boomer

Age: 51; Weight: 160; Score: 118

A man's metabolism starts to slow during his late thirties, and packing on pounds can speed the natural testosterone decline by 10 years, according to a study in the *Journal of Clinical Endocrinology & Metabolism*. Older men also swallow more statins, which reduce testosterone levels. Our tester's workout regimen of running and basketball has kept his metabolism high, prescription needs low, and weight steady.

somehow managed to collect all the testosterone from your entire body, it would barely fog the bottom of a shot glass.

But it gets more complicated. Testosterone occurs in the blood in three forms.

About 40 percent of total testosterone is tightly bound to sex hormone–binding globulin, or SHBG, meaning it's not readily available for use by the body. In fact, nobody knows for sure what function SHBG-bound testosterone performs.

"Free testosterone" isn't bound to other molecules. But it constitutes just 2 percent of total testosterone.

Fortunately, the balance of total testosterone is bound to albumin and other proteins, and those links are easily broken. So together with free testosterone, this "bioavailable" testosterone is there when the body needs it.

You could look at it this way: Your manhood is based on half of almost nothing. And there's less of it with each passing year.

BECOME MR. T

Five Easy Ways to Increase Your Manpower

A testosterone shortage could cost you your life. As if losing muscle mass, bone density, and your sex drive to low T levels weren't bad enough, new research shows the decline can also increase your risk of prostate cancer, heart disease, and even death. Follow thes%%e steps to lift your levels and lengthen your life.

Uncover your abs. As your waist size goes up, your testosterone goes down. In fact, a four-point increase in your body mass index—about 30 extra pounds on a 5'10" guy—can accelerate your age-related T decline by 10 years.

Build your biceps. Finnish researchers recently found that men who lifted weights regularly experienced a 49 percent boost in their free testosterone levels. "As you strengthen your muscles, the amount of testosterone your body produces increases," says David Zava, PhD, CEO of ZRT Laboratory. You need to push iron only twice a week to see the benefit.

Measuring testosterone is complicated, because the tests themselves aren't always reliable, and results can differ from one lab to the next. "Normal" levels can also vary dramatically from one man to the next. And they can vary from minute to minute in the same man; testicles seem to do everything in spurts. That's because testosterone levels fluctuate with the little wins and losses of daily life. So if a test suggests that you have a testosterone problem, do not despair: There's a one-in-three chance you'll be back to normal on a follow-up.

But none of this diminishes the mystery: Why would testosterone levels in the United States today be substantially lower than they were 15 years ago? When they saw their results, the Massachusetts researchers thought they'd made a mistake. "We'd used the same lab, the same assay, and the same analyst to gather the data over time," says Travison. "But even so, subtle changes in the way the assay was manufactured could have had some impact."

Then in the summer of 2006, Travison attended an Endocrine Society

---

Fill up on fat. Trimming lard from your diet can help you stay lean, but eliminating all fat can cause your T levels to plummet. A study published in the *International Journal of Sports Medicine* revealed that men who consumed the most fat also had the highest T levels. To protect your heart and preserve your T, eat foods high in monounsaturated fats, such as fish and nuts.

Push away from the bar. Happy hour can wreak havoc on your manly hormones. In a Dutch study, men who drank moderate amounts of alcohol daily for 3 weeks experienced a 7 percent decrease in their testosterone levels. Limit your drinking to one or two glasses of beer or wine a night to avoid a drop in T.

Stop stress. Mental or physical stress can quickly depress your T levels. Stress causes cortisol to surge, which "suppresses the body's ability to make testosterone and utilize it within tissues," says Zava. Cardio can be a great tension tamer, unless you overdo it. Injuries and fatigue are signs that your workout is more likely to lower T than raise it.

meeting where another researcher, Antti Perheentupa, MD, PhD, from the University of Turku, in Finland, presented evidence of a similar decline. The Finnish results suggested the change was happening among younger men, too. A man born in 1970 had about 20 percent less testosterone at age 35 than a man of his father's generation at the same age. "When I saw another group reproducing our results," says Travison, "that was convincing to me that we were seeing a true biological change over time, as opposed to just some measurement error."

One possible explanation for the decline is obvious: Men are fatter now. In the Massachusetts study, the average 60-year-old man in 1988 was already well past overweight (a body mass index, or BMI, of 25). But his 2003 counterpart was pushing obese (a BMI of 30). And obesity, says Travison, is "a very powerful predictor of low testosterone." Gain 10 percent in your BMI and you can expect your testosterone to drop by about the same amount. As a result, fat men typically have up to 25 percent less total testosterone than their trim counterparts do. (Fair warning: This doesn't make them girly men. SHBG—the stuff that locks up half your testosterone—also decreases with obesity. That means even a fat man with low total testosterone may have enough of the bioavailable stuff to crush you between his manboobs.)

Taking multiple medicines also tends to decrease testosterone, and a quarter of the Massachusetts test participants were practicing "polypharmacy"—taking six or more medicines at the same time. This was partly because the test group had aged. But in tandem with the obesity epidemic, participants also seemed to be experiencing an Rx epidemic. In 1988, 38 percent of the men were not taking regular medications. By 2003, not one man could make that claim.

Still, obesity and polypharmacy together weren't enough to explain the loss of testosterone. Nor was the dramatic decline in smoking among participants, though quitting can sometimes cause a decrease in testosterone. To filter out these effects, Travison's group looked at a subsample of 500 nonsmokers who were neither obese nor taking a large number of drugs. And even these apparently healthy men displayed the same exaggerated decrease in testosterone.

THE *MH* TESTOSTERONE TEST

When researchers at ZRT Laboratory, in Beaverton, Oregon, tested the testosterone levels of more than 8,000 men, they found that T peaked in the men's early twenties and sharply declined after that. Three *Men's Health* magazine staffers gave saliva samples to ZRT to check their levels. Each of them scored within or above the normal range for men (between 44 and 148 picograms per milliliter; multiply by five to approximate blood levels of T) and above average overall. A simple spit test can determine how you stack up. Ask your doctor.

Scientists have been arguing for years about whether they are seeing a worrisome pattern in male reproductive-health problems around the world—and also about whether environmental factors are to blame. Fertility, which moves in tandem with testosterone, has dropped not only in industrialized nations like Sweden, but also in Sri Lanka, without any apparent change in contraception or abortion rates. Increasing numbers of boys are being born with genital abnormalities, including undescended testicles and urethras that exit in odd places along the penis. In Denmark, 40 percent of young men have a subnormal sperm count, and the rate of testicular cancer is among the highest in the world. In the United States, testicular cancer has recently become the most common malignancy among Caucasian men ages 15 to 35. Some researchers have grouped these developments together as "testicular dysgenesis syndrome," or TDS, with "dysgenesis" meaning abnormal development of the male organ.

Plenty of experts question the evidence of such a syndrome. But Mitch Harman, MD, PhD, an endocrinologist at the University of Arizona College of Medicine and the director of the Kronos Longevity Research Institute, sees the shadow of Silent Spring. Back in 1962, when Rachel Carson published her environmental classic, estrogen-like substances in the insecticide DDT were making eggshells so thin that they were crushed by nesting parents; populations of eagles and other large birds plummeted. And today? Dr. Harman says, "I'm concerned that we're just pouring chemicals out into our environment that are endocrine-suppressing, estrogen-like compounds," possibly causing similar disruptions in human reproduction. The authors of a recent article in the *Medical Journal of Australia* likewise suggest that from early fetal life onward, male hormonal and reproductive functions are under "xenobiotic attack," meaning chemicals not naturally found in the body appear to be disrupting normal biological development.

For instance, 90 percent of American men have evidence of chlorpyrifos in their urine. This shouldn't be surprising, because 19 million pounds of the stuff was distributed across the United States in 1999 alone, much of it in household products such as tick-and-flea powder for pets, lawn treatments, and common insecticides. Though residential use is now restricted, chlorpy-

NINE WAYS TO KEEP YOUR BALLS IN PLAY

Toxins such as PCBs and dioxins not only slam the environment, but they also hit you below the belt by reducing your sperm count and lowering your testosterone. Here's how to safeguard your manhood.

Wear a dust mask. Old stone or cement walls—especially caulking from the 1960s and '70s—can release dangerous levels of PCBs when pulverized. As you breathe in, your testes can deflate.

Eat saltwater fish. PCBs and dioxins accumulate faster in bluefish, striped bass, and farmed salmon, because the fatty tissues absorb more toxins. Put wild salmon, skipjack tuna, or black sea bass on the menu instead.

Avoid sex toys and fishing lures. Gelled rubber—which makes fake worms and vibrators squishy—contains phthalates that can enter the body, decreasing semen quality in men. To be safe, swap in real worms in fishing, fingers and tongue during sex.

Support clean-water laws. Environmental groups such as Robert F. Kennedy Jr.'s Waterkeeper (waterkeeper.org) have the balls to protect yours. His group helped force General Electric to spend millions to clean up PCB contamination along 40 miles of New York's Hudson River.

rifos is still common in agriculture, as well as in some professional applications; for most people, diet is now the main source of exposure. In a recent Harvard study, men with the highest chlorpyrifos exposure typically had 20 percent less testosterone than those with the lowest exposure.

Carbaryl is another possible culprit. Detectable levels turn up in 75 percent of American men, and having it in your urine appears to be associated with reduced sperm count and liveliness, or motility, as well as increased DNA damage. And yet we still apply carbaryl to lawns and gardens at a rate of up to 4 million pounds a year, mostly by way of an insecticide known as Sevin. There should be a bumper sticker: Honey, the lawn shrunk my testicles.

Phthalates are also everywhere, almost certainly including your own body.

Toss old lawn treatments. In 2002, the EPA banned the sale of residential products with chlorpyrifos, an organophosphate proved to reduce testosterone in men. Time to dispose of (properly) the old weed killer. Industrial use is still okay; pay heed if the sign says "Keep off the grass."

Protect the pregnant. Women exposed to endocrine disruptors such as PCBs, dioxins, and phthalates give birth to male babies with higher rates of birth defects such as cryptorchidism (undescended testicles), hypospadias (malformation of the penis), and testicular cancer.

Buy a new bike seat. Narrow seats put pressure on your perineum, causing erectile dysfunction. Buy a seat that transfers pressure onto your hip bones during practice rides, and save the narrow saddle for race day.

Shop at the organic market. Pesticides are like debt: a little a day, over time, can develop into a big problem. Sidestep these testosterone killers by buying organic produce or growing your own testicle-friendly fruits and vegetables.

Read the ingredients list. A small study has shown a connection between lavender and tea-tree oils in cosmetics and the development of breast tissue in boys. Avoidance may be the best policy for now.

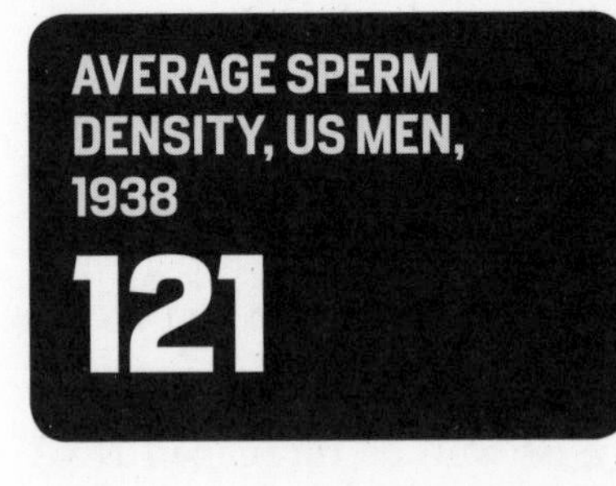

Manufacturers use them in colognes and cosmetics and as softeners in plastics. Baby bottles now come "phthalate-free," but hospital intravenous bags generally don't. And yet some phthalates seem to have all of carbaryl's unpleasant associations with reproductive health. And not just in men: Last year Greenpeace issued a warning against the danger of phthalates in your girlfriend's sex toys. Then the Danish Environmental Protection Agency came riding to the rescue, declaring such toys safe—as long as she keeps it to an hour or less a day.

Scientists can't say whether any of the suspect chemicals actually cause the reproductive effects that are occurring. They can only point out troubling associations. But these associations seem to be proliferating. About 50 new chemicals come onto the market weekly, says Dr. Harman, and while testing for carcinogenicity is required, "there's no systematized testing for subtle endocrine effects."

We're not likely to have good answers anytime soon. The reproductive problems of human males will remain understudied, says Dr. Harman, in part because federal research dollars are being diverted to issues such as biological warfare and terrorism. "We might just wind up disappearing from the planet quietly," he says, "because we were too busy fighting wars to figure out that our reproductive systems were going south."

All this could make testosterone therapy a more likely part of your life as you age. Demand is already booming. Last year, according to IMS, a pharmaceutical information company, U.S. doctors wrote more than 2.5 million testosterone prescriptions, and the market was worth more than $500 million to pharmaceutical companies. That's double what it was 5 years ago. If the decline in testosterone levels turns out to be real, the market could easily double again, with 6 to 12 percent of men in some age groups likely to qualify as "hypogonadal," to use the medical profession's distinctly depressing term. (Loosely translated, it means "tiny testicles.")

Misuse of testosterone-based steroids to build muscle is booming. It's already twice as common as heroin abuse among U.S. 12th graders. Baby boomers have also latched onto testosterone therapy as an antiaging remedy, despite a dearth of supporting evidence.

AVERAGE SPERM DENSITY, US MEN, 1964

97

At the same time, Australian andrologist David Handelsman, PhD, worries that doctors are failing to diagnose cases of genuine testosterone deficiency, resulting in "lifelong consequences" for younger men. As a result, testosterone therapy "suffers simultaneously from both overuse and underuse." And yet evidence about whether such therapy is safe or effective is "shockingly weak," says the Mayo Clinic's Victor M. Montori, MD. "There is no way for physicians to be certain when prescribing testosterone that, on average, it's doing more good than harm."

So is it safe to use testosterone therapy, even under a doctor's care? Does it cause prostate cancer, as some suggest? Here's where the debate stands now: First, the fear isn't that testosterone will cause prostate cancer. It's a natural product of the human body, and no evidence anywhere has ever shown it to be a carcinogen. Scientists worry instead that adding testosterone may fuel the growth of small cancers that already exist, undetected and harmless, in the prostates of many older men.

The only reliable way to gather scientific evidence on the prostate-cancer question would be the sort of large-scale, long-term study endocrinologists have tried and failed to get the government to undertake since 1999. That's roughly the same period in which testosterone use doubled in this country. So men are, in effect, undertaking the same experiment themselves, on their own bodies—haphazardly, and with no way to track the results.

The debate over testosterone levels was kind of a parlor game for me when I started researching this article. I'm married, a father of three, and neither overweight nor a smoker. I lift weights, and I row crew 6 miles a day in season. My appetites and my outlook on life have always seemed healthy. It never occurred to me that my testosterone levels might be low. Using testosterone therapy to

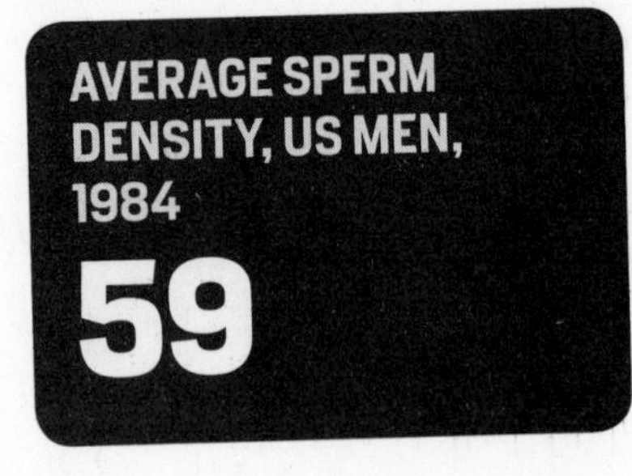

prolong the illusion of youth made about as much sense to me as hair plugs.

Then I had a blood test, and my total-testosterone level came back way low. It looked like the batting average of an okay hitter in a bad month near the end of his career. Suddenly, I listened a little more sympathetically when Abraham Morgentaler, MD, an associate clinical professor of urology at Harvard, started making the case for testosterone-replacement therapy. "What's amazing to me is the passion this testosterone issue generates in people," he said. "There are a couple of issues that come up. 'Why can't we just age normally? Why do we have to have 70-year-old men chasing their wives like they did when they were 25? Why can't they just be 70?' And I think it's the most ridiculous argument. Bad vision is age related, as are bad hearing, bad joints, bad hearts, bad blood vessels. Even cancer is age related. We treat all these things so we can live longer or happier. And the change in hormonal levels? If it's treatable and the therapy is safe, reasonably speaking, why would we want to withhold treatment from somebody?"

The case for considering testosterone therapy became even more compelling this past summer, when researchers at the University of California at San Diego released results from their long-term study of men over 50. Participants whose testosterone levels tested low in the early 1980s but who were otherwise healthy had a 33 percent higher risk of death over the following two decades. Another study, from the University of Washington, looked at men over 40 who already had health problems and found that low testosterone dramatically increased their risk of death.

But I didn't immediately try to alter my T levels. (See "Become Mr. T" on page 242 for natural ways to do it.) The standard medical guidelines for treatment are strict. I qualified on the first count: "unequivocally low serum testosterone levels." But I didn't have "consistent symptoms and signs" of low testosterone.

For doctors who take the conservative approach, the symptoms that matter most are physical changes, such as shrinking of the testicles, development of breasts, a decrease in spontaneous erections, or a loss of muscle bulk and strength. Doctors who take a looser approach often recommend therapy to men with the sort of complaints almost everyone experiences at some point: "Do you tire more easily? Is it more difficult to get and stay in shape? Is there less desire to exercise? Have you lost some of the zest for life?" I didn't fit either set of symptoms.

AVERAGE SPERM DENSITY, US MEN, 1996

38

Given the nuances involved, anybody thinking about testosterone therapy needs to consult a specialist. My doctor, an endocrinologist, pointed out that, despite the low total testosterone, my free testosterone was normal. He also discovered a slight thyroid hormone deficiency, a potential cause of low testosterone. So while he wasn't ruling anything out, it didn't look like T-time just yet.

Those are the kind of judgments a lot more men will be making over the coming years, as the population ages and further evidence comes in on health and reproductive issues. For some men, both young and old, testosterone therapy will seem like a miracle, a second chance at life as a man. But the effects can also vary dramatically from one person to the next. So for other men, it won't make much difference at all. "I'll be 64 in April," says one endocrinologist, whose total testosterone is "sky high" at 640, "and I don't feel the same as I did when I was 44. There's more to aging than hormones."

So which are you? And what should you do? A good doctor is the place to start, but even doctors have no certain answers, and your government has guaranteed doctors won't get answers for decades to come. So when it comes to doing the right thing about testosterone, the truth is that you're pretty much on your own.

The question remains: Are you man enough right now? Will you be, 10 years from now?

HAVE AN EXTREME BEDROOM MAKEOVER

EVERY LOVE LIFE NEEDS A LITTLE RENOVATION. OUR WRITER HEADS TO A SEX CLINIC AND DISCOVERS THE TOOLS FOR TURNING HER FIXER-UPPER INTO THE RELATIONSHIP OF HER DREAMS

BY LESLIE GOLDMAN

My husband and I make out in bars, grope each other on the couch, and generally screw with enthusiasm. So while our sex life is anything but broken, it could be even hotter. Allow me to elaborate.

Gripe No. 1: I believe I should orgasm faster than a 14-year-old boy with a copy of *Maxim*. When I can't, I give up. Gripe No. 2: Dan and I have different schedules, which means I'll return from a late workout, endorphins blazing, just as he's polishing off a chihuahua-size burrito. The really embarrassing bit is Gripe No. 3: Despite being a professional body image speaker and author, I'm as self-conscious about my butt as Nora Ephron is about her neck. When naked, I insist on walking backward away from the bed in a sort of modified grapevine, terrified that my husband (!) will catch a glimpse of cellulite.

Sex therapy may be an obvious fix, but I'd always pegged it as one of those things normal people don't do. I'd never even considered it, until the magazine asked me to write about the Berman Center, a Chicago clinic run by Laura Berman, PhD, aka the Dr. Phil of getting your freak on. Apparently my misgivings gel with popular opinion: "I've found that 50 percent of people are not satisfied with their sex lives," Berman says. "But only 10 percent of men and 20 percent of women seek help." Well, change begins with me, so I e-mail my concerns to Berman, and she recommends I sign up for an intensive 3-day retreat that will address everything from sexual inhibitions to stress management. Which brings me to . . .

DAY 1: 9 TO 10 A.M.: Q&A WITH THE SEX SWAMI

I meet Berman in her brightly lit downtown office, which looks more like a spa than a medical institution. Sitting in a red chair, her blonde hair held back with a black headband, Berman makes eye contact, shoots me an easy smile, and hands me a binder filled with my personalized schedule, a journal, and a slew of questionnaires, including a "depression inventory" and a "genital image scale." Holy crap, what have I gotten myself into?

I sink into the couch and set my water glass down on a kitschy "more medication, please" coaster. Before I know it, we're discussing my sexual background (four male partners plus a short-lived stint of drunken heteroflexibility that culminated in my waking up with a raging hangover and a naked 21-year-old named Valerie); the cues I received about sex and love from my family (tons of laughter and affection, no divorces, and "Put an aspirin between your knees and never let it fall" from my father before every high school date); and how Dan and I ultimately came to be (8 years of best-friendship followed by his dogged pursuit). It's a lot to cough up so soon, and just as we really start to dig in, she tells me we have to stop so that I can get to my Tantra lesson.

Tantra lesson?

11 A.M. TO 1 P.M.: BOOTY BREATHING

To help me rethink my orgasm-centric mentality, Berman has sent me to the TantraNova Institute, a Chicago clinic that teaches "the ancient art of sacred Tantric sexuality." I'm greeted by "beloveds" and business partners Elsbeth Meuth, EdD, 58, petite with ultra-short blonde hair and a thick German accent, and Freddy Zental Weaver, 51, a towering, handsome man with rich, chocolate brown skin. They lead me into a studio filled with candles, silk pillows, and a floor-to-ceiling painting of a figure with seven chakras ablaze. (For those of you who don't have the token yoga-obsessed friend, chakras are "energy centers" that run roughly from the base of the spine to just above the head. They're associated with a wide range of physical and mental states—the throat chakra with communication, the heart chakra with love, and so on.)

I sit cross-legged on the floor; the Tantric duo faces me. Freddy guides us through a meditation exercise. His voice is so smooth I can't believe it's not butter. As we inhale, Elsbeth explains the importance of breath: By circulating it through our bodies, we create energy, enhancing sex and, for the truly practiced and fortunate, paving the way to whole-body orgasms.

My homework, Freddy tells me, is to "self-love," perhaps the most PC term ever for masturbation. But orgasm is not the goal. I should encounter myself as my own lover, setting the scene with flowers, music, oils. The purpose of this exercise, Elsbeth explains, is to enjoy the sensations rather than rushing to completion. After caressing my hands, arms, and stomach, I may wish to move on to my "yoni" (Sanskrit for "cooch"). "Start by massaging her," Freddy encourages as I scribble down notes. "Dance on the edge of orgasm." I want to blurt out, "Didn't I see that in a Hallmark card?" but keep mum, engrossed in thoughts of tonight's assignment. Before my yoni gets any self-loving, though, I need to cab it back to Berman's to meet my husband for our first and only couples session.

1:45 TO 3 P.M.: DAN, ENTER STAGE RIGHT

"So, Dan, how would you classify your sexual relationship?"

My guy is such a sport. He really didn't want to air our sexual laundry on a national clothesline, but he's so supportive of my career—and our relationship—that he folded. He opens up to Berman immediately, describing it almost exactly as I would. "We're happy, extremely affectionate . . . lots of kissing and cuddling." He concedes that we are intimate less often than we used to be, due to dueling schedules and his back injury, and that he'd like to get it on more often.

We brainstorm ways to become more sexually proactive. Berman suggests scheduling sex, but we deplore the idea of PDAing our PDA. She counters, "Most young couples today have to make a paradigm shift: Instead of saying, 'Ugh, scheduling sex is a chore,' make it something you can look forward to." Or we can encourage nooky to occur more organically by freeing up time at night. I need to set boundaries between my work and personal life, Dr. B.

explains, for the sake of my mental and sexual health. Can I put aside 2 hours at night with no work? I balk. "Think about it as productive time for your relationship and it won't feel so gluttonous," she says. We compromise on an hour.

Then she brings up the rear: "What do you think about her butt issue?" she asks, looking at Dan.

He laughs, describing it as firm and strong, but I blurt out that he's lying, and before I know it, I'm crying. This is ridiculous. I was anorexic in college but have been recovered for more than a decade.

Berman posits that my caboose complex is a remnant of self-loathing I experienced with my eating disorder. For tonight I am assigned the charming task of standing before him, naked and ass-backward. Oh, and to have sex, too.

8 TO 9 P.M.: I TOUCH MYSELF

That night, I am surprisingly psyched for self-love. I close the bedroom door and cue up Sade. A citrus tea light twinkles from my dresser, guiding my way toward the bed, which I've covered with an old beach towel to protect the sheets from massage oil.

I take a few deep breaths and am ready to love all my 2,000 parts. "Smooth Operator" plays in the background as I stroke my arms, discovering that my wrists are pleasingly sensitive, especially when lightly tickled. I drizzle more oil over my stomach and breasts and enjoy dreamy rubbing for about 10 minutes. I know orgasm isn't the goal of this assignment, but a vibrator beckons from my bedside drawer, so I succumb, self-loving myself three times in a row. Bad student! I was supposed to massage my entire body but skipped my legs, back, and butt. I should have paid more attention to the directions rather than jump to my fast and furious conclusion. Obviously, this is an area I need to work on. But, hey, it was much easier to climax after all that caressing.

10 TO 11 P.M.: BRINGING SEXY BACK

I steel myself for the butt exercise. I position Dan on the edge of the bed, proudly presenting my front half—I love my perky breasts and toned stomach.

I don't know what scares me more: that my man, who loves me unconditionally, might be turned off, or that I might realize he really does love all of me—and then what will I have to obsess over? After a few frustrating minutes I say, "F@&! it," and rotate. Words like "cellulite" and "nutcase" zap through my mind. Dan kisses my back and whispers I am beautiful. We wind up having a nice heart-to-heart in bed, during which he gently confronts my perfectionism, asking me whether I would love him less if his butt were, say, not up to Brad Pitt standards. Okay, he's got a point. He kindly calls supermodel Gisele "an airbrushed freak," and because we're already horizontal, we switch off the light and continue the oral conversation.

DAY 2: 9:30 TO 10:30 A.M.: Q&A, TAKE TWO

I recount the butt experiment to Berman, explaining how caring Dan was and how hypocritical I, as a body image speaker, felt having to admit this eating disorder leftover. She explains that with my perfectionist tendencies, my tush is symbolic of my need for control. "When you have really high expectations—of how you look, what you're supposed to accomplish, how you do at work—you set yourself up for failure and disappointment," she says. Same goes for orgasms: If they're not happening right now, I think I've failed. Ironically, the more someone worries about climaxing, the more stress it creates, Berman explains. "An orgasm is the epitome of letting go." I need to be easier on myself and relinquish control.

This is starting to resemble conventional therapy, and I suggest we focus more on sex. Berman smiles firmly and shakes her head no. "Who you are is the sum of your life experiences—psychological, emotional, and sexual." While sex therapy, in its purest form, addresses sexual challenges in a relationship by helping you relearn behaviors, Berman likes to intertwine it with general as well as couples therapy, which explores the inner workings of the relationship.

My hour of psychoanalysis flies by in what feels like 10 minutes, and it's time for me to shut up and dance. Enter Miss Exotic World 2005, Michelle "The Ass That Goes Pow!" L'amour.

2 TO 3 P.M.: BURLESQUE IS BEST

I warm up in the Berman Center yoga studio, swiveling my hips to drum-thumping music with L'amour, 27, a tiny, hazel-eyed brunette. You might think you'd be too shy to faux-striptease with a total stranger, but that's because you've never met L'amour. She's like the straight-talking love child of Eartha Kitt and Shakira, sexy and unassuming in a pint-size package. She hands me a pink boa and satin gloves and shows me how to shimmy, to "present" my breasts (by cupping and lifting from beneath), and to tug my gloves off with my teeth. We talk about how burlesque appeals to women because it explores different definitions of "sexy": intelligent, humorous, playful. She describes it as "a very encouraging way to showcase curves." I can see why Berman has clients with body image issues try it. L'amour runs me through my routine once more and sends me home to show my husband some T&A.

11 P.M.: MEET THE NEXT PUSSYCAT DOLL . . . MEOW

Back home, Dan is waiting for me in the living room while I check myself out in the bathroom mirror. Black push-up bra, check. Matching thong, check. Gloves, check. Pink Hello Kitty boa from my 30th birthday party, check.

As "Fever" plays from my computer, I totter over to the couch in my patent-leather heels, a nervous smile plastered across my face. But I channel my inner Dita Von Teese and begin with a slow hip rotation, stroking my boa and sliding my satin gloves down my neck and around my breasts. I even do the move where I turn around, bend over, and slap that ass. I end up straddling Dan's lap. He has enjoyed the show. And even though the elaborate moves were seductive, he says the best part was seeing my near-naked body.

DAY 3: 10 A.M. TO NOON: FINAL SESSION

Back at the center, the topic of the day is control. Berman suggests that the control freak in me might surrender if Dan were extra-aggressive in the bedroom. In fact, she says, the most common fantasy women have is feeling powerless. Because I feel safe with Dan, I can give up the wheel and enjoy the ride. This will be therapeutic, Berman promises, so I deviously plot charging handcuffs and a whip to his Flexible Spending Account.

I dash off an e-mail to Dan—Subject: Your Mission, Should You Choose to Accept It—and stop at Freddy and Elsbeth's for a rousing round of Kegels, designed to enliven my sexual center and enhance orgasm. We do them together, chanting, "Squeeze, release, squeeze, release." It's Genital Jazzercise! They encourage me to do these every day: in the car, while writing. Soon my vagina will drop a size and crave protein bars.

Feeling tingly, I return home. I can't wait for tonight's hard-hitting homework assignment: caveman sex.

10 P.M.: NEANDER-THRALL

We're snuggling harmlessly in bed, and I get up to pee. When I come back, the room becomes a blur of bathrobe, boxer shorts, and bed sheets. Next, I'm against the wall, arms pinned overhead. Then I'm launched through the air, landing on a pile of pillows. Now I'm on my knees—but despite prior concerns I'm pretty sure my ass looks great. The sex is rough, and after all this talking and reflecting, I can finally let go and say, "Ahhhh."

TUNE-UP CENTERS

Overhaul your sex life at these clinics.

The American Association of Sexuality Educators, Counselors, and Therapists can help you find local certified sex therapy practitioners. Visit aasect.org.

CENTER	EXPERT	SPECIALTY	CONTACT	COST
The Berman Center	Laura Berman, PhD	Customized 3- or 5-day retreats for couples, singles, or women-only groups	800-709-4709; bermancenter.com	$500 to $750 per day
Loyola University Sexual Dysfunction Clinic	Domeena C. Renshaw, MD	Married couples undergo 7 vigorous weeks of couples counseling with a team of psychologists, gynecologists, urologists, nurses, and social workers.	708-216-3752; luhs.org/programs/sexdysf.htm	$1,400 for 7-week program
Sex and Couple Therapy Service at McGill University Health Center, Royal Victoria Hospital	Yitzchak Binik, PhD	This hospital-based program covers the spectrum of sexual, couple, and marital problems (from pain during sex to intimacy issues). Also offered: "Making Love Better," for those in good relationships who want to get even closer.	514-398-6094; sexandcoupletherapy.com	Up to $55 per session (sliding scale based on income)
The Pelvic and Sexual Health Institute	Susan Kellogg-Spadt, PhD, and Kristene Whitmore, MD	100 percent medical—pelvic pain and all types of sexual dysfunction	215-893-2643; pelvicandsexualhealthinstitute.org	$90 to $2,000 per session
Miraval, Life in Balance	Married cofounders David Taylor, MD, and Lana Holstein, MD	"Partners, Pleasure and Passion," a luxe 4-night retreat for couples in a spa atmosphere	800-232-3969; miraval-resort.com/act_sexuality.php	$6,200 to $7,300 per couple

DEFEND YOUR MANHOOD

A MAN'S REPRODUCTIVE ORGANS CAN ENCOUNTER A VARIETY OF TECHNICAL DIFFICULTIES. CONSIDER THIS YOUR TROUBLESHOOTING GUIDE

BY STEVE MAZZUCCHI

We men are a little uncomfortable with our genitals. Girls rock skirts sans undies (thanks, Britney), but most guys wouldn't dare don a kilt. R-rated movies showcase female pink parts, but they cover Borat's junk with a black rectangle. And while women have an entire area of medicine dedicated to the health of their private regions, if it weren't for the hernia check, we men would hardly drop trou at the doctor's office.

The result? When it comes to caring for some of our most critical equipment—the stuff we need to, you know, keep our species going—we're virtually clueless. And that ain't good, because a lot can happen to a man's penis, testicles, and prostate: itchiness, infection, pain, bumps, sores, growths, rashes, burning, drooping, swelling, clogging, and, hell, cancer. If you're not paying attention, you can wind up sick, sterile, or dead. With a little knowledge, though, you can cut much of the bad stuff off at the pass. Start here. These eight scenarios may make you wince, but at least you'll know what to do if they happen to you.

THERE'S AN AGONIZING PAIN IN MY SCROTUM

THE CAUSE: Assuming you weren't just kicked there, one of your testicles is probably twisted around something called the spermatic cord, cutting off the blood supply. "Think of a ball hanging on a rope," says Tony Makhlouf, MD, PhD, a urologic surgeon at the University of Minnesota medical center. "As the rope turns, it bunches, and the ball rises." This knotting—testicular torsion, it's called—instantly causes a sharp pain.

THE CURE: Head to an E.R. "If it isn't treated within 4 hours, you can lose a testicle," warns Larry Lipshultz, MD, a professor of urology at Baylor College of Medicine. "Why take a chance?" The docs at the E.R. will do an ultrasound to assess whether your testicle and cord are indeed twisted. If that's the case, a urologic surgeon will be called to untangle things. Then he'll suture each testicle to the inside of your scrotum to prevent the torsion from happening again.

THERE'S A SLIGHTLY LESS AGONIZING PAIN IN MY GUYS

THE CAUSE: The coiled tube that carries sperm from your testicles has probably become inflamed due to a bacterial infection. The most common culprits are gonorrhea, chlamydia, and, in men over 40, a urinary tract infection that migrated. The testicles themselves can also become inflamed.

THE CURE: Don't just pop some Advil and try to tough it out. "If you don't treat it, the tubes can become scarred and blocked," says Dr. Makhlouf. "You could become infertile."

So see your doctor, who will probably prescribe at least 2 weeks on an oral antibiotic to tackle the bacteria. Swelling and pain should begin to lessen within 3 days, but it could take months for all symptoms to subside.

IT FEELS LIKE MY SCROTUM IS A BAG OF WORMS, AND MY GOOLIES ARE DROOPIER THAN SOPHIA LOREN'S BUSTLINE

THE CAUSE: Sometimes the valves inside the veins of the scrotum don't close properly, so blood pools and they swell. The resulting bundle of enlarged veins, or varicoceles, doesn't always hurt, but the extra blood warms the testes. This jeopardizes sperm production (which requires temps cooler than 98.6°F) and causes the testicles to hang away from the body. About 20 percent of men will experience a varicocele at some point.

THE CURE: "If you notice you have low-hanging fruit, see a urologist who specializes in infertility," says Harry Fisch, MD, director of the male reproductive center at New York Presbyterian Hospital and author of *The Male*

Biological Clock. He or she can stop blood from pooling by tying off the veins or blocking them. It's minor outpatient surgery, and you can have sex again in 3 weeks, although you should schedule a follow-up semen analysis in 3 to 4 months. In 60 percent of infertile men, semen quality will improve after surgery, says Dr. Fisch. Even if you're not trying to conceive, he adds, the problem should be corrected if it's painful or creates a size discrepancy between testicles.

MY SEMEN HAS A REDDISH TINT, AND IT DRIPS OUT RATHER THAN SHOOTS WHEN I EJACULATE

THE CAUSE: When infections begin to heal, scar tissue can form and create a blockage in the ejaculatory duct. "It's like a five-lane highway becoming a two-lane highway," says Dr. Fisch. The red tint is blood from the initial infection. Your ejaculate volume may drop below the average of half a tablespoon and continue to dribble like an NBA point guard after you achieve orgasm.

THE CURE: You can function with a dribbly ejaculate, but it's kind of a buzz kill. Fortunately, there's a surgical solution.

The formal term is "transurethral resection of the ejaculatory ducts," but it's simpler than it sounds. "We just scrape out the scar tissue, and that opens it all up," says Dr. Fisch. You can resume sexual activity in 7 to 10 days.

I'M 25 AND IN GREAT SHAPE, BUT I HAVE TROUBLE MAINTAINING AN ERECTION

THE CAUSE: According to the American Urological Association, about 25 percent of erectile-dysfunction cases are psychological, and it could be anything from relationship issues to performance anxiety. For example, a man may have a sexual experience after heavy drinking and fail to get it up. "In subsequent sexual attempts without alcohol, he'll remember that episode, think something's wrong with him, and be unable to perform," says Karen Boyle, MD, director of reproductive medicine and surgery at the Johns Hopkins Brady Urological Institute.

THE CURE: Once physical factors have been ruled out, try seducing her after a romantic breakfast. Your testosterone levels peak around 7 a.m., so your hormones, and your penis, will be at full attention then. In many cases, such as the aforementioned alcohol scenario, a pharmaceutical option can also offer a helping hand. "A little added self-confidence—such as receiving some extra 'lift' from Viagra—goes a long way in this arena," says Andrew McCullough, MD, director of sexual health and male fertility at the New York University medical center.

If all else fails, seek counseling to address the underlying psychological issues.

I HAVE AN ITCHY RED RASH IN MY GROIN AREA

THE CAUSE: If it's on your thighs, it's often tinea cruris (aka jock itch), a fungus that thrives in warm, moist environments such as, say, gym shorts that haven't been washed since the Clinton administration. If it's bright red and right on the penis, it may be a yeast infection, which can be passed from women to men through unprotected sex.

THE CURE: Preventionwise, shed damp gym clothes and shower immediately after exercising, and dry the area thoroughly before dressing. For treatment, an over-the-counter medication such as Lotrimin can work wonders. "Continue using it for 1 to 2 weeks after the rash is gone to really knock it out and prevent it from coming back," says dermatologist Peter Kopelson, MD, of the Kopelson Clinic, in Beverly Hills. For a yeast infection, try an over-the-counter antifungal cream, applying it twice daily for a week. Don't treat either condition with hydrocortisone cream. By suppressing your immune system, "hydrocortisone will actually make the fungus worse," says Dr. Kopelson.

I HAVE CAULIFLOWER-SHAPED GROWTHS ON MY PENIS, A WATERY DRIP FROM MY PENIS, PAINFUL BLISTERS ON MY GENITALS, A THICK YELLOW DRIP AT TIMES, REDDISH CHANCRE SORES ON MY GENITALS, AND RAISED BUMPS ON MY GROIN

THE CAUSES: You have, in order, genital HPV, chlamydia, genital herpes, gonorrhea, syphilis, and molluscum. You haven't been wearing a condom, have you?

THE CURES: We're not here to lecture you on STDs, but there are a few new

WHEN CANCER STRIKES BELOW THE BELT

Don't be clueless. Face up to these facts and figures.

Testicular Cancer

Who's at risk: Ninety percent of cases occur between ages 20 and 54. White men and men with a history of undescended testicles are most at risk. There were an estimated 8,250 new cases in the United States in 2006.

Odds of survival: The 5-year survival rate for men with this cancer is 96 percent. If the cancer spreads beyond the lymph nodes, survival drops to around 70 percent.

Symptoms: Hard lumps or nodules (smooth rounded masses), or any change in the size, shape, or consistency of the testicles noticed during a monthly self-exam.

Treatments: The primary methods used are surgery (removal of the cancerous testicle), chemotherapy (cancer-fighting drugs), and radiation therapy (cancer-zapping high-energy rays).

Prostate Cancer

Who's at risk: More than 65 percent of cases are diagnosed in men 65 or older. The risk is highest among African-Americans. There were an estimated 234,460 new cases of this cancer in the United States in 2006.

Odds of survival: More than 90 percent of all cases are discovered in the local and regional stages. The 5-year survival rate for these patients approaches 100 percent.

things you should know. First, the FDA is reviewing the efficacy of a genital-HPV vaccine, Gardasil, for men. Currently, guys can get the three-shot treatment for a little over $300, says Stephen Tyring, MD, PhD, medical director of the Center for Clinical Studies, in Houston. His research team helped secure approval for the female version of the vaccine. Second, according to a CDC study, 8.2 percent of men between the ages of 16 and 24 are infected with chlamydia, but only 2.4 percent of those men have symptoms. And research by the New York City Department of Health and Mental Hygiene found that one in eight women treated for chlamydia were reinfected within

---

Symptoms: During a prostate exam, a PSA score of 0.7 or higher calls for annual PSA checks. If the PSA goes up more than half a point a year, further investigation is warranted.

Treatments: Careful observation for less-aggressive tumors. Surgery, radiation, cryotherapy, brachytherapy (radioactive-seed implants), chemotherapy, and hormone therapy for more-aggressive ones.

Penile Cancer

Who's at risk: Nearly two-thirds of cases are diagnosed in men older than 65. In parts of Africa and South America, penile cancer accounts for up to 10 percent of male cancers. In North America and Europe, it makes up just 0.2 percent.

Odds of survival: Data is limited, but the 5-year survival rate for all patients diagnosed with this cancer from 1995 to 2000 is 75 percent. The more localized the cancer, the better your odds.

Symptoms: A painless ulcer or growth; a reddish, velvety rash, small crusty bumps, or flat, bluish brown growths; and a persistent, foul discharge beneath the foreskin.

Treatments: The most common treatment is surgery. If the cancer's detected early, the surgery is a simple excision of the tumor. If detected late, part or all of the patient's penis may have to be removed.

a year. The point? If your girlfriend has had chlamydia, you should be screened and treated to avoid possibly reinfecting her. Third, "Molluscum [a viral infection] is the newest scourge we are seeing on campus," says Joel Schlessinger, MD, president of the American Society of Cosmetic Dermatology and Aesthetic Surgery. "The [raised bumps are] very contagious, and although they carry little or no risk, they can be a nuisance and require several treatments to fully eradicate." Keep one eye open, college boy.

THERE'S A BULGE IN MY GROIN AREA, AND IT HURTS WHEN I BEND OVER, COUGH, OR TRY TO LIFT HEAVY STUFF

THE CAUSE: You should have hired movers to lift that fridge. Inguinal hernias occur when part of the intestine protrudes through a congenitally weak abdominal wall. "It's often associated with a major straining episode," says Dr. Fisch, but a simple sneeze can set it off.

THE CURE: If it's small and doesn't bother you, no action may be needed. If it's growing or painful, lying down with your pelvis higher than your head can reduce the discomfort, but ultimately you'll need surgery. This will come in the form of either a herniorrhaphy, in which the edges of healthy tissue are sewn together, or the more modern hernioplasty, in which a piece of synthetic mesh is laparascopically inserted to cover the entire inguinal area. (A surgeon will recommend the option best suited to repair your particular type of abdominal-wall tear.) You'll be back to work within a few days.

UNLEASH HER DESIRE

DO I MAKE YOU HORNY, BABY? NOT WHEN THE PILL'S KILLING HER LIBIDO. HERE'S WHAT THE LATEST RESEARCH SAYS ON HOW TO GET IT BACK

BY LAUREN RUSSELL GRIFFIN

For 47 years, the Pill has given women the freedom to knock boots without getting knocked up. And while popping hormones does have its cons (such as a slightly higher risk for blood clots), you can't deny the perks: the convenience, the protection against uterine and ovarian cancers, the 99.7 percent effectiveness rate. But it turns out her trusty little OC can come with a caveat that might make her think twice about swallowing those little pills every day.

In the past decade, researchers have found that hormonal contraceptives—including the Pill, the Patch, and the vaginal ring—can dampen how often women want, think about, and even respond to sexual stimulation. And an online *Women's Health* magazine poll backs that up: They found that 36 percent of women firmly believe the Pill muffles their mojo.

Unfortunately, no official stats are available on how prevalent this problem really is. When asked to estimate how many of their patients on the Pill have suffered a blow to their sex lives, doctors' answers range from 10 percent to 40 percent—though some sexual-health specialists argue that 40 percent is a lot closer to reality. The phenomenon may be underestimated because many docs simply aren't clued in to the, well, ins and outs of their patients' sex lives.

"Sex drive is not a subject most doctors are comfortable discussing, because it's not something they learn about in detail in medical school," says Irwin Goldstein, MD, director of sexual medicine at Alvarado Hospital in San Diego. And while some European countries, including Germany, list decreased desire as a side effect on birth-control packages, there are no printed warnings about it in the United States.

THERE ARE REASONS WE BONK . . .

So, what drives your love machine? Even for women, a key component is testosterone. Women don't have enough juice to grow a goatee or develop a burning desire for an Xbox 360, but the amount they do have plays a role in their randiness, especially just before ovulation (when they're most likely to get pregnant). Every month at midcycle, women's brains signal their ovaries, which create 50 percent of the body's testosterone, to produce a surge of the lust-stimulating stuff. That makes perfect sense, given that their main biological goal is to propagate the species.

Testosterone also initiates bloodflow that causes her girly parts to become plump and sensitive. This leads to lubrication and, with any luck, one hell of an orgasm. According to the journal *Hormones and Behavior*, Canadian researchers report that women with higher levels of testosterone climax more often than those with lower hormone levels.

The problem is that daily contraceptives alter the body's testosterone production—and not in a good way. This occurs for two reasons. First, the hormones in the Pill put the ovaries to sleep, halting ovulation. Conked-out ovaries can't produce testosterone.

And what about the other 50 percent of her body's testosterone, which is produced by the adrenal glands? The Pill renders it useless, thanks to the super-potent synthetic estrogen it contains. After she takes each pill, her liver—convinced that she's consumed a potentially toxic amount of estrogen—starts pumping out a protein called sex hormone–binding globulin (SHBG). It works by glomming onto sex hormones (including estrogen, but also testosterone) like a mosquito to fly paper. As more of her testosterone glues itself to SHBG, less of it is available for her body to use. This "free" testosterone—whatever's produced that SHBG doesn't swallow up—partially determines her sex drive. In fact, a 2004 Boston University study found that subjects who reported the greatest sexual desire had higher levels of free testosterone. (Maybe that's A-Rod's problem.)

. . . AND REASONS WE DON'T

Now, even if she's been popping Ortho-Cyclen since puberty, the artificial flux might never affect her sex drive. That's because the Pill lowers testosterone in all women, but it only lowers libido in some. To demo the discrepancy, experts cite a 1995 study in which British scientists gave 150 women either an oral contraceptive or a placebo for 4 months. (All subjects were unable to conceive, either because they'd had their tubes tied or because they had partners with vasectomies.) For nearly half the women taking the Pill, sexual interest and intercourse frequency took a nosedive. However, sex drive did not stall for the others who took the drug.

"Unfortunately, we really don't know what the discriminating factor is," says Claudia Panzer, MD, a female-sexual-dysfunction specialist and endocrinologist at the Canterbury Wellness Center in Denver. But theories exist. The most popular is that nonhormonal factors help keep her sex drive in high gear. For instance, not having to worry about getting pregnant may increase her arousal and, in effect, cancel out the Pill's libido-squashing potential, says Cynthia Graham, PhD, a researcher at the Kinsey Institute for Research in Sex, Gender, and Reproduction. The adrenaline rush of a budding relationship can also override the effects of low testosterone.

BUT NOBODY LIKES A LAZY LIBIDO

If your life's missing more booty than the TV cut of *Basic Instinct*, we say it's time to play the field (of options). Ask her to ask her doctor to prescribe a different hormonal contraceptive: a new brand, a lower-estrogen pill, or the Patch. "Despite the fact that all forms of hormonal birth-control increase SHBG levels, 30 percent of women who switch somehow get their sex drive back," says Alan Altman, MD, a sexual-dysfunction specialist and assistant clinical professor of obstetrics, gynecology, and reproductive biology at Harvard Medical School. "We don't know why this happens; it may be just a placebo effect."

Or she can simply chuck her pills and see what happens. While it may not sound like the most cutting-edge remedy, it is what many doctors prescribe. "If you've determined that there's nothing else that might be impacting your sex drive, certainly the first thing I would recommend is a hiatus from

WHAT'S UP, DOC?

Need a hand bringing your sexy back? These three sites can help you find a sexual-health specialist.

aasect.org: The American Association of Sexuality Educators, Counselors, and Therapists

isswsh.org: The International Society for the Study of Women's Sexual Health

twshf.org: The Women's Sexual Health Foundation

the Pill," Dr. Altman says. Of course, ditching birth control pills is no trivial decision. Some women need the hormones to help treat medical conditions such as endometriosis or ovarian cysts. IUDs can be a long-term commitment, and messy barrier methods such as condoms and diaphragms put an end to spontaneity faster than an 80-hour workweek.

But if you decide that a hotter sex life is worth a little trial and error, suggest that she consider shelving her pills for 3 to 6 months, which should allow time for her to notice changes in her libido. With no artificial hormones swimming through her bloodstream, her ovaries will wake up from their snooze and start producing testosterone again.

If she goes OC-free and her libido's still in low gear, then the Pill probably isn't her problem. "Your sex drive is like a big pizza, and just one slice is hormones," Dr. Panzer says. Other common mood killers include depression, stress, and various prescription medications, such as some antidepressants and drugs to treat hypertension. Even antihistamines can dry out the vagina, making for painful intercourse. "And why would you be interested in sex if it hurts?" Dr. Goldstein asks.

Find yourselves a sexual-medicine specialist to help you discern the exact catalyst. (See "What's Up, Doc? above.) Just knowing what's wrong can be enough to help ease her frustration and get her excited about the prospect of putting the whoop! back in her whoopee. Once she's in the habit of generating some heat between the sheets, she'll feel more relaxed and confident—not only sexually but mentally as well. Just think of it as the sweet feeling of sex-cess.

ASK THE GIRL NEXT DOOR

THE HONEST TRUTH ABOUT WOMEN FROM OUR LOVELY NEIGHBOR

Why do women always want to fight?

I'm not going to pretend I don't know what you mean. Sometimes we crave intense emotional exchanges. We want passion from you, because passion reassures us that you're invested in the relationship. We know that men typically avoid confrontation, so if you engage, it must mean you care. If you feel like your girl is going ballistic for no reason, it may be because she's feeling alienated and wants to be closer to you but doesn't know a healthy way to get there. Women also start arguments when we're trying to communicate and our words don't seem to be sinking in. If your significant other has been yelling her head off, maybe it's because you haven't been listening. Grant her 100 percent of your attention and I'll bet she'll simmer down.

She's hung up on the fact that I'm divorced. How can I make her forget about it?

Her biggest concern is that your first marriage annihilated your faith in what pop musicians like to call "everlasting love." To convince her otherwise, you'll have to drill it into her head that, contrary to what your recent history suggests, you value commitment and hope to share the rest of your life with one person. Say it often; she won't become sick of hearing it. What she will become sick of hearing about is your ex-wife, so keep any and all mentions of the ex brief and matter-of-fact.

I like the house much neater than my girlfriend does. How can we sync up?

Complaining won't do it. Call her a slob, and she'll start ticking off a laundry list of your own flaws. The one thing we women can't resist is a straightforward, impassioned, do-it-for-me appeal. Explain that a clean, well-ordered house is integral to your happiness. That you can't think or relax when surrounded by clutter. Then ask if she'd be willing to put in the extra effort for your sake. Tell her you'd be grateful on a daily basis. How could she say no?

My girlfriend read a whole year's worth of my e-mail. Now she's pissed about stuff I wrote before we met. Help!

No matter what you may have written, you have the moral high ground. She invaded your privacy and betrayed your trust. (I mean, please—everyone knows it's wrong to read someone else's e-mail.) Don't waste your breath or validate her anger by defending yourself. Demand an apology.

My wife isn't interested in sex. How can I set up our bedroom to turn her on?

What you don't need to do is go overboard: Forget mirrors, black satin sheets, or a kiddie pool filled with Jell-O. In fact, something as simple as changing the lightbulbs may be enough to heat up the mood. Look for a 25-watt amber bulb. Amber glass casts a warm, sexy glow that will make your wife feel just a little more like Gisele Bündchen. Candles can work, too. Move any laundry, books, or other random crap off the floor and into the closet. Clutter makes us think of cleaning, which makes us reach for the DustBuster instead of you.

My new girlfriend says she's crazy about Leo DiCaprio, but I get reamed for saying Beyoncé is hot. What gives?

Here's what your woman is thinking: "Damn, Leo is sexy. I'd like to rip off his clothes, tie his wrists to my headboard, and lick peppermint schnapps from his navel. But then I'd be cheating, and I'd never do that. I wonder if he would cheat on me if Beyoncé offered to lick schnapps out of his navel. I bet he would, that bastard!" The next thing you know, she's refusing to sleep with you for a week. This is the female brain at work in the beginning of a relationship, when a girl has lingering suspicions that the guy she's dating might be a dog. Once your girlfriend is sure that the only place you'd two-time her is in your imagination, she won't care how wide your pupils dilate when Beyoncé bounces across the screen.

At what point should I slip the condom on during a hook-up?

The (only) thing I love about condoms is that they prolong foreplay. A lot more fondling and licking goes on because neither person feels like stopping to fish around in a purse or wallet. And for women, every additional second of foreplay increases our chances of having an orgasm. So the answer is, roll it on at the last minute. Take your time for added suspense.

What's a good, sexy, holiday gift that won't embarrass us both?

If you have some cash, give her a night at a gorgeous hotel where you can both forget about libido-killing holiday stress. The more posh the hotel, the sexier and less embarrassed you'll feel. Or try the new Erotic Massage Deck by Chronicle Books ($15, chroniclebooks.com). It's a sleek box of massage moves printed on loose cards. There are no graphic pics or sappy poetics, just clearly explained techniques that will put her in the mood.

AVOID RISKY BUSINESS

About 18 million men in the United States age 20 or older suffer from erectile dysfunction. According to a new study from the researchers at Johns Hopkins Bloomsburg School of Public Health, you are more likely to have erectile dysfunction if you fall into certain health categories.

A history of benign prostate enlargement: 43%

A weight problem (BMI 30+): 22%

PERCENTAGE OF MEN WITH ED WHO ALSO HAVE . . .

Prostate cancer: 93%

Diabetes: 51%

A history of cardiovascular disease: 50%

Hypertension: 44%

No regular exercise: 26%

High cholesterol: 23%

A smoking habit: 13%

PERCENTAGE OF MEN WHO CAN ALMOST ALWAYS GET IT UP:

Ages 20 to 39: 84.8%

Ages 40 to 59: 65.4%

Ages 60 to 69: 28.7%

Ages 70+: 11.2%

MAKE ENHANCEMENTS

Approach male-enhancement pills as you would salesmen at a flea market: There's a kernel of truth in what they claim, but believe only half of what you hear. "The effectiveness of those pills really depends on what you're trying to enhance," explains Michael B. Chancellor, MD, a professor of urology at the University of Pittsburgh. If you want to, say, increase the size of your manhood, as widely televised products have claimed to do, you're out of luck. Short of plastic surgery, "it's impossible to make your member any larger," says Dr. Chancellor. "You can chalk 'testimonials from satisfied users' up to overactive imaginations."

However, an overactive imagination is exactly what makes male-enhancement pills so potent for men with waning libidos. It's called the placebo effect, and a study in the *Journal of Urology* found that men given a sugar pill instead of Viagra still reported a 24 percent increase in their ability to maintain an erection.

To be fair, many enhancement pills do contain herbs that small studies have shown to enhance libido. (A report in the *Journal of Sex & Marital Therapy*, for example, found that men taking 15 milligrams of yohimbe a day saw mild benefits in bed due to improved bloodflow.) Even so, the pills' most potent quality is their influence on the male psyche, says Dr. Chancellor. "The mind is a powerful thing," he adds. "If you want something to work badly enough, it often does."

FIX YOURSELF UP

She loves you because you're not like anyone else. It's your charming quirks—bizarre enthusiasm for banjo music, the way you douse everything with Tabasco, your Sunday-morning bedhead—that make you adorable. But some physical imperfections can come between you and your happy place. Here's how to make up for the ways your bod might be just shy of ideal.

HER COMPLAINT: ROUGH HANDS

THE FIX: Make glove. The Fukuoku Five Finger Massage Glove ($60, xandria.com) houses a mini vibrator in each fingertip. Once you've high-fived your way to bliss, a lube such as Firefly Natural Moisturizing Lubricant ($19 for 4 oz, fireflylubricant.com), formulated with green tea extract and shea butter, will soften your fingers and make additional going less rough.

HER COMPLAINT: YOUR BAD BACK

THE FIX: She lies on her back, you lie on your side so your torsos are perpendicular. She lifts her legs up and over your waist. In this position, thrusting is easier on his back, says Rita Benasutti, PhD, a sex therapist in Boca Raton, Florida. Bending your knees will ease pressure on your lumbar even more, plus you'll have your hands free for extra-credit work.

HER COMPLAINT: SCRATCHY FACIAL HAIR

THE FIX: Wash and condition your beard daily, says Myriam Zaoui, cofounder of the Art of Shaving. After patting it dry, apply moisturizer to make the hair softer, she says. Try these special products made just for this purpose: Facial Wash with Peppermint Essential Oil ($22 for 4 oz), Conditioner with Rosemary Essential Oil ($20 for 8 oz), and Moisturizer with Calendula and Orange Essential Oil ($35 for 1.7 oz, theartofshaving.com).

HER COMPLAINT: SIZE ISSUES

THE FIX: If your Johnson's on the larger side, tweak missionary as follows: She keeps her legs together and straight, you straddle her thighs. Not so big? For deeper penetration in missionary, have her lift her legs straight up or

>>A MAN'S GUIDE POLL

"How would you describe your penis size?"

Massive: 7%

About average: 60%

Just right: 24%

Small: 8%

Way too small: 1%

cross them around your back, says Carol Queen, PhD, staff sexologist at Good Vibrations in San Francisco.

HER COMPLAINT: A BIG BELLY

THE FIX: Until your six-weeks-to-a-six-pack plan kicks in, work around the Buddha. When a guy has extra junk up front, his soldier has to do more than just rise to the occasion. It needs space. So set Willy free by placing a pillow under your butt when she's on top.

BRING ON HARMONY

Is your home in need of harmony? These three quick moves help bring peace.

CHANGE ONE SMALL THING. If you and your partner are always bickering about something, look for a simple way to shift the dynamic. If Wednesday is the busiest day for you both, but you end up always cooking, change the pattern: Make that your take-out pizza night.

TAKE A DEEP BREATH. Marriage researchers say that one of the keys to relationship satisfaction is to learn how to relax. It not only makes you happier but also calms your nervous system so you're less likely to overreact to perceived slights. Regular exercise, yoga, and meditation are good ways to lengthen your fuse.

SAY "PLEASE," "THANK YOU," AND "I LOVE YOU." It's easy to take the most important person in your life for granted. Go ahead and get mad once in a while, but in between, make sure you treat her with the same kindness you show your neighbors and friends.

MAKE UP OR BREAK UP?

As the host of TLC's *Shalom in the Home*, marriage counselor Rabbi Shmuley Boteach counsels couples on the brink of divorce, often after an affair, to determine whether the marriage can be saved. Although he uses a battery of tests, the most important factor he looks for is also the simplest: signs of love. Love, he says, is the only thing that will enable a couple to overcome an affair. Here, the relationship rabbi (and best-selling author of 17 relationship tomes) explains the dynamics of infidelity.

WHY DO PEOPLE CHEAT? Men generally cheat for the novelty of it and to boost low self-esteem, whereas women cheat because there's a fundamental flaw in the relationship.

HOW DOES THAT AFFECT THE OUTCOME OF AN INFIDELITY? Studies show that two-thirds of couples in which the husband cheats end up staying together, whereas two-thirds of couples in which the wife cheats end up divorcing. When a man cheats, he's looking for a quick confidence booster. But when a woman cheats, 95 percent of the time it's because of neglect. If your wife cheated, you need to ask yourself, Why did she have to find love in another man's arms?

WHAT SIGNS TELL YOU THAT LOVE REMAINS? Protective gestures, such as jumping in to defend a spouse in conversation. Perhaps surprisingly, contempt is a good indicator, too. If your wife has given up on you and doesn't love you, why would she want to show you contempt?

WHAT IF IT'S NOT THAT TRANSPARENT? Ask yourself: (1) When I get good news, who do I want to tell? (2) When I see a beautiful sunset, who do I wish were by my side? (3) When someone flirts with my wife, do I get jealous? (4) When someone criticizes my wife, do I rise to her defense? If your answers include someone other than your wife for the first two questions, or if you answer no to the last two questions, it's a sign that there's not enough love left to fix your marriage.

SPLIT, OR COMMIT?

Sometimes you have a moment of clarity about a woman—such as when you find her indexed, 7-year collection of *Brides* magazines. Other times, the signals are harder to read. Here's help.

SHE HAND-FEEDS FREE-RANGE CHICKEN TO HER DOG

Stay or go: Stay

Why: She may seem like a coddler, but dogs can lower stress and blood pressure, making her a healthier and more stable person. "Dogs make you more extroverted and outgoing," says Katherine C. Grier, PhD, author of *Pets in America*. Even if the dog fits in your pocket and has a name like Tinkerbell, playing puppy papa will improve your health, too. But when you walk it, remove the bow first.

SHE CAN'T MAKE A DECISION WITHOUT CALLING HER PARENTS, BEST FRIEND, THERAPIST, AND PSYCHIC

Stay or go: Go

Why: Her insecurity means she tells everyone about the finer points of your relationship. "She doesn't know who she really is, so how can you know who you're really with?" asks Caroline Tiger, author of *How to Behave: Dating and Sex*. If she's constantly on her BlackBerry, make her put it away for a day. If she freaks, move on.

SHE "WUVS" THE "CUTIE-OOTY" BABY TALK

Stay or go: Go

Why: "Hey, baby" isn't so bad, but the coochie-coo stuff, especially in bed, is just creepy. "She may be trying to avoid adult issues in the relationship, like problems or sex," says Tiger. It's also a mark of high maintenance. "She wants to be treated like a baby, like a precious princess plaything," Tiger says. She'll throw a tantrum when you drop her, but you'll feel good back in the adult world.

SHE DOESN'T KNOW LINES FROM *A BRONX TALE*

Stay or go: Stay

Why: Relax. So she doesn't lean over and unlock your car door. (You should have automatic locks anyway, Calogero). It's not her fault she didn't see this classic film. A Scorcese knockoff about gangsters and racism isn't exactly leading the chick-flick queue. Just Netflix the movie and watch it together. She'll get the point.

SHE OVERQUOTES HEGEL AND OTHER DEAD WHITE GUYS YOU SHOULD HAVE READ

Stay or go: Go

Why: Aside from the obvious fact that the know-it-all act is annoying, she's not comfortable in her own skin if she's cloaking herself in book smarts. Now, if she talked in movie quotes, that'd be different. Lock that one down—especially if they're lines from *A Bronx Tale*. Now yuze can't leave.

SHE'S A BOHEMIAN WHO HASN'T HAD A STEADY PAYCHECK. EVER

Stay or go: Stay

Why: The arty vibe hooked you, and it's not a huge leap to help her turn that creativity into a career. Plenty of companies need creative minds. "Tell her she'll bring art into everyday life, not limit it to the occasional gallery visit," says Rachel C. Weingarten, author of *Career and Corporate Cool.*

NAVIGATE THE BREAKUP

We enlisted psychologists and breakup experts to explain the compulsions men and women experience after a split. Here's how to ensure smooth sailing after the relationship reaches its end.

1 DAY AFTER DUMP-DAY

Protest stage: "At this point, emotions range from despair to rage to intense love and hatred," says anthropologist Helen Fisher, PhD, a relationship expert and the author of *Why We Love*.

He: Picks a fight

A University of Illinois study found that men are more likely to funnel negative emotions into physical aggression. So you're more likely to punch a wall, or a jerk at the bar. Hit the gym instead; cardio and resistance training reduce anger, fatigue, and tension.

She: Cries her eyes out

Women cry five times as often as men do, and 85 percent of women say they feel better after weeping. If you swung the ax, don't let her tears melt your resolve. If she ended it, her crying doesn't mean she's having second thoughts.

1 WEEK AFTER D-DAY

Obsession stage: An MRI study conducted by Fisher and her colleagues found that the recently dumped show elevated activity in several brain regions, including those that control obsessive thinking, anger suppression, and output of dopamine, a neurotransmitter associated with risk taking.

He: Broods

Men exhibit "verbal nonfluencies" ("uh . . . um . . . ") if they rap about the break, according to research by David Sbarra, PhD, a psychologist at the

University of Arizona. Don't dwell. Join a hoops league, or hit the road with a pal. "Men recover by doing things with peers, not by talking it out," says Fisher.

She: Justifies

Women settle in with friends. "They rely on close social networks to talk about their breakups," says Fisher. All your secrets are punch lines, your flaws fatal, and your sexual prowess panned. This is how her friends see you now. Brace yourself for their slicing glares and icy shoulders.

1 MONTH AFTER D-DAY

"Worst-is-over" stage: Researchers at the University of Virginia studied people one month after a split and found that the recently dumped were as happy as those still in relationships.

He: Drunk-dials his ex

Most breakup sufferers pursue their exes at least once, says a University of Nebraska study. Instead, vent in a journal, but keep it to yourself. "Our studies show you'll always feel worse after making contact with your ex," says Sbarra.

She: Blames herself

Even if she called it off, she's likely to blame herself for a breakup, says Melanie Greenberg, PhD, a psychologist at Alliant International University. This, coupled with loneliness, makes her miss you. Keep your distance. Play "friend" too soon and you risk prolonging her pain and yours.

6 MONTHS AFTER D-DAY

Acceptance stage: "You'll know you've reached acceptance when you wake up one morning and realize that you've gone a whole week—or longer—without thinking of your ex," says Fisher.

He: Asks out a coworker

Men achieve emotional calm a year before women. "After 6 months, you'll start returning to a state of equilibrium," says David Wexler, PhD, a psychologist and founder of the Relationship Training Institute. You're ready to swan dive back into the dating pool.

She: Seeks closure

"Women stress this fuzzy concept of closure," says Caroline Tiger, author of *How to Behave: Dating and Sex*. "It may mean telling you 'I never loved you,' or showing you she's better off without you." Either way, kill her ploy with kindness. Wish her well.

MOOD KILLER

How ironic: Her birth control could be snuffing out her sex drive, says the journal *Psychoneuroendocrinology*. Kinsey Institute researchers found that oral contraceptives lower women's testosterone levels, which could lead to fewer erotic thoughts and less interest in sex. Before and after going on the Pill, 61 women reported how often they had sex and how regularly it crossed their minds. Researchers say the frequency of dirty thoughts dropped for some after 3 months on the Pill.

If you've hit a sex-drive slump and ruled out other likely causes, ask her to ask her doc about birth control options. Pills with less estrogen may reduce the effects of decreased testosterone, says study coauthor John Bancroft, MD. (See "Unleash Her Desire" on page 267.)

PATCHED UP

For the 26 percent of women who suffer from low sex drive after having had their uterus and ovaries removed, a testosterone patch may increase libido and sexual satisfaction. In a study published in the *Journal of Sexual Medicine*, 64 surgically postmenopausal women used the Intrinsa patch for 6 months; 52 percent reported having at least one additional bed-sports session per week.

The patch restores testosterone, vital to arousal, to premenopausal levels, says lead researcher Sheryl Kingsberg, MD. It's not FDA-approved, so ask her to ask her doc about it. Also inquire about DHEA, a hormone that's converted to T in the body.

CHEAT THRILLS

Most Americans aren't bed-hopping at Wisteria Lane rates. Still, almost half of 70,000 men and women admit to having cheated at some point in their lives, according to an MSNBC survey. Researchers found that it most often happens with a friend 3 to 5 years into the relationship. Lead researcher Janet Lever, PhD, offers restless women this advice: "Consider couples therapy to try to improve deficiencies. If your husband refuses, consider individual therapy to learn how to better communicate your needs." See the survey in "He Said/She Said" below.

He Said/She Said

	HE	SHE
Have engaged in online sexual talk or webcamming	15%	7%
Have desired someone else but not acted on it	68%	43%
Would be more upset if their partner fell in love with someone else than had sex with that person	47%	65%
Would be more upset if their partner had a sexual affair than fell in love	53%	35%
Have had sex with someone else while married	28%	18%
Are glad they cheated	12%	13%

SORE SPOT

New baby? If sex makes her cry like your newborn in the next room, you're not alone. Nearly one in three women still experiences painful sex a year after giving birth, says a survey of 482 women in the *Journal of Clinical Nursing*. Not only do cuts and tears down there take time to heal, but breastfeeding puts the kibosh on estrogen production, which can lead to vaginal thinning and dryness, says Andrew Goldstein, MD, director of the Center for Vulvovaginal Disorders in Washington, DC.

To ease pain during intercourse, try a lubricant such as K-Y Intrigue, or ask her to ask her doc for a prescription for a vaginal estrogen such as Vagifem tablets, which last longer. And steer clear of progestin-only birth control pills, such as Ovrette. They make vaginal thinning even worse.

CONDOM EXCUSES

A new survey by the Kinsey Institute found that 40 percent of men reported losing an erection while putting on a condom at least one of the last three times they had intercourse. Worse, nearly half of those men removed the condom before finishing sex.

William Yarber, HSD, a coauthor of the study, suggests applying a water-based lube to the penis before putting on the condom, because it "improves the fit and makes intercourse more pleasurable." Or treat the sheathing as part of foreplay: "It becomes an arousing experience instead of an interference."

ED HELP

Sometimes erectile dysfunction can't be solved by swallowing a pill. Yet by opening your mouth, you may still find a fix. Group therapy may cure ED, concludes a new study out of Brazil's University of São Paulo. After 398 men with ED participated in four group-therapy sessions, 75 percent were able to stand tall in the sack, probably because their brains had been behind the dysfunction.

"Talking with other men with ED allows you to overcome unrealistic performance goals, as well as the social stigma of being impotent," says study author Tamara Melnik, PhD. Need a lift but afraid of a live audience? Start by finding an online support group, such as the male sexual forum at healthboards.com.

SLEEP THERAPY

Research from Northwestern University suggests a new twist on the ancient wisdom that you shouldn't go to bed angry. It should be "Don't go to bed sad"; your stress hormones will spike in the morning. In the study, more than 150 people recorded their feelings at bedtime for 3 consecutive days, and researchers measured the participants' levels of the stress hormone cortisol the following mornings. Those who went to bed feeling overwhelmed or downcast had higher amounts of cortisol than those who didn't. Elevated levels of the hormone raise a person's risk of heart disease and depression.

"If you're feeling sad and disconnected from your partner, resolve it before bed," says Emma Adam, PhD, the study's author. One way to make up: a hug. "Hugging releases oxytocin, the cuddle hormone," says Ian Kerner, PhD, a relationship therapist and the author of *She Comes First*.

PROBLEM SOLVING

Don't be afraid of conflict. Negative emotions can be good for a relationship. A study at Baylor University found that "hard" negative emotions, such as anger and contempt, helped couples instigate conflicts that led to solutions. "Soft" negative emotions, such as concern and disappointment, helped couples persevere in resolving issues.

Discuss problems promptly, says study author Keith Sanford, PhD. Start a clash by using the word "you" ("You hog the sheets"), but when it's time to resolve things, switch to the softer "I" (as in "I can't sleep when I'm cold").

LETHAL LOVE SPATS

Unfortunately, hot makeup sex won't fix this: One-sided arguments can harm your heart, according to a University of Utah study. After 150 healthy couples discussed a contentious topic—family, money, chores, and so forth—for 6 minutes, researchers performed CT scans and discovered that the men who had tried to dominate the argument had significant (and lasting) hardening of their coronary arteries. The result wasn't any better when the women flexed their power: The men on the receiving end also experienced stiffened arteries.

A seriously unbalanced argument can initiate a damaging stress response in a man's body, says lead study author Tim Smith, PhD. "Disagreements are unavoidable, but the way we talk during them gives us an opportunity to do something healthy."

MONEY 1, HAPPINESS 0

No matter how many things she has, she wants more. Brigham Young University researchers studied 600 married couples and found that when the wife was materialistic (35 percent were), both spouses were dissatisfied with their marriages.

One possible reason: The wife hassles her husband for more cash, regardless of the couple's financial standing. If she doesn't get what she wants, she thinks you failed as a husband, explains study author Jason Carroll, PhD. There is no easy fix here, but he suggests starting by "making her aware of those who have less and of exactly what you both have."

PART 6

SURVIVE RELATIONSHIPS

LUST OR BUST?

ONE EAGER LIBIDO. FIVE RISKY SEXCAPADES. OUR FEARLESS REPORTER DETERMINES WHICH DESERVE A SPOT ON YOUR HOT LIST

BY LESLIE GOLDMAN

"Drape a sheer scarf over the lampshade to create a sultry mood."

"Watch an erotic flick like *9½ Weeks* to inspire action."

Blah, boring, blah.

I've ignored such tips for revving up my sex life because, well, come on. I've sowed oats much wilder than those found in Kim Basinger's kitchen, doing the deed in public and making out with two siblings in one night—and they were not brothers.

But if these schemes are as contrived and silly as they sound, why do the experts keep recommending them? Do such simple suggestions have the power to send couples to their happy place faster than you can blurt out "French maid costume"? The magazine wanted to find out, so they sent me on a sex-charged adventure to test five intriguing but possibly overrated scenarios and report back which ones are worth trying—and which you should ditch faster than a vibrator with dead batteries.

SCENARIO #1: DO IT DOUBLE-BLIND

The last time I closed my eyes for too long during sex, I set fire to a pillow, leaving me with the knowledge that a Brita pitcher is not a good fire extinguisher. So I was hesitant about both me and my husband wearing blindfolds. But I bit the bullet and bought a pretty pink satin number for myself and a manly black one for my masked avenger (Pipedream Satin Love Mask, $8, amazon.com).

We started in the living room. But moving to the bedroom proved more challenging. I began breaststroking through the air like a charades player miming "blind Captain Nemo" until Dan took the lead and we landed on the bed, fumbling with our clothes. I headed south, arriving at what I thought was my Marco's polo but was actually his thigh. He reoriented me by planting my mouth at his navel. But I felt disconnected. Only when we kissed did the act feel familiar again. Then Dan sighed, "Oh, I wish I could see you." Way to make a girl feel good!

LUST OR BUST? The novelty quickly wore off and left me craving that visual connection. But once we tossed the blindfolds, the sex was fun, fast, and furious.

SCENARIO #2: MEET IN A BAR AND PRETEND TO BE STRANGERS

I arranged for Dan to meet me at a lounge up the street from our condo at 11 p.m. so we could play "strangers in the night." At 9 p.m., I joined some girlfriends at a wine bar to down a whole lotta Riesling—liquid courage necessary before I could don . . . The Wig. Unbeknownst to Dan, I'd decided to show up in a cascade of chest-length, sunshiny waves and tousled bangs (versus my normally pin-straight, dark blonde ponytail).

The key to picking up your partner at a bar is playing it cool so as not to ruin the mood. But upon spotting my mark through the haze of hair, I was so drunkenly excited for him to see me in all my Shakira-like glory that I stiletto-jogged over and lunged for his lips, all 6 feet of me nearly tripping over the barstool next to him. A party next to us tittered, and I realized they probably thought that, with my Amazonian height and Barbarella wig, I was a hooker or a transvestite.

Dan, poker face firm, extended his hand.

"Do I know you? My name's Billy."

Billy, I learned, had founded a nonprofit to save abandoned puppies. I was Candy, a manicurist.

We bantered back and forth for a while, painstakingly staying in character. It was frigging exhausting.

An hour in, we broke character and I admitted a dire craving for french fries. We hit the Hoagie Hut, then went home. I used up what little energy I had left climbing the stairs.

LUST OR BUST? Wearing such a dramatic wig was a blast, but as for the role playing, it was too cliché—and so tiring we didn't even end up having sex.

SCENARIO #3: PUT TANTRA TO THE TEST

I prepared for our Tantric tête-à-tête by reading *The Essence of Tantric Sexuality* ($12, amazon.com). Authors Patricia Johnson and Mark A. Michaels liken the typical orgasm to a "genital sneeze." But there has to be more to great sex than "God bless you!" and a Kleenex.

With my vagina (or "yoni") ready for enlightenment, I read aloud to Dan about "an altered state of consciousness," one achieved by prolonging the excitement phase of sex, leading to a strong orgasm with or without ejaculation.

In bed, we assumed Tantra's classic female-superior "Yab Yum" position (seated with legs wrapped around each other). Dan seemed distracted, but I assumed he was concentrating on flowing energy from his "lingam" into my yoni. We rocked back and forth. We breathed deeply. We spoke with our eyes. His cried, "I've had chronic back pain for 3 years; this is killing me!" And with that, he literally tossed me aside like a rag doll so he could execute a full-body stretch.

LUST OR BUST? A few nights later, we found ourselves Yab Yumming again (this time with a pillow behind Dan for lumbar support). And while we didn't have 6-hour sex, our foray left our "genital noses" itching, so we ended with a good old Western ahchoo.

SCENARIO #4: SURPRISE HUBBY AT HIS OFFICE DRESSED IN JUST A TRENCH COAT AND HEELS

This might work in balmy San Diego. But I live in Chicago, and the day I prepared to strip down to my birthday suit and slip into an unlined khaki trench, the newspaper headlines read, “Cold Delays Flights, Cracks Water Pipes.” Holy crap! If the minus-20-degree windchill could reroute 747s and make metal pipes burst, what would it do to my sensitive little flower?

Putting on a brave face, I undressed, goose bumps dotting my arms and legs even inside our 72-degree condo. Outside, as the wind whipped furiously, I heard a soft whimpering sound and realized it was my poor Brazilian-coiffed yoni crying for a reprieve. “It’s okay,” I whispered, turning back toward the door. “We’ll try again in the summer.” Because when your clitoris gets frostbite, the terrorists win.

LUST OR BUST? I can’t wait to try again during the next heat wave.

SCENARIO #5: WEAR A PEARL THONG FOR A DAY

The last time a semiprecious stone came this close to my nethers, it was on a hand holding a speculum. Yet I was oddly excited when I opened my K. Bella Pearl and Lace Thong ($58, kbella.com). I ran my fingers along the smooth, pinkish white strand attached to a black stretch lace waistband, wondering how something that looked so nice around a neck could be so naughty—not to mention tacky—down below.

As I pulled it on the next morning, here’s how I envisioned my day:

Walking to the bus: Orgasm #1

Crossing my legs at my desk: Orgasm #2

Afternoon Starbucks break: Orgasm #3 (Grande)

Thirty minutes on the elliptical: Priceless

In reality, my day was completely normal. The strand was mostly unnoticeable and only occasionally rubbed me the wrong way. I tried tugging on it when nobody was looking but felt pervy.

Then . . . at my gym that evening, a stability ball led to unexpected pleasures. One crunch, two crunch, three crunch, whoa! There I was, climaxing in the stretching area next to an old man doing biceps curls. More crunches yielded still more bouncing bliss.

LUST OR BUST? Sure it took all day, but it was totally worth the wait. And even though my man didn’t benefit from this scenario directly, I’m going to be greedy and give it five stars.

FIX IT UP

OUR FAVORITE SEX DOC ANALYZES THE DRAMAS OF FOUR REAL COUPLES—AND OFFERS THEM ADVICE YOU'LL WANT TO STEAL

BY IAN KERNER, PHD

True story: Ten years ago, in my first week of private practice as a sex therapist, I walked into my office to find a couple sitting on the couch completely nude. "Um . . . so why have you decided to . . . get . . . naked?" I asked, trying to regain my bearings. The husband responded, "Aren't you going to watch us have sex and tell us what we're doing wrong?" I struggled to keep a straight face. "No," I explained, "sex therapy is talking therapy. Any assignments I give you that involve sexual intimacy happen in the privacy of your bedroom." They actually seemed disappointed. Turns out they'd always wanted to have sex in front of a stranger and were hoping sex therapy would fulfill their fantasy.

I learned two lessons that day: (1) Everyone's an exhibitionist, and (2) most people don't know what sex therapists do. So allow me to share some of what I've learned over nearly a decade of successfully getting people naked (once they leave my office). These four cases—I changed the names or I'd get sued—represent the most common reasons couples book time with me. And the advice I give them will no doubt keep your bedroom fires burning.

THE CASE: SHE WANTS EXCITEMENT

THE COUPLE: Jenny and Jack, late twenties, living together

When they first started dating, Jenny and Jack got it on often and everywhere. But once they moved in together after 10 months, the dynamic shifted. While Jenny wanted to keep the novelty alive by experimenting with even more adventurous sex, Jack was content to cuddle and make love a couple of times a week. As a result, Jenny felt restless and bored, and Jack began viewing sex as a source of pressure. "She's always pushing me to do something new: sex toys, threesomes, making a sex tape," Jack complained during one session. "What happened to just making love? I want emotion; all she wants is adrenaline."

THE RX: Meet in the middle. I explained that when you're swimming in the waters of fantasy and adventure, there's a shallow end and a deep end. When two people show signs of being sexually incompatible, it usually means they have to find a midpoint where they're both comfortable. Jack and Jenny needed to find ways to share fantasies that were satisfying to both of them. They eventually decided to make love the way Jack liked it—intensely and with lots of eye contact—in front of a camera, as Jenny desired. The trick: agreeing not to watch until Jack, if ever, felt ready. Jenny was surprised to discover that the best part of making a sex tape was the imagination and role playing that went into it, not watching the results, and that they could discover plenty of thrills in their own bedroom. As for Jack, let's just say that any initial camera shyness went poof once he discovered his "inner director."

THE CASE: THEY'RE BOTH FAKING IT

THE COUPLE: Denise and Frank, mid-thirties, dating seriously

Denise and Frank prided themselves on their wild sex life, which included watching porn and acting out scenes, complete with lots of theatrical screaming and moaning. So it took a lot for Denise to confess that she'd been faking orgasms more often than Ashlee Simpson goes under the knife. But here's the double whammy: Frank had been doing the very same thing! They'd been so caught up in the performance of what they thought sex was supposed to be that neither was enjoying it.

THE RX: O-mission. Frank and Denise needed to start over. So I recommended a 30-day sex detox, which meant they could be physically intimate but weren't allowed even to think about orgasm. I also suggested they take porn out of the picture; it distracted them from nurturing a genuine one-on-one connection. Though skeptical at first, Denise and Frank eventually developed a whole new set of "sexpectations" that have nothing to do with what's playing on Cinemax and a lot more to do with their own feelings for each other. The bonus? No more faux-gasms. Denise has discovered that Frank's "tongue is mightier than his sword" and that she needs lots of leisurely foreplay to reach her high point.

Frank can let go and allow his orgasm to happen naturally now that he doesn't have to worry about Denise's. And when orgasm just isn't in the cards, neither one of them feels like they have to fake it. (Tip: If you've been pretending to hit your peak, it's best to admit it, as long as you assume some responsibility for the situation and don't lay all the blame on your partner.)

THE CASE: NOBODY'S GETTING ANY

THE COUPLE: Steve and Sara, early thirties, married

Low mojo is the number one complaint I hear from patients. When Steve and Sara first got together, they had a great sex life. But 4 years and one kid later, they were both exhausted and stressed. And because Sara no longer worked at the ad agency where the two had met and fallen in love, they seemed to have less in common. They tried to schedule sex, but the pressure it created made skipping the deed much more appealing. They came to me worried that the hots they'd once had for each other had all but fizzled, leaving them no other choice but to split up.

THE RX: Call in sick. There are two types of sexual arousal. Psychogenic arousal begins in the mind and triggers a potent neurochemical cocktail; you get all tingly the second your partner walks into the room. Reflex-based arousal is purely physical and isn't as overwhelming; you need 10 minutes of vigorous rubbing to get turned on. Most relationships start with the former and ease into the latter, which can feel like a letdown. And surprisingly, even though the problem shows up in the bedroom, the fix is outside it, where new experiences will get your sex hormones pumping again. I recommended that Steve and Sara play hooky together one afternoon every other week, during which they could have lunch at a new restaurant and maybe do some risqué shopping at a sex-toy boutique, all before it was time to pick up their daughter from preschool. They tell me that now, even though they have "naughty nooners" only once or twice a month, the anticipation every day in between has recharged their relationship.

THE CASE: SHE HAS A "WORK HUSBAND"

THE COUPLE: Claudia and Andre, early forties, married

I see more and more women involved in close friendships with men, usually

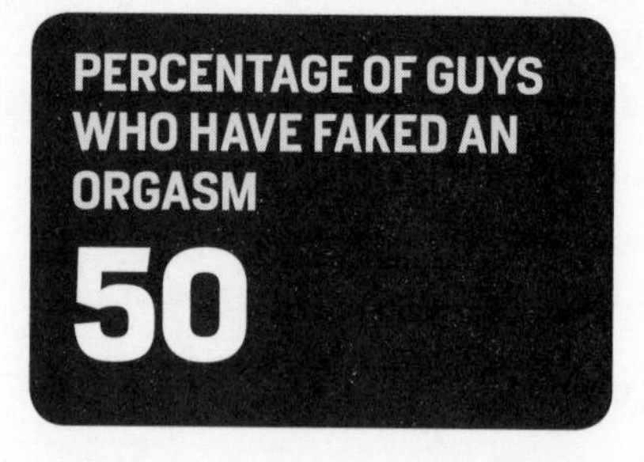

guys they've met at work. These friendships are as intoxicating as an episode of *Grey's Anatomy* but steal emotional energy you'd normally reserve for your actual beau. What happened in this situation is that Claudia began to have a flirtatious friendship with a male coworker (let's call him Lance), which she found herself hiding from Andre. She would take phone calls from Lance in private and duck into the bathroom with her BlackBerry to send him e-mails. Ultimately she spent more time discussing problems in her marriage with Lance than she did with Andre. Claudia realized it was going too far when she started fantasizing about Lance during sex with her husband.

THE RX: Make the friendship transparent. Be open with your partner about when you see your friend and what you talk about. Not that you can't have buddies of the opposite sex, but if you've got something to hide then something's potentially wrong. And never talk to your friend about problems at home, especially if you're not sharing them with your partner. When Andre got suspicious and snooped, he was doubly devastated by what Claudia had been saying about their marriage. Claudia has since requested that Lance not call her, and she doesn't exchange e-mails with him at all. By limiting her contact with Lance, she redirected energy into her marriage and is now getting more of the love and affection she craves.

NO HOLDING BACK?

Men are just as likely to fake it as women. Yep, I assure you, we can and we do. Whether we surreptitiously sweep an empty condom out of sight or pretend to fill 'er up, guys are more than capable of feigning the kind of orgasm even Meg Ryan would envy. We fake it for the same reasons women do: not wanting to hurt a partner's feelings, or wanting to feel close without necessarily being in the mood to have sex. And sometimes it's because, believe it or not, all we really want is to snuggle, watch *Heroes*, and eat Cool Whip right out of the tub.

ASSESS THE STATE OF YOUR UNION

HALF OF WHAT YOU KNOW ABOUT TYING THE KNOT IS WRONG—AND THAT'S A GOOD THING. WE UNTANGLE MARRIAGE FACTS AND FICTION AND REVEAL THE STRATEGIES THAT KEEP MEN AND WOMEN TOGETHER, HAPPILY EVER AFTER

BY ANDRÉA MALLARD

Between celeb nuptials that last a nanosecond and reality shows featuring 20 women eager to humiliate themselves for one Flavor Flav, it's easy to think that the state of marriage is imploding faster than a Mentos in Diet Coke. But when you dig into the research, it turns out our culture isn't as commitment-phobic as it seems. "Marriage has changed more in the last 30 years than in the previous 3,000," says Stephanie Coontz, a professor at Evergreen State College and author of *Marriage, a History*. And these changes are actually for the better. Whether you've taken the plunge or plan to someday, it's time to make sense of all this matrimonial madness so you're guaranteed a hot and happy union.

WOMEN ARE TOO BUSY TO BE BRIDES

Around the time you were born, most women were walking down the aisle at the same age you drank your first legal beer. Today, the median age for women at the time of their first marriage is more like 25; 27 if they went to college. If she's getting a law degree or an MBA, she'll hit the big 30 before she gets hitched. But women aren't stretching out the single life because they're procrastinating or waiting for the perfect guy to come along. Even after college, they pack way more into their twenties than their mothers did (or had the opportunity to)—getting an advanced degree, renting their first place, lining up thankless

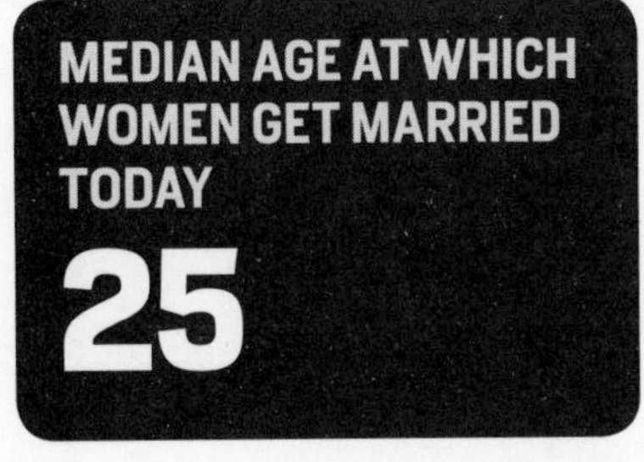

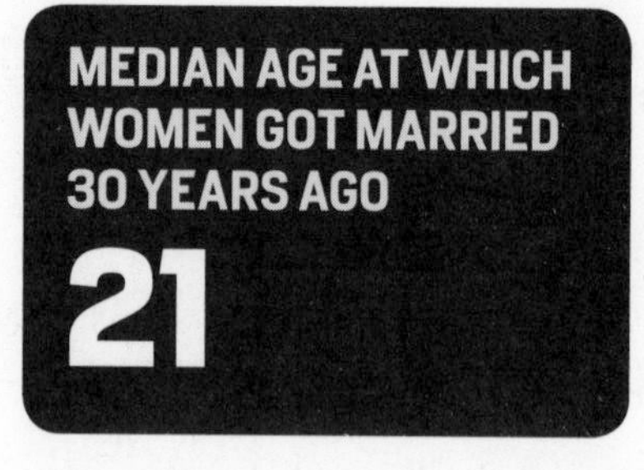

internships to pave the way to promising careers.

"Young women are postponing marriage because they're busy," says Terri Orbuch, PhD, a marriage therapist in Detroit and the project director of the Early Years of Marriage study at the University of Michigan's Survey Research Center in Ann Arbor. "The past decade has been a whirlwind of personal growth for me," says recently married Heather Harding, 31, of Toronto. "All of which I needed to experience before getting married. I went to grad school, I lived abroad, I tried on a couple of careers. Tying the knot just wasn't on my priority list in my early twenties."

GOOD NEWS: Research shows that when women take the time to score some goals before they settle down, it makes long-term happiness more likely. And, according to statistics, when women marry young (before their 25th birthday), it bumps up the risk of divorce by 24 percent. Some experts—and probably your mom—claim that with a quarter of a decade under a women's belt,

CHOOSING THE IDEAL BRIDE

Plenty of preexisting factors can lower your chances of divorce. Forget the Vera Wang dress and diamond-studded tiara; here's how to really rock down the aisle.

Hit the books. When a woman goes to college, it ups her chances of marrying and reduces her risk of divorce or separation by 13 percent. Fewer money woes and a better ability to negotiate help the relationship work.

Play the waiting game. Wait until she's older than 25 to marry, and you'll cut your chances of splitting by 24 percent. With a few extra years to explore the world and the people in it, she's better prepped to choose the right mate.

Look for a Daddy's girl. Women who have poor relationships with their fathers are more likely to divorce. Being close to Dad helps her understand men better. If hers is out of the picture, your marriage isn't doomed. Studies show that a good relationship with her husband's father can fill the void.

she knows herself better and so can choose a wiser match.

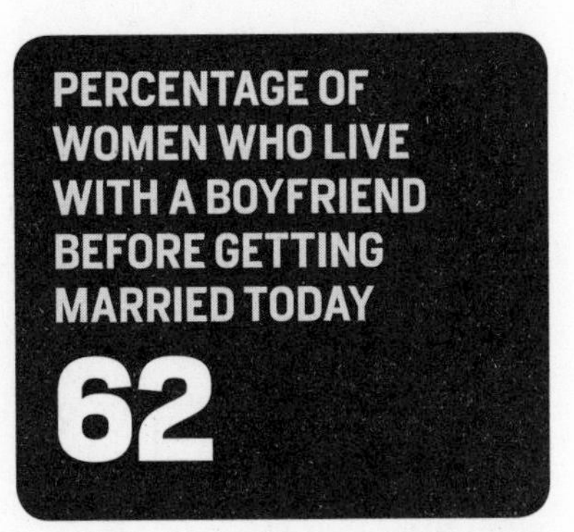

WOMEN TRY BEFORE THEY BUY

Nowadays you're a rebel if you don't swap keys before swapping rings. Mekayla Beaver, 27, of Somerville, Massachusetts, has been living with her boyfriend, Greg, for almost a year. "I expect to marry him someday," she says. "But neither of us was ready to take that step when we first moved in together." Within a few months, though, Beaver had relinquished any lingering doubts that he's the one. "It's just a matter of time before one of us proposes," she says. For most of us, living together is a dress rehearsal; 55 percent of cohabiters get married within 5 years.

Moving in with a beau does have some baggage that's worth unpacking. Research from the 1980s and 1990s suggested that people who lived together before marriage faced a higher risk of divorce—fodder for conservative groups

---

Find God. Having a religious affiliation decreases your odds of divorce by up to 19 percent—though it's likely because most religions frown on divorce, not because married believers are necessarily happier.

Ask for a raise. Couples who earn at least $50,000 a year reduce their chances of divorce by up to 34 percent. Experts believe (duh) it's because they're less likely to argue over money.

Knock her up later. Having a baby—wait to conceive for at least 7 months after you've been married—lowers risk of divorce by 24 percent. Couples who wed after procreating often marry because of the kid, not because the relationship is strong.

Marry an older woman. Marriages in which the bride is older than the groom are up to 5 percent less likely to dissolve. Experts aren't exactly sure why, but we're willing to follow Ashton Kutcher's lead on faith alone.

IT TAKES TWO

Below, 2,000 *Women's Health* devotees and 2,000 *Men's Health* fans share their opinions on getting and staying hitched.

The Big Day

58% of single men claim they'd like to seal the deal.

60% of bachelorettes want to walk down the aisle.

The Other Side of the Fence

60% of men don't feel sorry for their bachelor friends.

71% of women don't pity their single gal pals.

Living in Sin

70% of guys would move in with a woman before buying a ring.

67% of women would shack up sans sparkler.

The Marriage Bed

47% of guys aren't afraid the sex will change once they're married.

60% of women aren't worried about it either.

Who Makes Bank

9 in 10 men would let their wives bring home most of the bacon.

1 in 10 women is happy to oblige, and 1 in 5 already does.

Raising Kids

2 in 3 guys would agree to be stay-at-home dads.

1 in 3 women would rather work—even if they don't have to help with the bills.

Melding Minds

75% of men want to marry their intellectual equal.

83% of women refuse to put up with a dumbass.

Staying Together

56% of men would do anything to make a marriage work.

50% of women would fight just as hard for love.

to claim that those couples had a blasé attitude toward commitment that would lead straight to Splitsville and wreak havoc on the traditional notion of family. But newer, more sophisticated studies suggest otherwise. And because cohabitation has become so mainstream, some experts now consider it a natural extension of dating, rather than a diversion from marriage. Although it doesn't protect us from divorce, it doesn't make it any more likely.

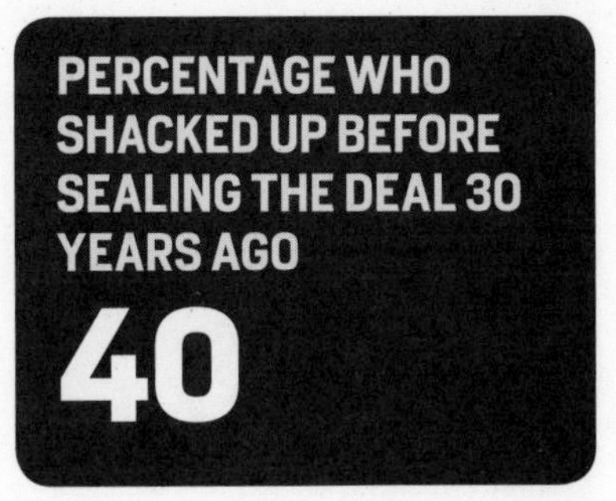

And what about that old saying that a guy "getting the milk for free," won't bother taking the next step? Not true. If anyone is going to put off marriage at this stage, it's probably the girl. "In long-term cohabitating couples, research shows that the woman is more likely to be dragging her feet to the altar—not the man," says Dorian Solot, coauthor of *Unmarried to Each Other* and cofounder of the national Alternatives to Marriage Project. Hardly surprising, given that what being a wife has meant historically—cooking, cleaning, raising kids—isn't so appealing on its own anymore. "Women want to pursue their own goals," Solot says. "And they want to be sure that getting married is going to allow them to be who they want to be."

WOMEN LOVE SEX—AND ALWAYS HAVE

Researchers say the number of Americans having prenuptial nooky hasn't changed much since the 1940s—and it didn't necessarily start then either. "Premarital sex was common in the medieval era," Coontz says, "and throughout history." The idea that our generation (or even the past few) is the first to embrace unmarried sex is hogwash. Not only did your mom do it, but there's a good chance Grandma did, too.

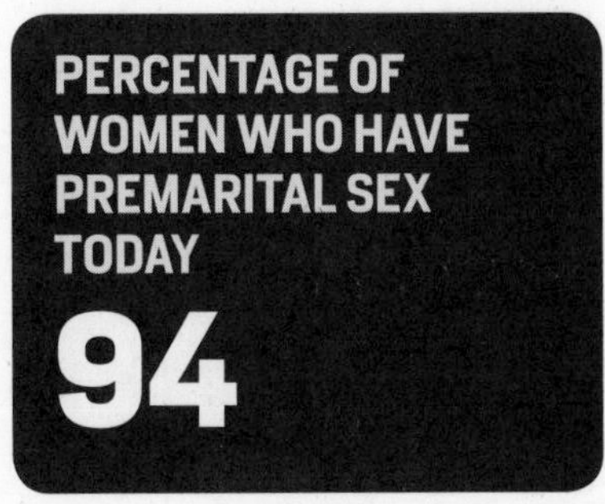

So, if we've always given in to the heat of the moment, what's changed? "Over the past

30 years women have become more comfortable owning up to their sexual desires and behavior," Coontz says. "A woman's value isn't tied to her virginity the way it used to be," she adds. "So women don't feel pressure to play the naive sexual role." This kind of openness translates into healthier sexual relationships. "Research shows clearly that today's husbands and wives report far more satisfying and enjoyable sex than couples did in the past," she says.

WOMEN ARE SMARTER, AND THEREFORE HOTTER

Back when the Doors were topping the charts, college-educated women were less likely to marry than their peers, making the old saying "men don't make passes at girls who wear glasses" pathetically true. Back then, traditional breadwinner-housewife roles in marriage were as rigid as a Botoxed upper lip. But for our generation, the girl in Armani specs and a power suit is the most likely to marry of all. "Studies show that young men today want the same qualities in a woman that were traditionally considered desirable in a man," says Jean Elson, PhD, a sociologist at the University of New Hampshire. In other words, someone smart and successful who can share the financial load. But it's about being on the same page intellectually as much as financially. "Men aren't looking for someone to play fetch anymore," says Christine B. Whelan, PhD, author of *Why Smart Men Marry Smart Women.* "They want to volley with an equal." According to her research, 71 percent of high-achieving men said a woman's career or educational success makes her more irresistible.

PERCENTAGE OF COLLEGE-EDUCATED WOMEN WHO TIE THE KNOT TODAY

94

And while it seems counterintuitive, women with degrees have the strict-est views on divorce. "In a recent study, 62.5 percent of college-educated women said getting a divorce should be tougher," says Steven Martin, PhD, a sociologist at the University of Maryland. "In the 1970s, it was 36 percent." Experts believe that because college-educated women have stronger support systems and better problem-solving skills, they're more willing to try to work things out.

PERCENTAGE WHO DID 30 YEARS AGO

70 to 80

WOMEN ARE COMMITTED TO GOING LONG

Every marriage is haunted by the knowledge that roughly one in two will fail. But your own chances of divorce aren't exactly the coin toss implied by the stats. At the time of any couple's wedding, certain factors are already present that can dramatically increase—or decrease—their odds of success. And here's an eyebrow raiser: The divorce rate isn't actually going up; it's on the decline. The high point of divorce occurred almost 30 years ago and has been inching its way down ever since. Sure, it was far lower in the 1960s, but the comparison is unfair. There's less stigma around divorce today, and it's much easier to get one thanks to laws that speed the process along. Women have greater financial power than ever and can leave a relationship more easily. And the standards for a good marriage are much higher now. "In the past, all you had to do to qualify as an acceptable husband was be a provider for your family," Whelan says. "The idea of marriage being based on love and mutual respect is very new," Coontz adds. "For most of history, it was more like a business relationship." Couples in the past didn't expect to find the partnership enjoyable—just practical.

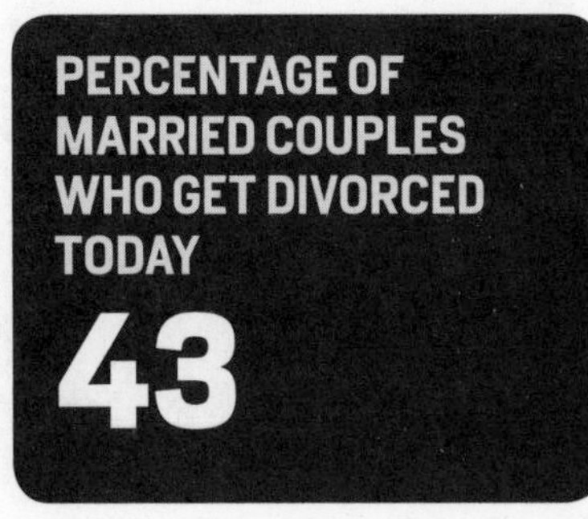

Is today's divorce rate still too high? It's impossible to tell, because no one knows what the rate of divorce should be, or whether marriages in the 1960s would have lasted had divorce been less taboo and easier to obtain. And some experts consider the current rate as

proof that our generation is uniquely committed to being happily married. "My research shows that people take marriage much more seriously now as a quality relationship," Coontz says. "And that's part of the current divorce rate. Women today believe it's better not to be married at all if the marriage doesn't meet this new standard." Which is why women are the ones to haul off to divorce court more than two-thirds of the time. Crystal Lopez, 26, of Atlanta, recently divorced her husband of 2 years. "The decision was difficult," she says. "But I see it as evidence of my commitment to marriage, not a lack of it." In spite of a long courtship, after getting married Crystal found that she and her husband had very different life goals. "I didn't want to miss out on the chance to have a fulfilling marriage in the future, and it became apparent that it would never be possible if I stayed in this one."

WOMEN ARE MORE HAPPILY MARRIED THAN EVER

Despite everything that has changed, the institution of marriage is still going strong. Yes, Bridget Jones had women freaked out for a while. But women's chances of getting married are just as good as they were 100 years ago—even if it doesn't seem that way when they're single and nearly blind from browsing eHarmony ads.

Most encouraging of all, tying the knot has become a choice rather than a necessity. It's hard to believe that just 30 years ago marriage was a woman's ticket to financial security, and dual-income families were as rare as a redneck at a Tori Amos concert. But over the past three decades, women have become better educated than men (58 percent of college students are female). And they're just as financially independent: Single women are now twice as likely as single men to buy homes, and nearly

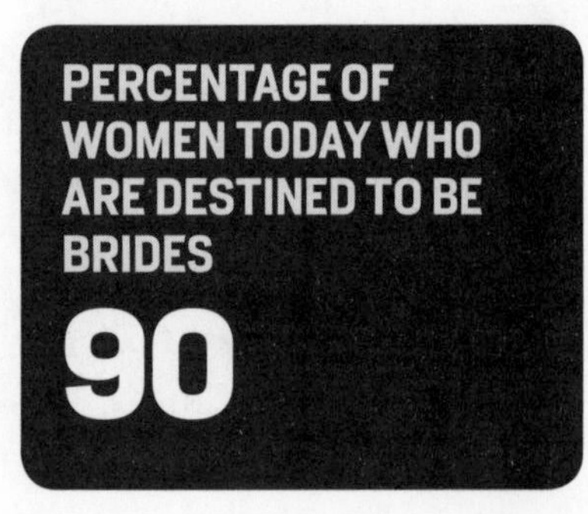

40 percent of babies are now born to unmarried mothers (compared with 5 percent in 1960 and 18 percent in 1980).

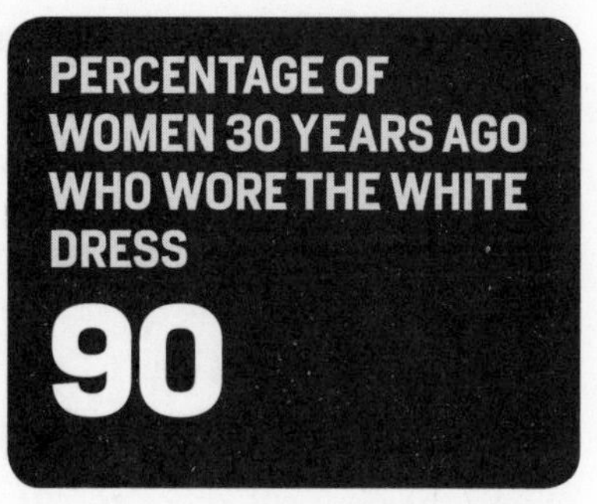

So if women can do it all themselves, what keeps them coming back? Maybe they just can't help it. "All cultures have some type of marriage ritual, suggesting that we're hardwired at the species level to want to marry," says James Cordova, PhD, a professor of clinical psychology at Clark University who specializes in marriage studies. But the explanation might be even simpler: As social creatures, humans function more effectively in teams. "We do better when we are in a positive, long-term relationship," Cordova says. "We live longer, we eat and sleep better, our immune systems function more effectively, we're less susceptible to depression, and our children are more likely to thrive." Now that women are not under as much pressure to get—and stay—married, they're more interested in the quality of the partnership. All of which adds up to powerful incentive. "As a relationship," Coontz says, "marriage is more satisfying now than at any other point in history."

STAYING POWER

Want to make your marriage last? Turn conventional wisdom on its head.

Talk less. "Love is not all about talking," says Patricia Love, EdD, coauthor of *How to Improve Your Marriage Without Talking About It.* "It's about connection." Her research reveals that while women release the bonding hormone oxytocin through talk, "men need physical stimulus to feel connected," she says. Touch him a lot a few hours before tackling big relationship issues. And don't hold back. "Men need two or three times more touch than women do to feel bonded," she says. Even if it's not sexual. "Stroke him on the arm or brush him as you walk by," she says.

Go to bed angry. Seeing red at midnight? Sleep on it. "The worst time to resolve conflict is when you're angry," says Terri Orbuch, PhD, a marriage and family therapist. Marriage researcher John Gottman discovered that conflict causes hormones to "flood" the body, which encourages us to fight harder against a perceived threat. The results—pounding heart, shallow breathing, that overheated feeling—make it tougher to concentrate on the conversation at hand. "The body needs at least 30 minutes to return to normal levels," Orbuch adds. So suck it up, tuck in, and calmly continue the discussion tomorrow.

Sweat the small stuff. Fostering a constant curiosity about each other keeps relationships growing. "And by slowing down and noticing interactions, our partners become richer and more complex," says James Cordova, PhD. "Cultivating curiosity about your partner is the same cognitive trick as slowing down to appreciate a delicious food." Just as savoring a juicy bite of steak lets you taste its complex flavors, relishing a detail about a joke your spouse made or asking about her day helps you appreciate her.

WHISPER SWEET NOTHINGS

BABYCAKES. DREAMBOAT. CORN DOG? IN THE MINDS OF MEN, TERMS OF ENDEARMENT ALWAYS MEAN SOMETHING

BY CHRISTIAN MILLMAN

The first time I called my wife "my apple blossom of a thousand perfumes," she started making noises I'd never heard before. I was reaching around her to begin the Heimlich maneuver before I realized they were simply helpless, grunting guffaws.

Maybe I was a little overenthusiastic, but this was early in our marriage, and in those heady times, sweet nothings were still really something. A weekend apart was enough to make me compose sorrowful poems. (To my own horror, I once wrote one that began, "My heart is heavier than the clientele at the Old Country Buffet.") A 6-month anniversary was a chance to write headlong haiku. And if things got a little hackneyed or trite now and then, well, it could be blamed on the recklessness of passion. But marriages change over time, and so do terms of endearment. Recently I told Michelle that I loved her like a corn dog.

Which brings up an important point: It may seem like a bit of the fire is lost in a relationship when something like this happens, but going from a fragrant flower to batter-covered meat on a stick is not a bad thing. Understanding why that is means taking a closer look at both the mechanics of a sweet nothing and the peculiarities of the male mind.

WHAT'S IN A NICKNAME?

When I composed those fanciful phrases early in our relationship, they were made of air and light, wisps of my imagination. When I told Michelle that I loved her like a corn dog, it was far higher praise than it sounds. For starters, I really like corn dogs. And so do our three sons. We've eaten them at many of our happiest times together. They are the default meal at our kids' birthdays, on visits to the state fair, and at roadside restaurants. Corn dogs have become a reminder of all those moments filled with love and laughter and ketchup.

The funny thing is, Michelle doesn't even like corn dogs. This lends still more affection to the term because it makes me think of how she pops them in the oven just for us while she nibbles on celery or a deviled egg or one of the other ingredients of a party meal.

Pet names and sweet nothings have become my linguistic shorthand, an unplanned language developed over the years that describes the state of our union at any given moment. Most of the time I call her "honey" or "babe," the pet name equivalents of gray sweatpants. There's nothing wrong with either—the problem with both comes from overuse. Too many straight weeks of "honey" is an indication that our relationship is flying on autopilot and a signal that we need to book a babysitter soon if we're going to avoid turbulence ahead. If I trot out a "Babycakes" or a "Love Puddle" at least a handful of times each month, then our relationship is going pretty well. If I make something entirely new up, things are rosy indeed.

I wish now that I had written down more of these made-up affectionate labels because I've forgotten most of the things I've called my wife over the years. If I had put them on paper, each would have reminded me immediately of that particular phase in our relationship—where we were, what we were doing, how we felt about each other. Scientists say that smell is the sense most closely linked to memory, but what if the scent is an imaginary one, made of a thousand apple blossoms? I'd argue that it's just as powerful as any noseful of Chanel.

NAMING RIGHTS

I've found that terms of endearment are generally a male specialty. Most women don't use them, or if they do, the ones they pick are pretty generic. A friend of ours calls her husband "Bud," for example, even though his name is Matt. She doesn't know where "Bud" came from. It just sounded good to her. Michelle calls me "my love" from time to time, which is sweet and all, but she uses the same term for the boys, the dog, and, occasionally, her warmest flannel pajamas.

I think it's mostly a male trait because men learn early on to express affection through pet names. We never called the guys in the school hallway or locker room by their real names. If we ran into a good friend, we used a name that was always some combination of cured cheese, the male organ, and the smell of decomposition. It was somehow easier than saying, "Hey, great game and thanks for falling back and protecting the goal when I let that guy get by me. By the way, I love you like a brother."

Even my father-in-law, a pretty conservative fellow by most measures, emotional and otherwise, was unabashed in his use of pet names. Only once did I hear him tell my mother-in-law he loved her, though he clearly did. But he had a litany of loving names for her. He usually alternated between "Hot Lips" and "Resident Love Goddess." He got the former from the TV show *M.A.S.H.* and the latter from a newspaper columnist somewhere. I'm sure there's a story behind his choice of each, but he's not around to ask anymore. He's been gone more than a year now, and my mother-in-law continues with the highly emotional process of deciding which things of their marriage to keep and which to set aside, both for healing's sake and for closet space. One thing she cannot part with: a stained and chipped coffee mug with "Hot Lips" printed on the side. To me, there's no better proof that sweet nothings really are everything.

These days, the pet names I come up with may appear less elaborate than those of the early years, but they are actually far more intricate. They may not be as flowery, but they possess something even more important: the memories of almost everything my wife and I have come to hold dear. My most fervent wish is that years from now, when I am dead and gone, Michelle will take her morning coffee onto the back porch and sip it from an ugly old mug with "Corn Dog" lettering the side—and that she will remember just how much I loved corn dogs.

JUST ASKIN', GUYS . . .

Besides her name, what do you affectionately call your girl?

1. Schmoopie
2. Penguin
3. Sugarpants
4. Babe-o-licious
5. Beans
6. Queen
7. The Goddess
8. Tigger
9. Foxy Mama

Source: MensHealth.com

BRING JOY TO YOUR WORLD

YOU FORESEE A SLOG FROM THANKSGIVING TO NEW YEAR'S. SHE'S PICTURING A WHIRLWIND OF SNOW-GLOBE GIDDINESS. HERE'S HOW TO STAY CLOSE—AND SANE

BY SARAH MILLER

I love the holidays. But then, I would: I'm a woman. Cue reindeers, cue childhood memories (and regrets), cue soul-crushing pressure on my man when November rolls around. But relax. It's just the holidays, and you don't have to do it all perfectly. Just a few things.

My gift to you: simple directions to ensure that this year you'll do something naughty under the tree besides accidentally setting off the audio chip in My Little Pony.

START SOONER WITH HER GIFT

You know the success of your gift to her will make or break your holiday season. So don't spend Christmas Eve—again—wandering the picked-over aisles at Target.

There's a better way. It's called paying attention. When she's browsing in a store or reading a magazine, she'll point to a handbag or jewelry or shoes and say, "Look—how cute!" Listening to the radio or reading the paper, she'll comment that she's interested in reading a certain author or growing herbs or learning Italian. All of this, friend, is her way of saying, "Here are 100 ways to avoid wandering around Target on Christmas Eve." Remember, though: You always score extra points for any gift that has meaning.

There is nothing sentimental about electronic gadgets, though they may indeed make her cry.

MAKE AN EFFORT: Gift certificates say, "I gave up." And gifts marketed as trendy say, "You're like every other woman," says author and gift consultant

Sherri Athay. A personal, handmade item, such as a collage of the year's photos, shows that you spent time thinking about her. And exchange gifts in private, say Sheri and Bob Stritof, the guides at marriage.about.com. She'll be able to express her appreciation uncensored.

HIT ALL THE PARTIES

Call off that fight you were just about to have—the one about whether you're spending the second Saturday night in December at her friend's party or your friend's party. You're going to attend both of them, bub.

Arrive at one party right when it starts. Stay an hour and a half. By the time you leave, everyone will be loaded and have no idea that you're even gone. And when you hit event number two, everyone there will also be loaded. They'll think you've been there all along. The trick: no grand entrances, and absolutely no goodbyes.

BRING MORNING-AFTER GOODIES: Buy baskets and fill each with muffins, pancake mix, syrup, and a bag of good ground coffee. Present one to the host of each party you attend, with a note that says, "You entertained me tonight, so I'd like to return the favor tomorrow morning."

MAKE YOUR RELATIONSHIP THE PRIORITY

Your parents want you to arrive sometime around Thanksgiving and leave after Groundhog Day. Her parents are hoping for a longer stay. Your cool new friends (who just happen to be rich) want to take you two to Crete on their sailboat. And then there's that much-anticipated alone time. The laws of physics will prevent all of this from happening at once. They will not, however, prevent the two of you from sitting down with a couple of beers and a calendar and saying, "Okay, what's going to keep us happy and sane in the weeks to come?"

Family is probably the first piece of this puzzle. If your relationship is new and one family or the other lays a guilt trip on you, it'll be tempting to use opposing families as scapegoats. This is not a good idea. You want these people to like one another. Unless your family is the mafia, you do not have to see your relatives every single holiday. Expand your calendar of possible dates beyond the obvious ones. Emphasize that it's the togetherness that counts, not the calendar page. Who knows, they may buy it.

KEEP YOUR SANITY: If you're driving from family to family, consider staying at hotels. And during the day, duck out every now and then. "Offering to do errands is a great way to buy some time for yourselves," says Herb Rappaport, PhD, an adjunct professor of clinical psychology at Temple University.

USE THE BUDDY SYSTEM

The crowds, family meltdowns, battery-powered beeps, and general decadence of the season can be brutal, and the two of you need to find an oasis of peace within it.

You must maintain your essential bond and take time out to appreciate each other. A quiet night at home, a short overnight trip, or, if things are really crazy, even just a long lunch (preferably with sex and without cell phones) can be crucial to reminding yourselves that you still have each other. When you do venture out, suggest a pledge to remain allies in the heat of battle. You can make up a game: "When I tap my nose twice, get me out of here." It will amuse you. It will create the illusion of control. It will be an excuse to go down to the basement and have sex.

BE AN ARMY OF TWO: Watch each other's backs at family gatherings, says Rappaport. Don't disappear to watch football in the den and leave her to fend off those "When can we expect grandchildren?" questions. Rescue her with a well-timed "I need to introduce her to so-and-so."

INDULGE A FEW CORNY TRADITIONS

Women are weird about the holidays. They, like, care. They want to walk through winter wonderlands holding hands. They want to sing songs about angels. All you want to do is drink hot buttered rum, though you would also consider licking it off something.

Do two stupid holiday things. That's all. And throw yourself into them with full enthusiasm. Take her skating. Rent *It's a Wonderful Life*. And maximize the quiet, soulful activities. Go see some kids play bells at a church, or swap your downhill day at Longline Mountain for snowshoeing and cocoa instead.

Yes, you're extremely hip and the holiday thing is so embarrassingly clichéd, but here's another cliché: Snow falls gently outside. Lights twinkle as your woman lowers her naked body onto a bearskin rug, murmuring, "Darling, this is the most wonderful time of year!"

See how this works?

START A TRADITION: Go to the nicest holiday store you can find and pick out ornaments that best depict each of you. Think angels, dirty Santas, and candy canes. It'll spark a collection you can build together over time, says Athay, as well as many shared and meaningful smirks.

>>A MAN'S GUIDE POLL

Traditional Holiday Turn-Ons: 200 women tell us which holiday traditions make them melt in our arms.

1 = No fun 10 = Love it

Dressing up for parties: 7.5	Having a snowball fight: 7.5
Getting jewelry: 8	Watching football: 3
Shopping for kids: 5	Baking cookies: 10
Sitting by the fire: 8.5	Trip to Grandma's: 4.5
Ice skating: 6	Making a snowman: 8

GO A LITTLE CRAZY

JUST BECAUSE YOU'RE A RESPECTABLE GROWN-UP DOESN'T MEAN YOU CAN'T BE WILD, IRRESPONSIBLE, AND DRIVEN MAD WITH LUST

BY COLIN McENROE

Astronaut Lisa Marie Nowak was arrested in 2007 after she drove 950 miles in a diaper—well, in a car, but also in a diaper—and pepper-sprayed her love rival. She was held up to ridicule, but I didn't feel superior to her.

Who doesn't go nuts every once in a while? Especially in the service of love? And Nowak got points in my book for being in her forties, as was (for that matter) the to-pee-for object of her desire. The woman who was pepper-sprayed was at least 10 years younger. Good! Well, not really. But it was nice to see a couple of midlifers taking back the night, so to speak.

How recently have you been there, in the grips of passion that made you do crazy things? If it has been 5 years or more since you drove through the night to make (or profess) love to someone, maybe that's not such a good thing.

I'm under the limit. I'm within 3 years of being so crazy in love, so deprived, so suspicious, so full of ache and desire that I routinely showed up at the woman's house at dawn. With the late moon and the early sun together in the sky, I threw pebbles at her upstairs window to get her to wake up and come down and unlock the door. I was 49.

One night, with a snowstorm pretty much shutting down the whole state, I drove to be with her. It was 2 a.m. On the highway, the only vehicles were plows and long caravans of 18-wheelers, creeping along like elephants linked trunk to tail. And one insane guy in a car. I gently spilled down an exit ramp. The world was quiet, as if humanity had died out. When I folded myself into her bed, the sex was an ocean of surging, crashing emotions.

Hmmm. I had forgotten some of that until just now. The relationship burned itself out. Eventually, she was the one more likely to be on dawn patrol. And then neither of us showed up.

It didn't feel great to be that wild and needy. But it doesn't feel great not to be, either.

"We glorify the cult of passion a lot, perhaps more than any culture in the world," says Pamela C. Regan, a psychology professor at California State University at Los Angeles. "We say there is The One, and that if you keep looking for this person and this feeling, you will find it. I think these are really hurtful emotional ideas in terms of what they do to people's expectations."

But those images of uncontrollable ardor are largely confined to the young, she says. "We don't really know what to do with older adults who engage in those behaviors," says Regan. "The only thing we can say is they're crazy; there's something wrong with them. We don't know a lot about the mating dynamics and the love and lust of people older than 22, because 99 percent of the research is conducted on 22-year-olds."

Of course, we're expected to learn from our lives and acquire better judgment. If I told you I was going to quit my job and move across the country on the off chance that a certain relationship might work, you might be a little worried about me. I'm 52. If I were 22, it would make more sense to you.

I still have weird impulses. Last night, I drove 40 miles to a local university to be just about the only grown-up anywhere near the mosh pit for the Dropkick Murphys, a Celtic hard-core punk band. My 17-year-old son called to make sure I was safe.

I've done even crazier things in the grips of love, here in my middle years, but several of them are not ready for mass consumption. Let's just say I'm lucky to be alive for reasons that have nothing to do with driving through a massive snowstorm.

I could easily apply all this bad judgment to a love relationship again, I think. I just haven't found the right wrong woman.

Do women like wild overtures? You especially may be wondering this if you're newly single, out of practice, and worried about—more than anything else—making a fool of yourself.

The answer is that women like urgent, ardent behavior as long as it appears to spring from confidence as opposed to desperation. Unflinching, yes. Needy, no. Women want to be held worthy of pursuit, of love letters, of flowers, of serenades, of poems. But don't be a pest. The single, huge gesture that strikes to the heart—think of Dennis Christopher singing an Italian love song in *Breaking Away* or John Cusack holding the boom box over his head in the rain in *Say Anything*—is much better than 15 text messages and 7 voice mails a day.

Interesting, though, that the two examples I just gave involve the very young. Hollywood doesn't give us much to go on about the madness of midlife love. Except, of course, *Something's Gotta Give*, the Diane Keaton–Jack Nicholson comic masterpiece of heart attacks and crying jags. The craziness of those two people and the untreatability of their conditions—that's what we should all be going for.

But wait. Some of you are married. Long married. How crazy can you possibly afford to go?

Allow me to suggest the Crazy Astronaut Simulation. You and your wife must agree to pretend to be a little more star-crossed than you actually are. And you must conspire to introduce a small element of danger into your sex life. Imagine that you are, in fact, married to other people and having an affair with each other. That's an old trick, I know, and it usually winds up with the two of you going to some dumb love motel, and if that works for you, fine.

What I have in mind is sort of the X Games version of that. I want you to do it in a place where you might get caught. And I want you to do it in a way that's a little uncomfortable. Stash a sleeping bag in a remote wooded patch of the nearest state park. Meet there, arriving by alternate routes, around 7:30 a.m., at a time of year when it's a little cold at that time of day, so that her nipples perk up from the chilly air and your Mr. Happy faces the little extra challenge of low-temp performance. Slither into the bag, out of your clothes, and inside her in one long chuckling operation. And then do it a little more quietly than you want to, because some idiot jogger or bird-watcher may be in the vicinity.

If you're indoor types, meet at your office or hers on a deserted Sunday. Screw on a desk or a swivel chair or something even more improbable.

On a commercial flight, ask for a blanket and then bring each other off by hand. Meet down by the ferry slip in separate cars. Drive a short distance away and do each other in the backseat of your car (have you ever even been in the backseat of your car?), maybe in a place where there's half a chance some cop might shine a flashlight in on you.

If this seems like a lot of trouble to go to, well, yes! Anybody can go to a freakin' love motel with his wife! Are you just anybody? No! I am urging you to go to a little extra trouble—and possibly even get into some.

Try, as you do these things, to slip into the mind of the desperate lover, the person who has no option but to risk everything—loss of reputation, standing, dignity, circulation in the extremities—for this sharp stab at ecstasy. Imagine that there is another man who lays claim to her, a hard, controlling, powerful bastard who cannot possibly worship her and ravish her as you do. A man who would shoot you both if he caught you.

Get in touch with your inner Lisa Marie.

Will any of this work for you? It depends on your own comfort level with the raptures of love.

Long Island couples therapist Joel Block says we are governed by a blueprint based on what love and relationships looked like during our childhoods.

"The burned child is eventually drawn back to the fire," says Block. "So I'd say there is something that has a vague familiarity in these passionate love affairs that sometimes go over the edge."

That's a good question to ask yourself if you're feeling drawn to the wild side: Are you stuck in some pathological pattern you learned from your dysfunctional parents?

Or are you just happy you're still crazy after all these years?

SEXY OR STALKER: A SELF-TEST

How to tell whether your moves are smooth or scary: The list progresses from sexy to stalker.

You call the morning after to say you had a nice time.

You text her three times a day to say "Hi, hon" and ask for detailed reports on her pedicure.

You memorize the names of her last three boyfriends—and where they live.

You check her text messages when she leaves the room. You tattoo her name over the name(s) of the last girl(s) you dated.

You hack into her e-mail account (just this once), and call to hear her voice and then hang up.

You join her Pilates class and sleep with her best friend to be close to her.

You watch her undress through the window, and call her with your voice disguised. You act surprised by the restraining order.

PRESENT A UNITED FRONT

MOM VS. DAD: DIFFERENT STYLES OF RAISING—AND DISCIPLINING—CHILDREN CAN LEAD TO SERIOUS MARITAL STRIFE. HERE'S HOW TO JOIN FORCES

BY WILL PALMER

It's not easy to sit still while your toddler cries in the next room. But that's what my wife insisted we do. It was time, she said, for our Grace to be Ferberized.

At nearly 3 years old, Grace was still not going to sleep without a parent in the room, which was exhausting for two overworked parents. That's when my wife, Ruth, heard about a method of getting a child used to sleeping alone by starting with a few minutes and building up to a whole night—even if it meant letting her cry her eyes out at first. Ferberizing is what they called it (after Richard Ferber, MD, author of the somewhat controversial *Solve Your Child's Sleep Problems*), and it was more than my overprotective heart could bear.

Ruth and I were having the first of many skirmishes about the right way to raise our child, and we weren't alone. Researchers at Seattle's Relationship Research Institute, a couples counseling center, have found that about two-thirds of couples experience a sharp decline in relationship quality when they first become parents. Researchers isolated "fundamental differences in parenting" and used this as a predictor of divorce with 80 percent accuracy.

"Couples disagreeing on parenting styles is a very serious issue," says Toru Sato, a professor of psychology at Shippensburg University in Pennsylvania. "We don't want to send inconsistent messages to children who are growing up in a world that is already confusing enough."

In the end, I came around. So did Grace after a few painful nights, and I had learned a few things about handling differences in child rearing.

KNOW THYSELF. Some parents have "emotion dismissing" attitudes (best summed up as "Just suck it up, kid"), while others have an "emotion coaching" philosophy (e.g., "Let's talk about your feelings"). Both parents should try to identify where they fall on the spectrum and—if they have wildly different approaches—discuss how to reconcile their differences, says John Gottman, founder of the Relationship Research Institute and coauthor of the best-selling book *Seven Principles for Making Marriage Work* and the just-released *Baby Makes Three*. "Unless parents talk about this and arrive at a way of honoring both attitudes—toward their own emotions and their kid's—they won't get anywhere," he says.

NEGOTIATE BEHIND THE SCENES. Even the best of us have insecurities, and it's not uncommon for those issues to sneak into the parent-child relationship. And that can lead to conflict between the two partners. "If you don't like your spouse's decision, first ask yourself why it bothers you," says Sato. "Then express that, and then listen. Half of the disagreement is resolved when we feel that our feelings are being respected by the other person."

DON'T PLAY GOOD COP, BAD COP. "Putting one parent in charge of discipline isn't fair to that parent," says Elizabeth Tingley, a professor of child development at Bank Street College of Education in Manhattan. "See yourselves as parents who are equal partners operating together."

TAKE A TIME-OUT. Not your kids—you. There will be times when you are outraged by your wife's approach and the kids are in the room. Don't question her in front of them; just go with the decision and come back to it later, says Sato. "This will show that you respect your wife as a parent. Take a time-out and discuss the issue after you've both cooled off."

ENROLL IN A PARENTING CLASS. The Bringing Baby Home workshop, a new offshoot of the Relationship Research Institute, is an intensive course branching out to hospitals across the country (bbhonline.org). There's no certification process for parenting courses, but good recommendations—and experience being a parent—are the things to look for in an instructor. "You're dealing with the needs of at least three individuals here," says Sato, "and taking those needs seriously is never a waste of time."

FIRE STARTERS

Here are the most common ways parents annoy each other.

Things You Do

The 8 p.m. wrestling match. Hop on Pop seems like a great idea when you come home from the office, but your wife sees it as undoing all of her hard work to calm the kids before bedtime. If you get the kids riled up, it's your job to calm them down.

The 10 p.m. shoulder tap. At the end of an exhausting day, this is what a woman dreads most, according to Julia Stone, coauthor of *Babyproofing Your Marriage*. "Women think, 'Can't he put a little more effort into wooing me? Or just go to sleep?'"

The midnight game of playing possum. You both hear the baby crying, but you keep your eyes closed and hope your wife thinks you're still sound asleep. "When you're both tired, thinking the other person is trying to trick you into doing more work is pretty aggravating," says Stone.

The vanishing act. The uncanny psychic ability to disappear seconds before your wife needs help. She knows it's not a coincidence.

Things She Does

"The baby needs a sweater." Your wife can't help her overprotective instincts. Humor her and put the sweater on. You can always take it off later.

"You washed the delicates on permanent press!" "Women have to let go of the reins," says Stone. "Husbands may not do things the same ways wives do, but the men can do it." Delicately suggest that dad cycles are different but equally effective.

"Sure, you can play golf . . . when the kids go to college." Everyone needs a break, but typically, men reach that point first. Suggest that you take the kids for an afternoon, then gently ask if you could get a half day off yourself.

"Ugh, not tonight." The cliché that launched a thousand sitcoms can do long-term damage. "When a man is rejected over and over, it's devastating to him emotionally as well as frustrating physically," says Stone. "He'll no longer want to expend the effort to pursue his wife romantically."

GIVE GOOD GIFT

GOT MONEY ISSUES WITH YOUR HONEY? WE'VE GOT ANSWERS

BY REBECCA ASCHER-WALSH

You're officially a Committed Couple. How fun! And with this status comes the need to juggle gifting for two sets of friends and family (not so fun). On a good day, deciding who shops and pays for your dad's wine rack or her niece's American Girl doll can be a nightmare. On a bad one, divvying up responsibilities can spark a tree-kicking tantrum. So, to preempt holiday cash spats, we grilled financial advisor Bambi Holzer, author of *Financial Bliss: A Couple's Guide to Merging Money Styles and Building a Rich Life Together*; Burlington, Vermont-based etiquette expert Peter Post, author of *Essential Manners for Couples: From Snoring and Sex to Finances and Fighting Fair*; and anthropologist Helen Fisher, PhD, a relationship expert and the author of *Why We Love*, on how to shop sanely—solo and together. Love is nice, but no one ever said it'd be cheap or easy.

Q: At what point in your relationship should you give joint gifts to your families?

Fisher: You should be close to getting engaged. From an evolutionary perspective, the whole point of pair bonding is to have babies. When you give a gift together, you're announcing to your kin group that you're going to be joining their DNA with this person's, whether they like it or not.

Post: Agreed. If you haven't discussed marriage or haven't been living together, you shouldn't be putting both of your names on a gift tag.

Q: If your lives are commingled but your finances aren't, what should you do if she wants to spend more on gifts than you do?

Fisher: Some people, usually those who have higher levels of serotonin (a chemical that regulates mood and sex drive, among other things), may be more likely to be frugal. That means you're dealing with a biological temperament, not just stubbornness. So both partners need to remember that the other person isn't trying to control or undermine them; they're just doing what feels sensible for them. The only solution is to compromise and settle on a middle price; or make a list of gifts you need to buy and pick one or two to splurge on.

Q: What if one person really doesn't have any money to spend? Does he or she have to bake cookies?

Holzer: You don't need to buy something to give something. Print out a gift certificate for dinner at your house or scour used-record stores for copies of the giftee's favorite '80s albums on vinyl. These can be nicer gifts, because they have a personal touch. But if one half of a couple has the cash and wants to spend it, the decision's up to him/her. Write the check and say it's from both of you, because that's the point of a joint present.

Fisher: Start baking cookies.

Q: If she left the shopping to you, it would never get done. So now she's shopping for everyone, including your family. How can you keep her from becoming resentful?

Fisher: First, try carving out time to shop together. If that doesn't work, fend for yourself. My boyfriend always puts his wallet next to the bed, so I make a list of who he needs to shop for, leave it there, and make a joke of it. He can do it or not, but he accepts the consequences either way.

Holzer: Put a list on the fridge and cross off names once their presents are bought. That way, you can see who's been left until the last minute.

Q: If you don't share a bank account but you end up buying all the gifts on both your lists, do you ask your girl to settle up at the end of the month?

Holzer: Hopefully, you've agreed ahead of time on who's paying for what. Finances aren't romantic. They're the one part of a relationship that should have no mystery. Before you start shopping, set up a budget, and split up your list of recipients according to the kinds of shopping each of you is better at. Maybe you take the guys and she takes the women, or you take the adults and she takes the kids.

Fisher: If you're shopping for and buying all the gifts, she should pay for at least half. And maybe you should charge her interest for your time!

Q: What if you do share finances, but you don't want to admit how much you tip your barber or doorman for the holidays? Can you keep it a secret?

Holzer: It depends on how much money you're talking about. If what you're "sneaking" is more than a couple hundred dollars, there's a problem, and it's not worth being deceptive about it.

Q: Should you agree on how much you plan to spend on each other? Or does that suck the romance right out of gifting?

Fisher: Different personalities will handle this differently. If either partner is uncomfortable with setting a budget, don't do it—though you can say, "Sweetie, I'm not going to give you much this year."

MOVIE AND A MAKE-UP

Study these holiday scenes to fast-forward your own love life.

It's a Wonderful Life

Scene stealer: Jimmy Stewart and Donna Reed get distracted looking into each other's eyes when sharing a phone receiver.

Your turn: "Eye contact differentiates between sexual attraction and love. It signifies there's more than just chemistry," says Ian Kerner, PhD, a relationship therapist and the author of *She Comes First*. "We're the only mammal that gazes into the eyes of those we love during sex. It separates us from all other creatures."

Love Actually

Scene stealer: Colin Firth learns Portuguese to ask his beloved's father for her hand in marriage.

Your turn: Learning a new skill, such as a foreign language, for someone you adore is effective because "it's personally relevant to your significant other," says Patricia Love, EdD, coauthor of *How to Improve Your Marriage Without Talking About It*. She says big gestures are "proof positive that you care for me and you've been paying attention."

Q: She wants to throw a holiday party, but you don't. Should you make her pay for it herself?

Holzer: Yes, that means she has to pay for it. And she should. She wants to have it; you don't.

Fisher: If you're going to be there playing the role of cohost, you should cough up some dough. If you really don't want to be involved, you should make other plans for that night.

Q: You're headed to her parents' house for your first holiday together. Should you bring just one gift, or a gift for each of her family members?

Holzer: I would give one household item, such as a serving dish, and spend about $100. You don't want to look cheap.

Post: If you don't have tons of money, you could put together a gift

---

An Affair to Remember

Scene stealer: Cary Grant surprises Deborah Kerr with a Christmas Eve visit.

Your turn: "Long-term relationships, by definition, have a degree of dependency, responsibility, and predictability," Kerner says. "Keeping passion alive demands the opposite. You have to constantly look for ways to introduce the unknown and surprise your partner. Popping up unannounced is a perfect example."

The Holiday

Scene stealer: Jude Law declares his love for Cameron Diaz—despite his two kids, her commitment phobia, and an ocean between them.

Your turn: "All relationships have obstacles," says Debby Herbenick, PhD, researcher at Indiana University's Center for Sexual Health Promotion. Find specific ways to show your partner you're resourceful, patient, creative, and caring enough to work on your commitment.

basket filled with wonderful breakfast stuff, such as gourmet pancake mix, real maple syrup, oven mitts, cloth napkins. Buy the items separately and wrap them together nicely; it's all about presentation. In the end it will look quite expensive.

Q: Let's say that last year your mother gave your girl a hideous gift that's too big to hide in a closet—but has no place in her house. You won't let her sell it because you're afraid of offending Mom if she asks where it is. Advice?

Post: That's ugly. Once you both agree it's not going in the house, tell Mom you really appreciate her thoughtfulness, but it doesn't match the décor and you've put it in storage for your next home.

Fisher: A woman's home is her nest. A man has to put his girlfriend or wife above his mother. He has to get his priorities straight.

Q: What about, say, re-gifting his mom's hideous present? Is that a clever way to spread holiday cheer—or just plain tacky?

Fisher: The gift is in the giving. At least rewrap it.

Post: I hate re-gifting. By nature it's deceitful and can cause trouble. If you're going to do it, don't hide it. Getting into a white lie isn't worth the effort of getting out of it. It would be a lot easier if people would just give gift receipts and tell the recipient it's fine to take it back to the store where it came from.

Q: A study by Expedia says that 42 percent of U.S. adults would prefer to blow money on a hotel than stay with family. If you've been warmly invited, is it rude to refuse?

Post: It comes down to how realistic it is for your family to fit comfortably into a single house. My advice is to call 3 months in advance and say, "We think it would be easier for you if we stayed in a hotel, so we insist." Use considerate rather than selfish language. Don't say, "Your kids are so loud, we'd never be able to sleep."

AVOID THE SURPRISE

SUDDEN DIVORCE SYNDROME: DIVORCE MAY BE THE WORST THING THAT CAN HAPPEN TO A MAN'S HEALTH, FINANCES, AND EMOTIONAL WELL-BEING. YET ONE IN FOUR MEN WHO WILL GET DIVORCED THIS YEAR DOESN'T HAVE ANY CLUE THAT IT'S COMING

BY JOHN SEDGWICK

Like every husband who suddenly turns into an ex, Martin Paul, a pleasant, unassuming 51-year-old, knows exactly where he was when it happened. He was sitting on the back porch of his pricey hilltop house in the Boston suburbs one sunny Saturday morning, relaxing over coffee.

Paul is a professional collector, primarily of coins, but of other rare objects as well: Sonny Liston's ring belt, a submarine that appeared in the James Bond film *The Spy Who Loved Me*. It wasn't easy to build up his collecting business, but he had finally got it humming, and he was pulling down close to seven figures a year. Plus, the oldest of his three sons had suffered a frightening brain injury, but after two years of treatment, he had finally recovered enough to go to college. For the first time in a very long while, life was good.

And so, that Saturday, he wanted to tell his wife he was thinking about finally easing off a little. They'd started going on expensive vacations in Europe and Hawaii, and he figured she'd be pleased at the prospect of taking more trips together, or at least at the prospect of seeing him around the house a little more and not buried in his basement office. He had met her in graduate school more than a quarter century ago, and they'd had their ups and downs, but he was still crazy about her. And he thought that, with a little more time together, she'd be crazy about him again, too.

But no. She scarcely listened to any talk of retirement, or of vacations, or of anything he had to say. She had plans of her own.

"I want a divorce," she said.

Paul was so stunned that he thought he must have misheard her. But her face told him otherwise. "She looked like the enemy," he says. He started to think about everything he'd built: the thriving business, the wonderful family, the nice life in the suburbs. And he thought of her, and how much he still loved her. And then, right in front of her, he started to cry.

That night, he found a bottle of whiskey, and he didn't stop drinking it until he nearly passed out.

Things turned shitty very fast. His wife took out a temporary restraining order, accusing him of attempting to kidnap their youngest son. The claim was never proved in court. Then, with the aid of some high-priced lawyers, she extracted from him a whopping $50,000 a month—a full 75 percent of his monthly income. Barred from the house, he was not allowed regular access to the office he used to generate that income. (On the few times he was permitted inside, his wife did not let him use the bathroom. She insisted that he go outside in the woods.) "My lawyer kept telling her lawyers, 'You're killing the Golden Goose,'" recalls Paul. "But they didn't care."

Crushed by the payments and unable to work, he soon faced such a severe cash-flow crisis that he had to declare bankruptcy. His wife still did not relent. She charged that Paul had been abusive toward one of their sons. Paul says the charge is absurd, but it did its work, limiting his visitation rights.

Paul was sleepless and nerve wracked; his spirits plunged. He still missed his old life with his family. He missed the sound of it—the bustle of all the activity, the life. "I can't stand the silence," he says. "I miss hearing my wife breathe as she lay in bed beside me." In his desperation, he twice overdosed on prescription medication, but managed to call 911 each time before the drugs took full effect, and medics rushed him to the hospital in time. "I don't want to die," he says wearily. "I want to live. But I can't live with this torture." He did manage to keep a few mementos of his former life. Pictures, mostly. But also the kids' baby shoes. "I was always the emotional one," he says. "But that's all I have—the shoes, a few pictures. That's all. I used to be jovial, happy. But not now. I'm a broken man."

Sudden Divorce Syndrome. You won't find it in the *Diagnostic and Statisti-*

cal Manual of Mental Disorders, that bible of psychiatric illnesses, but you will find it in life. In a 2004 poll by AARP, one in four men who was divorced in the previous year said he "never saw it coming." (Only 14 percent of divorced women said they experienced the same unexpected broadside.) And few events in a man's life can be as devastating to his physical, mental, and financial health.

"I meet men all the time who are going through breakups, and it's very common for them to say it caught them by surprise," says Los Angeles–based sex therapist Lori Buckley, PsyD, host of "On the Minds of Men," a weekly relationship podcast on iTunes. The warning signs are usually there, claims Buckley, but the male mind is simply not very adept at recognizing them. "When women make up their mind that the relationship is over, they stop talking about the relationship," she says. "Men interpret a woman's lack of complaining as satisfaction. But more often, it's because she's simply given up."

To understand how common this scenario is, consider figures provided by John Guidubaldi, a former member of the U.S. Commission on Child and Family Welfare. Nationwide, Guidubaldi reports, wives are the ones to file for divorce 66 percent of the time, and, in some years, that figure has soared to nearly 75 percent. "It is easier to end a marriage than it is to fire an employee," says Guidubaldi. If she wants out, it's over. "You can get a dissolution of marriage on the basis of nothing."

Oftentimes, men have a divorce sprung on them in midlife, when their kids are more self-sufficient and they've finally started to think they were over the hump. Like Martin Paul, they could start to relax. But that's exactly the time of life when the instance of divorce begins to swell (another occurs shortly after marriage). Joe Cordell, of the law firm Cordell and Cordell, which specializes in representing men in domestic cases, attributes this to wives deciding as they approach age 40 that it's now or never for getting back into the marriage market. It's the same phenomenon as rich guys trading in their long-time partners for trophy wives. Only it's the women who are shedding men.

It didn't used to be this way. Although divorce has been legal for nearly two centuries, it was long a topic of such mortification that it was considered a last, desperate resort. The 1960s changed all that. The free-love decade both increased the inclination to divorce and dropped the social resistance to it. The rising financial independence of women began to free them from a need

MARITAL DIAGNOSTICS

Cars are easy: Change the oil, check the belts, rotate the tires, done. Relationship maintenance is a bit more difficult. So after consulting the experts, we developed this diagnostic check to help you assess the wear and tear on your marital vows. Instead of taking your marriage into the shop and having someone else look at it, these tools are about learning to listen to the important cues in your relationship, says professor William Doherty, PhD, director of the marriage and family therapy program at the University of Minnesota and author of *Take Back Your Marriage: Sticking Together in a World That Pulls Us Apart*. Here's how to make sure you and the missus are firing on all cylinders.

Checkup 1: Togetherness. When you gingerly mention that you'd like to go away for a weekend of fishing, what is your wife's reaction? Does she hassle you about spending more time with her? If the answer is yes, breathe easy. "When a woman is engaged in a relationship with all her heart, she's high-maintenance," says Doherty. (Uh, hooray?) But if she used to demand attention and doesn't anymore, don't chalk it up to her accepting you for who you are. "She may have given up her efforts to save your marriage," says Doherty, and moved on to her own time-consuming pursuits, things like "looking for apartments, finding a lawyer, and planning an exit strategy."

Checkup 2: Intimacy. Think about sex for a minute. Okay, it has been a little while—that's normal. Kids and jobs are lousy aphrodisiacs. "The first red flag is when there's a change in your sexual relationship," says Jennifer Berman, MD, founder of the Berman Women's Wellness Center, in Beverly Hills, California. Perhaps Saturday-morning cartoons used to mean you locked yourselves in the bedroom, but now it's when she schedules manicures. What about the rare weekends when you are alone together? Does she relish those nights? Ask yourself, "Is she just going through the motions and getting it over with?" says Dr. Berman. Tune in to make sure your wife is getting what she wants.

Checkup 3: Communication. All couples fight—not just Brangelina. The question

to stay in a stultifying or abusive marriage. As a result, divorce soared, doubling by most measures. But the stereotypical divorce story—man marries, starts a family, meets a younger woman, and leaves his wife—just isn't as common as we are led to believe.

---

to ask yourself is, What happens next? If your wife acts reasonably pleasant, do you assume she's over it and just go on with your day? If so, there could be trouble brewing. "Women will brood for months about words spoken," says Doherty. If you've cleared the air completely—for example, if she can laugh about it now—you're okay. If not, it's likely that she's "still hurting or expecting an apology." Warning: Pent-up resentment, like rust, is corrosive. Therefore, Doherty recommends approaching your wife after a blowup to ask how she's doing. "Yes, it's scary, because she might blast you again," he says, "but it's better to know that there's tension than not to know."

Checkup 4: Socializing. Who is she hanging out with? "If your social world involves playing basketball with other married guys, and she takes on new friends who are single—or pulls away from your married friends—you're orbiting different suns, and that will make you grow apart," says Doherty, adding that this move is often totally unconscious, but it can be dangerous. While a married woman is inclined to offer her female friend advice on how to overcome conflict with her husband, single women are more likely to say "Come join us!" After all, he points out, "Single people love having single friends."

Checkup 5: Jealousy. At a holiday party, you spend a few minutes chatting with a Gisele look-alike. When you get home, does your wife say, "Who was that floozy?" If so, feel good about your marriage, says Doherty. A hint of jealousy means that she thinks you're attractive, she expects other women to find you attractive, and she wants you all to herself. Sometimes men process a lack of jealousy as "a free pass to flirt with other women," says Doherty. Think about that. "If she really doesn't give a rip, it's not a good thing," he explains. It means she's less invested, and, he says, "she might be thinking that if you left for another woman, it wouldn't be so bad."

"Marriage changes men more pervasively and more profoundly than it changes women," explains sociologist Steven Nock, author of *Marriage in Men's Lives*. "The best way to put it is, marriage is for men what motherhood is for women." Marriage makes men grow up. Nock observes that many men before marriage are indifferent workers, and, after hours, are likely to be found in bars or zoned out in front of a TV. After marriage, they are solid wage earners, frequent churchgoers, maybe members of a neighborhood protection association. But divorce takes that underpinning away, leaving men strangely infantilized and unsure of their place in the world. They feel like interlopers in the stands at their children's soccer games or in the auditorium for their school plays.

Compounding this pain, men find the deck is stacked against them. The divorce system tends to award wives custody of the children, substantial child support, the marital home, half the couple's assets, and, often, heavy alimony payments.

This may come as startling news to a public that has been led to believe that women are the ones who suffer financially postdivorce, not men. But the data show otherwise, according to an exhaustive study of the subject by Sanford L. Braver, a professor of psychology at Arizona State University and author of *Divorced Dads: Shattering the Myths*. "The man is in a lot poorer condition than the popular media portray," he says. "This idea of the swinging, happy-go-lucky, no-worries single guy in a bar . . . that's just not it at all." The misconception was fueled by Harvard professor Lenore Weitzman's widely cited book, *The Divorce Revolution: The Unexpected Social and Economic Consequences for Women and Children in America*.

Weitzman's 1985 tome claimed that, postdivorce, women and children suffer on average a 73 percent drop in their standard of living, while the divorced men's standard of living increased by 42 percent. Years later, Weitzman acknowledged a math error; the actual difference was 27 percent and 10 percent, respectively. But Braver says even that figure is based on severely flawed calculations. Weitzman and other social scientists ignored men's expenses—the tab for replacing everything from the bed to the TV to the house—as well as the routine costs of helping to raise the children, beyond child support. Even the tax code favors women: Not only is child support not tax deductible for fathers, but a custodial mother can take a $1,000 per child tax credit; the father cannot, even if he's paying. As "head of the household," the mother gets a lower tax rate and can claim the children as exemptions. If the ex-wife remarries, she is still entitled to child support, even if she marries a billionaire. Indeed, every year men are actually thrown in jail for failing to meet their child-support obligations. In the state of Michigan alone, nearly 3,000 men were locked up for that offense in 2005.

But for many men, the real pain isn't financial, it's emotional: "Men depend on women for their social support and connections," says Buckley. "When marriages end, men can find themselves far more alone than they ever expected." In a large-scale Canadian survey, 19 percent of men reported a significant drop in social support postdivorce. Women are customarily the keepers of the social calendars and all that is implied by that, providing for what University of Texas sociologist Norval D. Glenn calls the "intangibles" that can create much of a man's sense of place in the world. More often than not, wives send out the Christmas cards; they stitched that cute Halloween costume their daughter wore in second grade; they recall the names of the neighbors who used to live two houses down. The men who bear all these unexpected burdens do so alone, in a strange place, while their ex-wives and children live in the houses that used to be theirs. For an ex-husband to enter that house can feel like trespassing, even though it was paid for with his own money, or sometimes, built with his own hands.

Long before his wife came along, a frame-store owner named Jordan Appel, 55, had built a fine house for himself atop West Newton Hill in one of the fancier Boston suburbs. He loved bringing in a wife and then adding two children. "It felt so wonderful to say 'my wife' and 'my children' and feel part of a community." He volunteered for the preschool's yard sale; his wife took up with a lover. Sometimes she slept with him in Appel's own house; in time, she decided to divorce Appel. As these things go, he was obliged to leave the house and, as it happened, the community, too. Money was so tight that he ended up sleeping in a storage room above his frame shop two towns away. His ex-wife works part-time on the strength of Appel's child custody and alimony payments and spends time with her boyfriend in Appel's former house. She lives rather well, and he has to make $100,000 a year to support her and the chil-

HER 7-YEAR ITCH

He has no idea she's miserable. Or that she has slept with another man.
As told to* Best Life *magazine.

He doesn't read.

It's not that he isn't smart. He is, but he's not educated, and he's not curious. He wants to talk about how we're adding on to the house, and all the decisions that go along with that, and, "When we retire, do you want to buy a Winnebago?" I want to talk about global warming. It's about conversation and—I hate to say it—intellect. Our conversations about anything are pretty short.

He's a very good husband in terms of sharing household responsibilities. He does laundry, he helps cook, he'll do all the normal, manly outdoor chores. He's a loving dad. We don't argue. He's someone I truly admire and think of as a wonderful person, but I don't think we are right for each other.

We've been married for 7 years. If I'm truthful, I had some doubts when we were dating. Then a close friend of mine died. That trauma made me question what I wanted in life, and this man cared for me and adored me. I was going for something I thought was good for me. He's offered me stability, both emotionally and practically, in buying a house and having money. Now I feel stable but uncreative.

I want him to have his own life, to be interested in things outside of me and our child. He has a few interests, and he's trying to develop them, but he doesn't have a lot of friends, so he's needy and dependent. He says, "If you're happy, then I will be happy." There's a weird pressure in that statement. It's selfish: I have to be happy so that he can be happy. It doesn't matter if I'm happy for me.

And, okay, can I tell you this? We haven't kissed in a long time, other than just a peck on the lips: "See you tonight." When we physically do the deed, it takes care of the basic needs, but I don't feel passionate about it. It's that lack of creativity and imagina-

dren, which amounts to 70-hour workweeks. One day, he went back to his house and discovered many of his belongings out on the sidewalk with the trash. "My body feels like it's dissolving in anger," he says. "I'm in an absolute rage every single day."

---

tion. If I found him to be a stimulating person, perhaps I could kindle more passion.

This idea of leaving him has been in my head for a couple of years. There was no event between the two of us. I think it started with me. I worry that he'd be so angry that he'd somehow try to keep me from my child. But I am naively hopeful that this would be amicable. I am concerned about money, but we've worked really hard to be in this place with our finances. I have these weird thoughts, like, We've hired an architect, and in April, we're supposed to start adding on to the house. If something's going to change, I don't want to be in the middle of that process, spending all that money.

And then, just recently, I had an affair.

The man was someone I had met and known and been attracted to. He's smart in ways my husband isn't. I'd never thought about acting on those feelings, but I was away from home and a big group of us went out for cocktails. I had the chance and a few drinks. I was curious. I wanted to know, If I slept with someone else, would it be a big deal?

It was the best f—king sex I've had in years. This man touched me in places I never let my husband touch me anymore. It was sweaty and passionate and awesome. It wasn't just the sex; it was that the person I was with, I wanted to be with. The experience has made me feel like perhaps there are other people in the world I would be compatible with. But I would leave my husband for myself, not for another man.

And yet I don't know if it has pushed me toward one decision or another. I'm back in my normal life, where I don't know how to broach the subject of "Are we happy?" I need to find a way to tell him I'm not happy and ask if he's willing to try some counseling. But I feel like I already know. I would hope having a counselor sitting there would make it easier for me to say, "This just isn't working for me. And I'm leaving."

"What are five of the biggest stressors a human being can face?" asks Ned Holstein, MD, executive director of Fathers and Families, a Massachusetts-based reform group for divorced dads. "One: the death of a child. Two: the loss of a spouse. Three: the loss of a home. Four: a serious financial reversal. And five: losing a relationship with a child. All of these except the first are combined in a father's experience of divorce. People always think the man is a lone wolf and he can take care of himself. Well, he's also a human being, and people don't think through what that means for men."

As hard as such deprivations are on the psyche, they can be devastating to a man's health. Recently divorced men are nearly nine times more likely to commit suicide than their female counterparts, according to a study by sociologist Augustine Kposowa. "It's not so much the loss of money," he says, "but the loss of children that propels men to suicide." Or it could be a combination. Infuriated by his obligation to pay child support for three children he rarely saw, Perry Manley snuck a hand grenade inside a federal courthouse in Seattle last year and was shot to death by security personnel after they spotted it. The death was termed "suicide by cop." Kposowa has also detected an increased incidence of motor-vehicle accidents among divorced men, either due to a lack of concentration, sleeplessness, or, more darkly, suicide "cloaked as an accident," he says.

Compared with married or single men, divorced men are nine times as likely to be admitted to the hospital, to report difficulties at work, or to suffer significant depression. According to a study in the *American Journal of Psychiatry*, they suffer the effects of divorce with the intensity that their wives experience the death of a close friend. And they suffer physical maladies. "Their blood pressure goes up, and so does their cholesterol, and that drives up hypertension, heart disease, coronary artery disease, and peripheral vascular disease," says psychiatrist Arnold Robbins, associate editor of the *Journal of Men's Health & Gender*. Researchers at the Texas Heart Institute have noted that emotional stress can lead to a dangerous ballooning of the left ventricle, which they term "broken heart syndrome." Says Dr. Robbins: "A lot of metabolic syndromes kick in too, like borderline and type 2 diabetes. There's cirrhosis of the liver from too much drinking. Even prostate problems. It's not a pretty picture."

Scientists have recently come to some possible conclusions as to why this might be so. It may be as simple as a loss of being touched. James Coan, PhD, a psychologist in the departments of psychology and neuroscience at the University of Virginia, found that, for a husband, just holding his wife's hand is enough to reduce the stress associated with the anticipation of pain. Regular sex helps insulate a man from chronic stress, and that can pay off in increased longevity: In a study of 1,000 middle-aged men by researchers at Queen's University in Belfast, men who had sex at least three times a week had half the risk of heart attack or stroke of men who had sex less frequently.

Distressed by such facts, men's groups are springing up around the country. "Think of it," says Stephen Baskerville, president of the American Coalition for Fathers and Children, in Washington, DC. "A father could be sitting in his own home, not agreeing to a divorce, not unfaithful to his marriage vows, and not abusive, and the next thing he knows, the court has taken his house, his children, and a lot of his money, and then forced him to pay his wife's legal fees and even her psychologist's fees. And he can be threatened with jail time if he resists."

So, how to avoid Sudden Divorce Syndrome? One way, of course, is to avoid marriage. Another way is by working on your marriage when it can still be salvaged. Statistically, end-stage marriage counseling is rarely effective, despite what the counselors might say. Instead, husbands might be wise to pay attention to the essential ratio that—according to John Gottman, founder of the Relationship Research Institute and coauthor of the best-selling book *Seven Principles for Making Marriage Work* and the just-released *Baby Makes Three*—governs marital success or failure: five to one. That means husbands (and wives) should direct at least five positive remarks or actions to their spouses for every negative one. Any less and the marriage is in trouble. Or, following the much-admired work of Howard Markman, PhD, who holds couples workshops (loveyourrelationship.com), husbands should attune themselves to their wives' "bids"—for attention, for affection, for all the things that

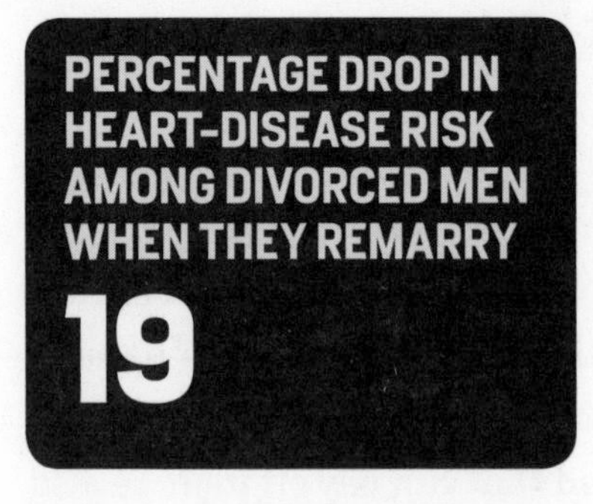

sustain a relationship—and do their best to provide for them. In truth, husbands are not built for the demands that wives often place on them; they are less inclined to talk things out or to display emotion. But then, marriage isn't easy for either party. When a wife wants out, it is usually not out of selfishness or senseless cruelty. Sometimes the love simply runs out. Husbands should do what they can to keep that love alive. That way, they might hang on to the many delights that marriage affords and spare themselves the countless horrors that divorce can bring.

But such advice comes too late for the many men such as Martin Paul and Jordan Appel, who have already fallen victim to the syndrome. For them, the best, and perhaps only, cure will be time—time to forge a new relationship that can undo the ravages of the previous one. After all, most divorced men, like most divorced women, do remarry. A second marriage is a triumph of hope over experience, yes, but it's the best chance to restore the health and security that so cruelly has been taken away. Even without remarriage, the overwhelming sense of upheaval will gradually fade if the men can only persevere. And, in time, the experience will evolve into a memory that, however bitter, yields a gift of wisdom.

ASK THE GIRL NEXT DOOR

THE HONEST TRUTH ABOUT WOMEN FROM OUR LOVELY NEIGHBOR

My fiancée wants me to change careers for more money, but I'm happy. What do I do?

Ask her point-blank how much joint income she needs to feel secure. If her number is wildly different from yours, go to a financial planner to find a fair solution, or, given that money problems are the number one cause of breakups, prepare to marry your future ex-wife.

We're writing our own vows. What does she want me to say?

Handle it the way presidents deliver the State of the Union and you're sure to win over both sides of the aisle: Begin with what you've accomplished. Describe the years you've been together as the best of your life. Next, tackle the issue of security by waxing poetic about the way your love grows stronger every day. Finally, bring it home with hope for the future and a request for support: There are sure to be ups and downs, but you know that together—with the help of family and friends—you can overcome anything.

The wedding is all my fiancé wants to talk about. How do I tell her she's becoming a bridezilla?

Um, I wouldn't use that word if I were you. Remember that time you called her a nag. Instead, try some romantic "dancing" around the subject. Tell her you don't want all the planning to overshadow "how great it is just to be engaged" and that you want to "sit back and enjoy her company without worrying about the future." Then suggest a window of time every day to talk cake, favors, and vows—say, during dinner. If you seem enthusiastic for an hour, she may let you off the hook for the other 23.

I want to go on a trip with the guys this year. How do I warm my wife up to the idea?

Whether or not your wife makes a fuss depends on where you're headed. Big-city trips (L.A., Vegas, God forbid) where the main event is getting trashed will make her blood run cold as she pictures you getting lap dances from an 18-year-old named Misty. Adventure trips such as backpacking, on the other hand, seem like innocent male bonding. Make it clear that your objective is to hang with friends—not make new ones in short skirts—and she'll support you.

After complaining about being fat, my wife asks me to pick up Häagen-Dazs. Should I refuse?

Never. Bring a pint of sorbet to share instead of the superfattening stuff. If she asks, tell her it's your new favorite.

Why does she think I have to handle every chore involving the garbage or a power tool?

Plenty of men out there can tackle the entire range of household chores with patience and skill. They lay sweaters flat to dry, scrape dried egg from forks, dust between blinds, and vacuum under the bed. And you might be one of those men, in which case your woman has no right to request that you alone handle stereotypically male tasks. But if you're not so good at the delicate household stuff, your significant other is probably just playing to your strengths. Unless you'd really rather be polishing silver with a Q-tip, why complain?

My wife says we should know each other's e-mail passwords. How do I escape this one?

Two options. The low road: Hand over your password after meticulously deleting incriminating e-mails and contacts with handles like vixen69. Then open a new account where you can resume your naughty shenanigans. The high road: Suggest creating a new, joint e-mail address so you can communicate with the world as a couple. But insist that your own e-mail is full of private messages from trusting friends. It wouldn't be right for you to let anyone else read them, even her.

How can I persuade her to switch to thongs?

Find out why your girl is reluctant to bisect her butt with a strip of fabric. Prod her with flattery: "You have a gorgeous ass. Why not show it off?" If she says her butt is too big, compliment her backside regularly. After several weeks of this mental reprogramming, she may feel confident enough to buy itsy-bitsy undies. If it's the permanent wedgie that she protests, suggest she keep a lace thong around for bedtime. You promise to peel it off within minutes. Just beware the "thongs are for skanks" response. You're better off dropping it than dealing with that trap-filled debate.

How can I make my wife mad with lust?

You have to get her excited for real: her blood pumping, her adrenaline flowing, her thighs tingling. Find a sport you can play against each other, such as racquetball or tennis, and let the sweating, trash talking, and score keeping commence. If competition isn't an option, try fear. Dare her to try something new and slightly dangerous, such as scuba diving or zip-lining. Or just take her to a horror movie that'll make her jump out of her skin. All the above will make her feel alive, exhilarated, and hungry for more stimulation. That's the stuff lust is made of.

I've heard "I'm not in the mood" from my wife too many times. I'm desperate. Have any tips?

It's probably the last thing you want to hear, but you have to back off a bit. Right now, she feels pressured to have sex, and that's turning booty into a chore instead of the pleasure fest it should be. Taking some time away from sex will reset her libido and make her want you as much as she did the first time. Declare intercourse off limits for an entire month. This way she'll know that when you start massaging her feet or kissing her neck, it isn't to get into her pants; you're just showing her some love and affection. With the pressure off of her, she'll begin to want more than just a good rubdown.

My wife says she doesn't want to do anything for our anniversary. Is this a trap?

Not exactly. She thinks it'll be okay if you don't celebrate or exchange gifts. But when the day comes around, a bad mood will creep in on her like that Japanese hair ball in *The Grudge*. Your only safe move requires some stealth. Buy a few things you know she'll love (gourmet chocolates, a gift certificate to a spa, a DVD of her favorite flick from the previous year) and hide them around the house. When she wakes up on your anniversary, give her a card with clues to where the goodies are stashed.

She snores, and it's driving me nuts. How should I handle this?

Try to make your point without offending her feminine sensibilities. Express your concern that she may have "slight breathing problems" and that you often wake up in the middle of the night, worried that she's struggling for air. Maybe she should see a doctor? If she goes, then the doc can tell her she snores.

DEFUSE HER STRESS

When you add it all up—parent-teacher conferences, the leaky new Labrador puppy, stacks of bills—and then toss in the daily rigors of work, it's not surprising that your wife is ready for words by the time you both get home. In fact, a study conducted by researchers at Harvard University and the University of California at Berkeley found that after a stressful day, female spouses were more likely to instigate fights and alienate themselves from their partners. Instead of following suit, use these three simple steps to calm her down and prevent long-term havoc to your marriage.

PICK UP THE PHONE. Call her just to check in at least three times a day. "Talking releases a rush of dopamine and oxytocin (the 'reward' and 'bonding' neurochemicals) in a woman's brain," explains Louann Brizendine, MD, author of *The Female Brain* and a neuropsychiatrist at the University of California at San Francisco. "It's the biggest neurological reward a woman can get besides an orgasm." First of all, this chemical reaction explains a great deal about women. Second, it gives you a powerful tool: A simple "I can't wait to see you tonight" is enough to distract her from the insanity of the day and reinforce the love circuits in her brain.

HAVE A HEART-TO-HEART. Once a week, ask her how she's doing and whether anything is bothering her, and then listen. "Women report that the more their husbands talk to them, the more satisfied they are in their marriages," says Dr. Brizendine. The reason? "Women use communication to navigate and ease the ups and downs of life," she says. Scheduling time to allow her to vent her frustrations is the key to preventing and resolving smaller problems before they escalate into larger issues.

MEET ON NEUTRAL GROUND. If you know your wife is having a bad day at the office, warn the babysitter you'll be home late and take your wife out to dinner after work. "Taking household responsibilities off her mind is a good way to reduce her stress," says Cathy O'Neill, coauthor of *Babyproofing Your Marriage*, "and it allows you to spend quality alone-time together," two things experts say contribute to long-lasting intimacy.

BUY HER THE PERFECT GIFT

Here are four gifts that are sure to please.

SIGNED FIRST EDITIONS: You wouldn't trust her engagement ring to a department-store jeweler or the brake work on her car to a high school mechanic. So when it comes to nurturing her mind, why not turn to an expert as well? Odyssey Books, in South Hadley, Massachusetts, has a First Edition Club run by an astute literary crew, and each month they send members a new autographed book that has received insider praise in the publishing world. It's not just a great read, but also a great investment: Past picks include Kiran Desai's *The Inheritance of Loss*, which won the 2006 Man Booker Prize. When it did, a signed first edition jumped in value from $25 to $700. odysseybks.com

ARTFUL ANCESTRY: Whereas most family trees trace roots through the splitting of branches, this one starts with your own rock-solid marriage and tracks its origins through the happy unions that preceded it on both sides. Chicago-based stationer Kelly Maron works with customers to create family marriage trees based on six generations of holy matrimonies. Start by sending Maron both of your histories via e-mail (if your parents or in-laws have trouble filling in the blanks, consult rootweb.com for access to dozens of genealogy resources). In about 14 days, you'll receive a handmade 12-by 12-inch letterpress diagram that's ready for framing . . . and presenting to your better half. $250, paperstories.com/familytree

YOUR LOVE, PRESERVED: If she's like most women, your wife probably keeps a paper trail of your love, in the form of cards, movie ticket stubs, and other shared memories. Such sentimental reminders of your commitment should be eternally preserved, not left to crumble in a drawer. The artisans at Kaas GlassWorks have come up with a permanent way to display a piece of personal ephemera—say, your wedding portrait or a playbill from your first date—in a decorative glass plate that she can hang on the wall or use as a jewelry dish. The process involves scanning the image and then fusing it behind slightly concave glass, available in circles or squares of various sizes. Your custom glass memory is mailed along with the original keepsake in about 2 weeks, so chances are she won't even know you've been snooping around her personal things. kaas.com

ANTIQUE COFFEE SET: Some things, like that stained Mr. Coffee carafe, should not be allowed out of the kitchen. For dinner parties and entertaining purposes, your wife deserves a serving set as classy as the rest of the show she's running, such as an early-20th-century antique set from famed Danish silversmith Georg Jensen. His sterling-silver "holloware" (the general term for vessel-like serving pieces) was made in five styles—Art Nouveau, Art Deco, Modern, Mid-Century, and the nature-inspired Blossom pattern from 1904—and a complete set consists of a coffeepot, sugar bowl, creamer, and tray.

"Jensen believed in the idea that beautiful, functional objects enhance your daily life," says Janet Drucker, author of *Georg Jensen: 20th Century Designs* and founder of Drucker Antiques, an online store that carries a rotating stock of vintage Jensen pieces (druckerantiques.com).

If you decide to go out on your own and shop for Jensen collectibles at an antiques store or auction, always check for the company's hallmark of authenticity: Original Jensens bear the company logo (GJ), product number, silver content, and country of origin (Denmark). Check out a reference book such as Judith Miller's *Antiques Investigator* for examples ($17, amazon.com).

SHAKE IT UP

Back when Eddie Murphy was funny, he told Nick Nolte in *48 Hours*, “My dick gets hard if the wind blows.” Of course, that was in 1982, when a stiff breeze was all it took for most of us. If you’re in your forties, however, there’s no guarantee you’ll be able to stand at attention on command every time. While the best way to prolong your virility is to eat right, exercise, and control stress, one expert has added another step: Get out the blender.

Ridwan Shabsigh, MD, associate professor of urology at Columbia University and director of the New York Center for Human Sexuality at New York–Presbyterian Hospital, in New York City, says you can stir up your sex life—and shiver her timbers—with a smoothie that’s also an aphrodisiac. “I call it the sex shake,” says Dr. Shabsigh. The recipe is in his new book, *Sensational Sex in 7 Easy Steps*, and it’s based on research that suggests certain basic nutrients—available in liquid or powder form at health food stores and online—can help maintain potency. The brands mentioned here are good examples, but there are many others you can try.

Zinc, an antioxidant, improves your lipid profile and blood circulation, which is crucial to erectile function. It may be especially important for testosterone and sperm production, and it’s vital for the functioning of proteins, enzymes, and hormones. Because heavy alcohol use depletes zinc, it’s critical for people who drink regularly. One good source is Zinc Liquimins, from Trace Minerals.

Gingerroot supports your cardiovascular system, which is crucial to every erection. The best way to get it is simply to grate it from a piece of gingerroot. Or you can buy ginger tincture, as called for in this recipe, at health food stores.

Ginseng helps in the production of nitric oxide, which is essential for smooth-muscle relaxation and erectile function. Try Chinese Red Root Ginseng, from Nature’s Answer.

Selenium is key to fertility; you need it to produce sperm. Allergy Research Group sells it in liquid form under the name Selenium Solution.

Choline bitartrate and phosphatidylcholine are nutrients that help sustain memory function and ejaculate volume. Choline bitartrate is widely available in powder form; phosphatidylcholine is available from Designs for Health.

As for the flavor, well, this is no Butterfinger Blizzard. But its aftertaste is a lot more intriguing.

THE SEX SHAKE

12 to 16 ounces fat-free milk

¼ teaspoon (50 mg) zinc sulfate

1 teaspoon grated gingerroot

12 drops ginseng tincture

1 drop (50 mcg) selenium

4 strawberries or ½ banana (optional)

1 teaspoon choline bitartrate powder or 1 tablespoon phosphatidylcholine powder

2 or 3 ice cubes

Place all the ingredients in a blender. Blend for 30 seconds.

RESTORE YOUR HOME

The straw that broke the camel's back was a brass monkey lamp. My wife, Julie, and I had saved for a year to refurnish our living room and dining room. It was final-decision time, but since we both work—and our weekends were already booked with errands and kids' soccer games—we had to squeeze a final shopping spree into a 60-minute window in the middle of a workday. Apparently, I had run out of steam. "Can't you decide on one little thing by yourself?" I spat. Whoops. Our lunch hour quickly derailed into an ugly argument. We turned our backs on the shiny lighted primate and stormed out of the store empty-handed.

Psychotherapist and best-selling author Mira Kirshenbaum calls ours one of the big mistakes harried couples make. We substituted time for us with time for taking care of business. According to Kirshenbaum, we were confusing the satisfaction of intimacy with the satisfaction of completing a project together.

In her latest book, *The Weekend Marriage: Abundant Love in a Time-Starved World*, Kirshenbaum lays out guerrilla tactics for harried couples who have so little time together during the week that they're forced to try to cram all of their intimacy into the weekend—which, of course, is already booked with those errands and soccer games.

The secrets, she says, grow out of the need to create more positive energy and reduce negative energy. How do you do that? Here are her top three tips for getting your marriage back on track.

TAKE CARE OF YOURSELF FIRST. "Do something for yourself to recharge your batteries, and you'll have more energy to give your partner," says Kirshenbaum. Recently, I took the kids out to dinner and a movie so that Julie could go swimsuit shopping alone for a luxurious 3 hours. The result: Julie got a blissful break from the kids, and I got a sneak preview of summer skin—plus a serious make-out session during the show-and-tell.

DON'T REHASH THE NEGATIVE. Kirshenbaum says that "problem talk"—

conversations that focus only on the negatives of your situation—will grind away the joy in any relationship. Julie and I have agreed to cut down on gripe sessions about lousy days at work. Instead, we're identifying the positive aspects of our days, which has led to more enthusiastic time together at night.

GRAB TIME-OUTS FOR SEX. One of Kirshenbaum's most fascinating guerrilla tactics is "love on the spot." Here's how it works: Find a small flat stone and write the letters LML on it (for "let's make love") with a marker. The deal is that whoever holds the stone hands it over whenever he or she feels the urge, and unless there's a really good reason not to, you have to make love right away. Then the other person gets the stone. I was the first to play rock hound. The result was some groping in the guest-room closet, from which, we learned, we could still keep tabs on the kids. Talk about a win-win.

Kirshenbaum says that once couples tip their energy back toward the positive end of the scale, they rediscover just how well suited they are. And for most modern marriages, that happens just in time.

COME HOME

From the moment I walk through my front door each evening, my attention is focused 100 percent on my family. That is, until I pass the potatoes.

By then, I've caught up on "What was school like today?" and "Did the baby nap okay?" My wife and I have flipped for who's driving to band practice in the morning. And now, in a lull at the dinner table, my mind drifts back to my pointed conversation with Bob in manufacturing.

My mind, like my BlackBerry, receives messages from my job long after I've left the building. But unlike electronic work tools, it has no off switch.

In its most recent national survey, the Families and Work Institute found that 44 percent of American men believe an 8-hour workday doesn't give them enough time to complete their work. Many of us, as a result, tend to bring unfinished business home—if not in our briefcases, then in our minds.

Why can't a man turn off work in order to be fully present at home? "Probably because work issues feel more urgent than what you're trying to replace them with," explains Mario Alonso, PhD, a clinical psychologist.

Alonso offers a radical idea: Don't fight it. "Give attention to the noisy residue of the day before you try to let it go," he says.

REPLAY THE POSITIVES. "Chances are, you're being self-critical about your performance," says Alonso. Try focusing only on what went right. It'll bring closure to your day.

USE YOUR IMAGINATION. If you're obsessing over unfinished tasks, picture yourself resolving them . . . tomorrow. "Convince yourself that you can deal with this distraction later and give yourself permission to clear your head," explains Alonso.

RUN AWAY. Or ride a bike, practice yoga, or lift weights. Physical activities "break the cycle of infiltrating thoughts," says Alonso.

TALK TO YOUR COO. That's the chief operating officer—of your household (aka your wife). "Retelling workplace problems to a supportive person gives you control over a previous situation in which you felt passive," says Alonso.

Most men have difficulty talking about a problem for which they don't have a solution. "It puts them in an uncomfortable one-down position," says Alonso. But it's something we should try. Indeed, a little talk therapy worked for me. Telling my wife, Kathy, about a recent conflict at work did two things: It made her feel more engaged in my career, and her perspective kept me from making a huge business mistake.

GET WHAT YOU WANT

My wife and I both work full-time. She hates to cook. I don't. The result is an expectation that I'll juggle the family skillet. I don't mind, until Thursday night or so, when resentment begins to simmer. Is it too much to ask, I stew, for her to sling hash every now and then?

Evidently. For I've never asked.

According to family therapist Terrence Real, this flaw is clearly my fault. In his latest book, *The New Rules of Marriage: A Breakthrough Program for 21st-Century Relationships*, Real postulates that you'll get what you want—more sex, time off for poker night, sweet-potato linguine with walnuts—only if you ask for it. I never ask for a break from cooking, so I never get one. Instead, I resent that my wife (who is overworked herself, I'll admit) rarely volunteers to step up to the literal plate. She has no idea that I find this situation, in Real's words, "constant, cumulative, and corrosive." How could she? All she has to go on is the cold shoulder I give her once Thursday night rolls around.

To break the impasse, Real prescribes a mind-set that is deliciously selfish. Ask her, "How can I help you give me what I want?" In my case, it means stopping on the way home to buy the ingredients she's going to need to cook dinner. It might even mean I'll need to fold clothes while she chops walnuts.

The underlying message is that men need to take action to break the stalemate. Get off the couch. Get engaged. Get the clothes out of the dryer. The upside: You'll get more of what you want . . . whatever that is.

Here's Real's program for 21st-century married men who are still playing by 20th-century rules:

RUN YOUR MARRIAGE LIKE A BUSINESS. "Start asking for what you want," says Real, "instead of complaining about what you're not getting."

MAKE A DEAL. Come up with a plan ahead of time. Say something like, "I'll cook if you'll do the dishes."

VOLUNTEER YOUR SERVICES. When she needs something, ask yourself what it would cost you. "Often, it will only cost pride," says Real, "and holding on to that isn't manly, it's dumb."

SCHEDULE CHECKUPS. Take time each week to check in on each other. Pour some wine, put your feet up, and say, "Honey, let's talk about how we're doing."

DON'T BACK DOWN. If you're unhappy with the situation, take her on in a constructive way. Explain that you've worked on giving more, but she isn't holding up her end of the bargain.

PUT YOUR IN-LAW IN ORDER

When I said "I do" 8 years ago, I thought I was marrying the hottie in the white dress. I had no idea I was also tying the knot with the older lady in the front row, or that she'd turn that knot into a noose by moving 10 minutes away to help with our newborn. And wouldn't you know it, my wife and I had been doing everything wrong. At least that's what we're told . . . daily. It could be worse, though: A survey by the National Association of Home Builders found that a quarter of all new high-end homes are built with mother-in-law suites. That's right: Many men actually live with their mothers-in-law. So what am I—and those less fortunate—to do? The key is to muffle her meddling without locking horns, says clinical psychologist Albert J. Bernstein, PhD, author of *Emotional Vampires*. Here's how.

GET YOUR WIFE ONBOARD. Some women tell their moms everything, but it's not in everyone's best interest for her to know about, say, your Zoloft prescription or junior's academic shortcomings. "Sit down with your wife and discuss what to keep private regarding money, children, and health," says Bernstein. The more info you give your mother-in-law, the more likely she'll be to opine, advise, and raise your blood pressure.

ESTABLISH AN EARLY WARNING SYSTEM. "Don't encourage unrestricted dropping in," says Nina W. Brown, EdD, a professor of counseling at Virginia's Old Dominion University. If your mother-in-law feels she can arrive unannounced, she'll also feel comfortable enough to offer her two cents at will. "Ask for prior notice, and always return the favor," says Brown.

STAY POSITIVE. In-laws and children share one thing in common: They test parental limits by pushing buttons. "The best response is not to respond at all," says Brown. A negative reaction will only fuel defensiveness. Walk away, cool off, and follow the next step.

WEAR KID GLOVES. If your mother-in-law countermands one of your orders, acknowledge her positive intention (real or not), explain your dictate, and ask for help in carrying it out. Your mother-in-law wants to be part of the parenting team, says Brown, and if you make her feel like the MVP, that's what she'll become.

LET HER MEDDLE (A LITTLE). Your mother-in-law knows a thing or two about parenting. She raised your wife, didn't she? "So seek her advice on small issues," says Bernstein. "A little respect almost always provokes a positive response." Shortly after I asked my mother-in-law to teach my kid how to put on her own shoes, for example, brownies appeared on my desk. Even small victories taste sweet.

TALK YOUR WAY OUT OF TROUBLE

Use this peace-talk primer to stop fights before they go nuclear. "Women are always scanning for proof you're still trustworthy," says Scott Haltzman, MD, a clinical assistant professor of psychiatry at Brown University and author of *The Secrets of Happily Married Women*. Sound harrowing? Not to worry. Here's how to react the next time you trip her trust alarm.

SHE CATCHES YOU CHECKING OUT HER HOT SISTER, COUSIN, OR FRIEND

This isn't anonymous eye candy you're "appreciating." The social proximity jacks up the potential for infidelity and, therefore, jealousy.

SAY, "I'm sorry. You have absolutely nothing to worry about—there's no one else I'd rather be with than you."

Be sincere and take ownership of your mistake, and keep ironclad blinders on your eyes from now on. She knows you look at other women (she's on guy patrol, too), but wonders why you can't control your impulses. Her peripheral vision will be working overtime.

DON'T SAY, "What are you talking about?" "Denial makes her feel like you don't understand why she feels bad," says Janice Levine, PhD, author of *Why Do Fools Fall in Love?*

SHE LEARNS YOUR PAL WASN'T ALWAYS A PLATONIC ONE

Secrecy adds suspicion of what could happen, says psychologist Patricia Love, EdD, coauthor of *How to Improve Your Marriage Without Talking About It.*

SAY, "I wasn't trying to hide it. She's been platonic for so long, I didn't think to mention our past."

Ask her how she'd like you to handle your former flame. Letting her dictate your interaction shows that you put the relationship above the friendship.

Invite her next time you hang out with your friend, so she can see how innocuous the friendship is.

DON'T SAY, "There's nothing going on there. I didn't mention it because you'd blow it out of proportion." She'll think it's a convenient excuse. "It's cowardly and shows you don't trust her," says Levine.

SHE FINDS E-MAILS FROM YOUR EX

Despite your noble effort to shield her from the details, her instincts tell her "where there's chemistry and exclusivity, there's the potential for intimacy," Love says.

SAY, "I don't want to get these e-mails any more than you want to read them. Let's figure out what to do together."

Offer to let her read the notes, Love says. Then use the opportunity to set the ground rules for how to handle situations like this.

DON'T SAY, "She's insane. Don't worry about it." This leaves the door ajar. You'd go a little nuts if she kept the lines of communication open with her ex, right? Don't do it to her.

SHE HEARS A RAUNCHY STORY ABOUT A BACHELOR PARTY YOU HAD DOWNPLAYED

Even if you dodged the stripper all night, your omission makes her worry you may have covered up other parts of that evening.

SAY, "Okay, if you want to know, make some popcorn and grab a seat."

Offer up full disclosure if she asks, but chances are she won't. No woman likes to imagine a half-naked dancer gyrating atop her man, but if she's worth your time, she'll get over it.

DON'T SAY, "The strippers? I didn't really pay too much attention." Now she knows you're lying. Think about Bill Clinton: It wasn't Monica Lewinsky that led to impeachment, it was the lie.

BENEFITS OF A CLEAN CASTLE

You can imagine your honey as a French maid, but don't treat her like one. After interviewing 1,128 married women, Pew Research Center researchers found that a man's willingness to do housework is a major predictor of marital bliss. "It takes just a small amount of resentment regarding her share of the cleaning for problems to arise," says Debby Herbenick, PhD, researcher at Indiana University's Center for Sexual Health Promotion.

Divvying up duties is about more than mold-free showers, says Suzanne Bianchi, PhD. It's about knowing that your spouse is willing to shoulder some dirty work so you don't have to.

So team up, scour the homestead, and then reward yourselves with home-made margaritas. Give her a hand, or hire a real maid.

YOUR HOME, INC.

Keeping a house in order is a full-time job—one that would pay women better than it would men. According to new research from Salary.com, women

»A MAN'S GUIDE POLL

Percentage who say this is important for a successful marriage

1. Fidelity

1990: 95%

2007: 93%

2. A happy sexual relationship

1990: 67%

2007: 70%

3. Shared household chores

1990: 47%

2007: 62%

4. Adequate income

1990: 46%

2007: 53%

5. A comfortable home

1990: 42%

2007: 51%

6. Shared religious beliefs

1990: 45%

2007: 49%

7. Shared tastes and interests

1990: 44%

2007: 46%

8. Children

1990: 65%

2007: 41%

perform tasks at home that would require paying a janitor and a housekeeper a total of $138,000 a year. By comparison, men do the work of a maintenance worker and a groundskeeper, which has a value of $125,000. In reality, both sexes earn zip.

SATISFACTION

Ask not what your wife can do for you; ask what you can do for your wife. A study in the journal *Family Process* followed 38 newly married couples for 4 years. Researchers had them rate the quality of their relationship and say how much they agreed with statements like "It can be fulfilling to give up something for my partner."

Results showed that people who enjoyed making sacrifices for their partner had happier marriages. Six years later, "those with higher initial sacrifice scores were much more likely to be happily married," says study coauthor Sarah Whitton, PhD. Even giving in on minor matters can make a difference. So eat at her favorite Chinese place when you really want Thai. She just may return the favor.

COOKING SCHOOL

Couples who cook together are happier.

COUPLES WHO . . . ALWAYS COOK TOGETHER

Rate relationship as excellent: 83%

Communicate well and don't fight: 45%

Have a satisfying sex life: 58%

COUPLES WHO . . . RARELY COOK TOGETHER

Rate relationship as excellent: 26%

Communicate well and don't fight: 19%

Have a satisfying sex life: 30%

Source: Survey of 1,500 couples for Sears, Roebuck & Company

RITUAL REWARDS

Taco Tuesday, Sunday-morning sex: Having fun rituals boosts commitment in a relationship, says a study in the journal *Sexual and Relationship Therapy*. Researchers asked 100 unmarried couples what they did for fun and how satisfied each person was with his or her partner. People in relationships who rated rituals as meaningful scored 27 percent higher on the satisfaction scale than those who found them less important.

"By engaging in behaviors both partners enjoy, the couple is able to maintain a strong friendship, which is crucial to a stable, long-term relationship," says lead author and graduate student Kelly Campbell. Make what you both love—trail runs, movie nights, eating out—as routine as flossing—or more so.

RECYCLED HAPPINESS

See a comedy on your next date. Couples who reminisce about funny experiences they've shared are more satisfied with their partners than those who recall cracking up alone, found Appalachian State University psychologists. A funny memory serves as an inside joke, which creates cohesiveness between two people, says study author Doris Bazzini, PhD. Need material? She advises couples to use amusing nicknames for each other that are based on a humorous recollection. This way the mood-boosting power of the memory can be used often.

TALK THERAPY

Tell her to quit biting her tongue: Women who keep mum during spats with spouses increase their risk of mortality, reports a study in the journal *Psychosomatic Medicine*. Researchers surveyed 3,682 people over 10 years and found that women who stayed silent during arguments had four times the risk of dying from any cause. Bottling up your feelings may make them seem unimportant, which can create depression-like symptoms that wreak havoc on your health.

Move angry moments to neutral ground such as coffee shops, LeslieBeth Wish, EdD, advises. It can make for calmer voices and a more comfortable atmosphere for speaking your mind.

CHATTY CLARKS

Women have long been labeled society's motor mouths, but a study in the journal *Science* reports that both sexes speak the same number of words in a day: 16,000. In a 6-year study, nearly 400 people wore a digital recorder for several days. Every 12.5 minutes, the device switched on for 30 seconds. Based on those excerpts, researchers estimated how many words were uttered in a day. Women may get slapped with the big-mouth label because they tend to say more during heated conversations, which we remember the longest, says lead researcher James Pennebaker, PhD.

CONTROLLING INTEREST

It's classic: She yaps, and your eyes glaze over. Well, it might not be your fault. According to Duke University scientists, men unconsciously reject the wishes of a nagging partner. When men who said they had controlling spouses were asked to solve anagrams on a computer, they performed significantly worse after seeing the names of their wives flash on the screen. "Our participants weren't even aware that they had been exposed to their spouses' names, yet that subliminal exposure was enough to trigger an act of defiance," says study coauthor Gavan Fitzsimons, PhD. Conversely, men who didn't view their wives as controlling performed better after their names flashed. Think your wife can be a nag? Explain to her that you'll probably cooperate more if she just relaxes the reins.

THE PERFECT GIFT

Think you know just the right gift for your wife or girlfriend? Think again. Better yet, stop thinking and start paying attention. The closer you are to someone, the less likely you are to give her what she wants—so says a study in the *Journal of Consumer Research.* You know so much about her that you may ignore her hints. Sherri Athay, author of *Present Perfect,* says women read messages into gifts. A spa certificate says, "Take time for yourself," while a gold necklace when she wears only silver says, "I'm not paying attention." Write down ideas as they come to you, Athay says. Last-minute gifts reek of panic.

INDEX

Underscored references indicate boxed text.

M

N

S

T